EUROPE

AFRICA

SOUTH
AMERICA

THE METRIC ENCYCLOPEDIA

METHICS

Since 1952

THE METRIC
ENCYCLOPEDIA

" SI "

Compiled and Edited by

A. L. LeMaraic

and

J. P. Ciaramella

PUBLISHED BY ABBEY BOOKS
Metric Media Book Publishers
Somers, N.Y. 10589
ISBN Prefix 0-913768

FOREWORD

The Metric Encyclopedia presents in succinct and simplified form accurate information concerning the new metric system — The International System of Units, generally known as the SI. It endeavors to present important facts in a concise manner to meet the practical needs of those who, seeking information, want it presented briefly, clearly, and accessibly.

The Metric Encyclopedia makes no pretense of being a conventional encyclopedic compilation in the usual sense, in fact, it is a radical departure from the customary format of such compendiums. While striving for brevity, clarity, and the prudent use of limited space to its utmost possibility, all phases of the new metric system have been included and given ample treatment to answer the questions with which the average person may be confronted.

The Metric Encyclopedia is a comprehensive and practical compilation of the metric system based on modern principles derived from the latest information available from official sources.

The Metric Encyclopedia is so arranged that it can be used by teachers, students, and adult learners as a source or reference book in many ways. It presents the basic and unchanging principles of the new metric system in a concise, easy to understand manner which eliminates much tedious reading of technical texts to obtain desired information.

While simplicity and brevity have been kept constantly in mind during the preparation of this compendium, all phases of the SI have been defined to the maximum degree possible within the space limitations of this book. The material has been carefully selected and edited from the practical point of view. It was simplified and condensed to enable the average person to acquire easily a good understanding of the SI so as to put it to practical use quickly and deal with almost all but exceptional metric problems of highly technical nature. In short, The Metric Encyclopedia provides sufficient data to enable the average individual to resolve practical daily problems of weights and measures.

The compilation of a systematized presentation of the subject for practical use was a matter of utmost importance for it must be conceded that if an educational book is to serve its intended purpose it must be thorough, interesting, and above all, easy to understand. While it is not always possible to provide every human requirement within the covers of one book, whatever the subject, a sound foundation can be provided to induce constructive thought or action by the individual to involve him in learning the more advanced phases of the subject. We believe that these objectives have been achieved to an appreciable degree in this compendium.

May 1975   A.L. LeMaraic
                                                  J.P. Ciaramella

CONTENTS

CONTENTS

CONTENTS

SPECIAL SI TABLES

ACKNOWLEDGMENT

All the basic material used in this book is derived from the translation approved by the International Bureau of Weights and Measures of its publication "Le Système International d'Unités." Grateful acknowledgment is made to the following for permission to include excerpts from their publications in this compendium.

Conférence Générales des Poids et Mesures	(CGPM)
Consultative Committee for Units	(CCU)
International Bureau of Weights and Measures	(BIPM)
International Committee of Weights and Measures	(CIPM)
International Organization for Standardization	(ISO)
National Aeronautics and Space Administration	(NASA)
National Bureau of Standards—U.S.A.	(NBS)
South African Bureau of Standards	(SABS)
South African Metrication Advisory Board	(SAMAB)
United States Department of Commerce	(USDC)

HISTORICAL NOTE

Almost four centuries ago, in 1585, the Flemish mathematician, Simon Stevin, conceived the idea of a decimal system of measurement and advocated its development without success. During the next century astronomers, mathematicians, and other scientists again proposed a system based on decimal units of measurement, however, not until the latter part of the 18th century, when the French Revolution brought on many radical changes, did the metric system gain momentum.

The French revived the idea of creating a universal system of measurement to serve mankind for all time in 1790, and in 1793 they proposed the metre as a unit of length and the gramme as a unit of mass. The idea was favorably received throughout Europe and continued to thrive, gradually gaining broader acceptance all over the world.

The growing use of the metric system in various countries created the need of a central authority to supervise and maintain uniform standards of measurement universally. Accordingly the French government convened conferences in 1870, 1872, and 1875 for that purpose with good results.

The International Bureau of Weights and Measures (BIPM) was set up by the Metre Convention signed in Paris on May 20, 1875 by seventeen States during the final session of the Diplomatic Conference of the Metre. This Convention was amended in 1921.

BIPM has its headquarters near Paris, in the grounds of the Pavillon de Breteuil (Parc de Saint-Cloud), placed at its disposal by the French Government; its upkeep is financed jointly by the Member States of the Metre Convention.

The task of BIPM is to ensure worldwide unification of physical measurements; it is responsible for:

—-establishing the fundamental standards and scales for measurement of the principal physical quantities and maintaining the international prototypes;

—-carrying out comparisons of national and international standards;

—-ensuring the co-ordination of corresponding measuring techniques;

—-carrying out and co-ordinating the determinations relating to the fundamental physical constants.

BIPM operates under the exclusive supervision of the International Committee of Weights and Measures (CIPM), which itself comes under the authority of the General Conference of Weights and Measures (CGPM).

The General Conference consists of delegates from all the Member States of the Metre Convention and meets at least once every six years. At each meeting it receives the Report of the International Committee on the work accomplished, and it is responsible for:

—discussing and instigating the arrangements required to ensure the propagation and improvement of the International System of Units (SI), which is the modern form of the metric system;

—confirming the results of new fundamental metrological determinations and the various scientific resolutions of international scope;

—adopting the important decisions concerning the organization and development of BIPM.

The International Committee consists of eighteen members each belonging to a different State; it meets at least once every two years. The officers of this Committee issue an Annual Report on the administrative and financial position of BIPM to the Governments of the Member States of the Metre Convention.

The activities of BIPM, which in the beginning were limited to the measurements of length and mass and to metrological studies in relation to these quantities, have been extended to standards of measurement for electricity (1927), photometry (1937) and ionizing radiations (1960). To this end the original laboratories, built in 1876-1878, were enlarged in 1929 and two new buildings were constructed in 1963-1964 for the ionizing radiation laboratories. Some thirty physicists or technicians work in the laboratories of BIPM. They do metrological research, and also undertake measurement and certification of material standards of the above-mentioned quantities.

In view of the extension of the work entrusted to BIPM, CIPM has set up since 1927, under the name of Consultative Committees, bodies designed to provide it with information on matters which it refers to them for study and advice. These Consultative Committees, which may form temporary or permanent "Working Groups" to study special subjects, are responsible for co-ordinating the international work carried out in their respective fields and proposing recommendations concerning the amendments to be made to the definitions and values of units. In order to ensure worldwide uniformity in units of measurement, the International Committee accordingly acts directly or submits proposals for sanction by the General Conference.

The Consultative Committees have common regulations (Procès-Verbaux CIPM, 1963, 31, 97). Each Consultative Committee, the chairman of which is normally a member of CIPM, is composed of a delegate from each of the large Metrology Laboratories and specialized Institutes, a list of which is drawn up by CIPM, as well as individual members also appointed by CIPM and one representative of BIPM. These Committees hold their meetings at irregular intervals; at present there are seven of them in existence.

1. The Consultative Committee for Electricity (C.C.E.), set up in 1927.

2. The Consultative Committee for Photometry and Radiometry (C.C.P.R.), new name given in 1971 to the Consultative Committee for Photometry set up in 1933 (between 1930 and 1933 the preceding Committee (C.C.E.) dealt with matters concerning Photometry).

3. The Consultative Committee for Thermometry (C.C.T.), set up in 1937.

4. The Consultative Committee for the Definition of the Metre (C.C.D.M.), set up in 1952.

5. The Consultative Committee for the Definition of the Second (C.C.D.S.), set up in 1956.

6. The Consultative Committee for the Standards of Measurement of Ionizing Radiations (C.C.E.M.R.I.), set up in 1958.

Since 1969 this Consultative Committee has consisted of four sections: Section I (measurement of x and γ rays); Section II (measurement of radionuclides); Section III (neutron measurements); Section IV (α-energy standards).

7. The Consultative Committee for Units (C.C.U.), set up in 1964.

The proceedings of the General Conference, the International Committee, the Consultative Committees, and the Inter-

national Bureau are published under the auspices of the latter in the following series:
—Comptes rendus des séances de la Conférence Générale des Poids et Mesures;
—Procès-Verbaux des séances du Comité International des Poids et Mesures;
—Sessions des Comités Consultatifs;
—Recueil de Travaux du Bureau International des Poids et Mesures (this compilation brings together articles published in scientific and technical journals and books, as well as certain work published in the form of duplicated reports).

From time to time BIPM publishes a report on the development of the Metric System throughout the world, entitled Les récents progrès du Système Métrique.

The collection of the Travaux et Memoires du Bureau International des Poids et Mesures (22 volumes published between 1881 and 1966) ceased in 1966 by a decision of CIPM.

Since 1965 the international journal Metrologia, edited under the auspices of CIPM, has published articles on the more important work on scientific metrology carried out throughout the world, on the improvement in measuring methods and standards, of units, etc., as well as reports concerning the activities, decisions and recommendations of the various bodies created under the Metre Convention.

A joint Resolution of Congress was introduced in the 92nd Congress as Senate Joint Resolution 219 and House Joint Resolution 1192, 1132, and 1169 stating the national policy on conversion to the metric system in the United States. The full text of this Resolution appears at the end of this book.

As of December 31, 1972, forty-one States were members of this Convention: Argentina (Rep. of), Australia, Austria, Brazil, Belgium, Bulgaria, Cameroon, Canada, Chile, Czechoslovakia, Denmark, Dominican Republic, Finland, France, Germany, Hungary, India, Indonesia, Ireland, Italy, Japan, Korea, Mexico, the Netherlands, Norway, Poland, Portugal, Rumania, Spain, South Africa, Sweden, Switzerland, Thailand, Turkey, U.S.S.R., United Arab Republic, United Kingdom, U.S.A., Uruguay, Venezuela, Yugoslavia.

[2]For the meaning of these abbreviations, see page X

VARIATIONS IN METRIC WRITING STYLES

There exist some variations in metric writing styles used in established metric countries and those used in the United States. In this compendium we strive to adhere as closely as possible to the official rules of the SI.

Almost all established metric countries use the comma as the decimal point instead of the period, as we do. There are also variations in the spelling of the metric units of length, mass, and capacity, and their multiples and submultiples. In most foreign countries using the metric system they are spelled "metre" - "gramme" - and "litre" in keeping with the form established in the SI. However, in the United States "meter" - "gram" - and "liter" are considered acceptable, even though they do not conform with the spelling used in most established metric countries.

The metric writing style guides as stated by the National Bureau of Standards are given verbatim hereunder.

METRIC WRITING STYLE GUIDES OF
THE NATIONAL BUREAU OF STANDARDS

1. CAPITALS
   Units: When written in full, the names of all units start with a lower case letter, except at the beginning of a sentence. Note that in degree Celsius the unit "degree" is lower case but the modifier "Celsius" is capitalized. The "degree centigrade" is obsolete.
   Symbols: Unit symbols are written with lower case letters except that the first letter is upper case when the name of the unit is derived from the name of a person.
   Prefixes: Except for tera (T), giga (G), and mega (M), all symbols for numerical prefixes are written with lower case letters. All prefixes are written in lower case letters when written out in full, except where the entire unit name is written in upper case letters.
2. PLURALS
   a. When written in full, the names of units are made plural when appropriate. Fractions (both common and decimal) are always singular.
   b. Symbols for units are the same in singular and plural (no "s" is ever added to indicate a plural).

3. PERIODS

A period is NOT used after a symbol, except at the end of a sentence.

4. THE DECIMAL POINT

The dot is used as the decimal point and is placed on the line. When writing numbers less than one, a zero must be written before the decimal point.

5. GROUPING OF DIGITS

a. Separate digits into groups of three, counting from the decimal sign. The comma should not be used. Instead, a space is left to avoid confusion, since many countries use a comma for the decimal point.

b. In numbers of four digits, the space is not recommended, unless four-digit numbers are grouped in a column with numbers of five digits or more.

6. SPACING

a. When writing symbols or names for units having prefixes, no space is left between letters making up the symbol or the name.

b. When writing a symbol after a number to which it refers, a space must be left between the number and the symbol (except for degree, minute, and second of angle).

7. COMPOUND UNITS

When writing the symbol for a compound unit that is formed by the multiplication of two or more units, a centered dot is used. For example N·m.

When writing the name for such a unit, a hyphen is recommended (or a space is permissible) but never a centered dot. For example, newton-metre or newton metre.

STANDARDS OF MEASUREMENT

Units of measurement should be distinguished from standards of measurement. Units of length are fixed distances, independent of any other consideration, while length standards are affected by the expansion and contraction resulting from changes of temperature of the material of which the standard is composed. It is therefore necessary to fix upon some temperature at which the distance between the defining lines or end surfaces of the standards shall be equal to the unit. The same is true of standards of capacity, which at some definite temperature contain a given number of units of volume.

XVI

The recommended standard temperature for commercial and industrial length standards is 20⁰ C.(68⁰ F). Some metric standards, especially those made in Europe until recently, are intended to be correct at 9⁰ C. In the past some length standards graduated in the customary units have been made to be correct at 62⁰ F (16.67⁰ C).

For measurements of high precision it is also necssary to specify the manner of support of the standards, whether at certain points only or throughout their entire length, and in the case of tapes it is also necessary to give the tension applied to the tape when in use.

In the United States the capacity standards, both metric and customary, are made to hold the specified volumes at 4⁰ C. Standards of capacity are usually made of brass and the capacity at any other temperature may be computed by the use of the coefficient of cubical expansion of that material usually assumed to be 0.000 054 per degree centigrade. In the purchase and sale of liquids a more important consideration than the temperature of the measures is the temperature of the liquid when measured, for the reason that the large coefficient of expansion of many liquids makes the actual mass of a given volume delivered vary considerably with temperature.

While the temperature of a weight does not affect its mass, it is nevertheless important that when two weights are compared in air they both be at the same temperature as the air. If there is a difference between the temperature of the air and the weights, convection currents will be set up and the readings of the balance will be thereby affected. Also, since weights are buoyed up by the surrounding air by amounts dependent upon their volumes, it is desirable that the weights of any set be of the same material. If two weights of the same density balance in air of a certain density they will balance in vacuo or in air of a different density.

Brass is the material most widely used for standard weights, although platinum and aluminum are quite commonly used for weights of 1 gram or less. In the absence of any knowledge as to the actual density of weights, those made of brass are assumed to have a density of 8.4 grams per cm^3 at 0⁰ C, while those of platinum and of aluminum are assumed to have densities of 21.5 and 2.7 grams per cm^3, respectively.

THE METRIC SYSTEM FOR EVERYDAY USE

By learning the meaning of 12 terms, viz. mega-, kilo-, deci-, centi-, milli-, metre, hectare, litre, gram, metric ton, pascal and degree Celsius, enough knowledge of the metric system is acquired to satisfy practically all ordinary needs. Please note that according to international agreement there is only one correct symbol for each term. These symbols are the same for all languages and are given in brackets below. They have no plurals and are consistently written without a period. The units of electricity and time are not affected by metrication.

METRIC PREFIXES

mega-	(M)	means	million
kilo-	(k)	"	thousand
deci-	(d)	"	tenth
centi-	(c)	"	hundredth
milli-	(m)	"	thousandth

These prefixes are the same for all types of metric units,

1 megalitre (Ml)	=	1 000 000 litres (l)
1 kilolitre (kl)	=	1 000 litres (l)
1 kilopascal (kPa)	=	1 000 pascals (Pa)
1 kilogram (kg)	=	1 000 grams (g)
1 kilometre (km)	=	1 000 metres (m)
1 decimetre (dm)	=	1/10th metre (m)
1 centimetre (cm)	=	1/100th metre (m)
1 millimetre (mm)	=	1/1 000th metre (m)

THE METRIC SYSTEM FOR EVERYDAY USE
(continued)

(a) LENGTH, DISTANCE

Base unit:
metre (m)   approximately equal to a long pace

Multiple:
kilometre (km)   = 1 000 metres (m)

Submultiples:
centimetre (cm)   = 1/100th metre (m)
millimetre (mm)   = 1/1 000th metre (m)

(b) AREA

SI unit:
square metre (m²)   = the area of a square with
                           sides 1 metre
Multiples:
1 square kilometre (km²) = 1 000 000 square metres
                            (m²)
1 hectare (ha)   = 10 000 square metres (m²)

Submultiples:
1 square centimetre
    (cm²)   = 1/10 000th square metre
                            (m²)
1 square millimetre (mm²) = 1/1 000 000th square
                            metre (m²)

Note: Hectare (ha) is a special name given to 10 000 m² and is
used in land surveying.

THE METRIC SYSTEM FOR EVERYDAY USE
(continued)

(c) VOLUME

SI unit:
cubic metre (m^3) = the volume of a cube
with sides 1 metre

Submultiples:
1 cubic decimetre (dm^3) = 1/1 000th cubic metre (m^3)

1 cubic centimetre (cm^3) = 1/1 000 000th cubic metre (m^3)

Note: The cubic decimetre (dm^3) was given a special name, the litre (l). The litre is used for measuring liquids.

Unit for liquids:
1 litre (l) = 1 cubic decimetre (dm^3)

Multiples:
1 megalitre (Ml) = 1 000 000 litres (l)
= 1 000 cubic metres (m^3)

1 kilolitre (kl) = 1 000 litres (l)
= 1 cubic metre (m^3)

Submultiple:
1 millilitre (ml) = 1/1 000 litre (l)
= 1 cubic centimetre (cm^3)

(d) MASS

Base unit:
kilogram (kg) = the mass of 1 litre (l) of water

Multiple:
1 metric ton (t) = 1 000 kilograms (kg)

Submultiples:
1 gram (g) = 1/1 000th kilogram (kg)
1 milligram (mg) = 1/1 000th gram (g)
NOTE: The megagram (Mg) = 1 000 kilograms (kg) and is called a metric ton (t).

THE METRIC SYSTEM FOR EVERYDAY USE
(continued)

(e) VELOCITY

Expressed in kilometres per hour (km/h) (h is derived from the Latin word "hora").

(f) PRESSURE

For practical purposes pressure is expressed in kilopascal (kPa). 100 kPa is practically equal to the pressure of the atmosphere at sea level.

SI unit:
pascal (Pa)	= a pressure of 1 newton per square metre (1 N/m²)

Multiples:
1 megapascal (MPa)	=	1 000 000 pascals (Pa)
1 kilopascal (kPa)	=	1 000 pascals (Pa)

(g) TEMPERATURE

Temperature is expressed in degrees Celsius (°C). Water freezes at 0 °C and boils at 100 °C. Body temperature is 37 °C and 20 °C is a pleasant room temperature.

(h) FUEL CONSUMPTION

Expressed in litres per 100 kilometres (1/100 km)

METRIC TABLES, SYMBOLS AND NOTATION

1. LENGTH

10 millimetres (mm)	=	1 centimetre (cm)
100 cm	=	1 metre (m)
1 000 m	=	1 kilometre (km)

2. AREA

100 mm²	=	1 cm²
100 cm²	=	1 dm² (square decimetre)
100 dm²	=	1 m²
100 m²	=	1 are (a)
100 ares	=	1 hectare (ha)
100 ha	=	1 km²

A piece of land 100 metres by 100 metres is therefore 1 hectare.

3. VOLUME

1 000 millilitres (ml)	=	1 000 cm³ = 1 litre (l)
1 000 litres (l)	=	1 m³

4. MASS

1 000 grams (g)	=	1 kilogram (kg)
1 000 kg	=	1 metric ton (t)

METRIC TABLES, SYMBOLS AND NOTATIONS
(continued)

5. PREFERRED UNITS, MULTIPLES AND SUBMULTIPLES

Length: 1 000 millimetres (mm) = 1 metre (m);
             1 000 m   = 1 kilometre (km)
Volume: 1 000 millilitres (ml) = 1 litre (l);
             1 000 litres   = 1 m³ = 1 kilolitre (kl)
Mass: 1 000 grams (g)   = 1 kilogram (kg);
             1 000 kg   = 1 metric ton (t)

Writing numbers: Large numbers should be divided into groups of three, counting from the decimal sign to the left and the right and these groups should be separated by a space and never by a comma. A space replaces the comma used previously because the comma serves as the decimal sign in many metric countries. In numbers less than units a zero should precede the decimal sign, for example, 0.239 and not .239.

A quantity is generally described in millimetres, grams or millilitres up to 999.9, thereafter in metres, kilograms or litres. 1 300 mm or g or ml is therefore written as 1.3 m (1.300 m for engineering drawings), 1.3 kg or 1.3 litres. When using symbols, no addition such as s, should be made to indicate plurality, e.g. 1 kg; 2 kg NOT 2 kgs.

It is important to use the symbols correctly, lower case letters should not be used where the accepted symbol is a capital letter, or vice versa, e.g. m stands for milli- (1/1 000 th), but M for mega- (1 000 000 times).

I. THE INTERNATIONAL SYSTEM OF UNITS - SI

1. INTRODUCTION

A most significant advantage of the SI over other measuring systems is that it is coherent, i.e. all SI units are formed by simple multiplication and/or division within a set of seven so-called base units and two supplementary units, and no factors other than the number one are necessary.

For example, in the imperial system the pound-force is often used as a force unit. This means that the factor **g** (acceleration due to gravity) appears in all calculations involving force, ass and acceleration because one pound-force acting on a mass of one pound does not produce one unit of acceleration but **g** units. In a similar way, use of the horsepower (defined as 550 foot pounds-force per second) results in the factor 550 appearing in calculations involving force, time and power.

Because of the use of the kilogram force, the old metric technical system suffered from similar disadvantages and even the centimetre-gram-second system is non-coherent where relationships between mechanical, electrical and heat units are concerned.

The property of coherence and the choice of base units (see Chapter 2) ensure that in the SI there is only one unit for each physical quantity (i.e. length, mass, energy, etc.). The measure of rationalization and simplification brought about by this is clearly illustrated if the joule, which is the SI unit of energy (irrespective of whether it is mechanical, electrical, chemical or any other form of energy) is compared with the present series of energy units in general use; e.g. The British Thermal Unit, foot pound-force, foot poundal, kilopond-metre, calorie, kilowatt-hour, ton (equivalent of TNT), electronvoit, erg, thermie, etc.

At present it is unfortunately not yet possible in practice to use only SI units. All the required units fall into the following three broad groups:

a) SI units

b) Multiples and submultiples of SI units

c) Units which do not constitute part of the SI buts which may be used with the SI subject to certain restrictions.

2. SI-UNITS

2.1. The three classes of SI units

SI units can in turn be divided into three classes:

base units

derived units

supplementary units

The SI is based on a set of seven base units, the metre (m), the kilogram (kg), the second (s), the ampere (A), the kelvin (K), the candela (cd) and the mole (mol) (see 2.2).

The second class, derived units, contains units which are formed by combinations of the base units and supplementary units according to the algebraic relationships between the corresponding physical quantities (see 2.3). As already mentioned, no factor other than the number one is used. For example, speed is defined by the algebraic ratio distance divided by time and consequently the SI unit of speed is the metre per second. Some derived units have special names, and these can again be used to form further derived units.

The third class contains only two units, the radian and the steradian, units of plane angle and solid angle respectively. The CGPM has not yet classified these units as either base units or derived units but refers to them as supplementary units. When calculating with these units they may be regarded as either base units or derived units.

Units which fall into these three classes form a coherent system and only these units are known as SI units. Multiples and submultiples of the SI units which are formed by using the SI prefixes (see Chapter 3) are *not* SI units and should be referred to as *multiples and submultiples of SI units.*

Example:

The metre (m), kilogram (kg), newton (N), watt (W) are the SI units of length, mass, force and power respectively.

The millimetre (mm) and the kilometre (km) are respectively a submultiple and a multiple of the SI unit of length.

2.2. SI base units

TABLE 1

THE SEVEN SI BASE UNITS

Quantity	SI base unit		
	Name	International symbol	Definition (CGPM)
length	metre	m	The metre is the length equal to 1 650 763,73 wavelengths in vacuum of the radiation corresponding to the transition between the levels 2 p_{10} and 5 d_5 of the krypton-86 atom. [11th CGPM (1960), Resolution 6].
mass	kilogram	kg	The kilogram is the mass of the international prototype kilogram recognised by the CGPM and in the custody of the Bureau International des Poids et Mesures, Sèvres, France. [1st CGPM (1889)].
time	second	s	The second is the duration of 9 192 631 770 periods of the radiation corresponding to the transition between the two hyperfine levels of the ground state of the caesium-133 atom. [13th CGPM (1967), Resolution 1].
electric current	ampere	A	The ampere is that constant current which, if maintained in two straight parallel conductors of infinite length, of negligible circular cross-section, and placed one metre apart in vacuum would produce between these conductors a force equal to 2×10^{-7} newton per metre of length. [CIPM (1946), Resolution 2, approved by the 9th CGPM (1948)]
thermodynamic temperature	kelvin	K	The kelvin, unit of thermodynamic temperature, is the fraction 1/273,16 of the thermodynamic temperature of the triple point of water. [13th CGPM (1967), Resolution 4].
luminous intensity	candela	cd	The candela is the luminous intensity, in the perpendicular direction of a surface of 1/600 000 square metre of a blackbody at the temperature of freezing platinum under a pressure of 101 325 newtons per square metre. [13th CGPM (1967), Resolution 5].
amount of substance	mole	mol	The mole is the amount of substance of a system which contains as many elementary entities as there are atoms in 0,012 kg of carbon 12. [14th CGPM (1971), Resolution 3]

Notes:

(i) The unit kelvin and its symbol K are also used to indicate temperature intervals or temperature differences. Besides thermodynamic temperature (Symbol T), expressed in kelvins, Celsius temperature (Symbol t) is also used. Celsius temperature is defined by the equation: $t = T - T_o$
where T_o = 273,15 K by definition. Celsius temperature is in general expressed in degrees Celsius (Symbol °C). The unit "degree Celsius" is therefore equal to the unit "kelvin" and an interval or difference in Celsius temperature is also expressed in degrees Celsius (°C).
Note that the Celsius temperature of the triple point of water is 0,01°C, which accounts for the factor 273,16 in the definition of the kelvin.

(ii) Whenever the mole is used, the elementary entities must be specified, and may be atoms, molecules, ions, electrons, other particles or specified groups of such particles.

2.3. SI derived units

SI derived units are formed according to the rule in 2.1 and may be devided into three classes. Examples of each are given in the following table.

2.3.1.

TABLE 2

EXAMPLES OF SI DERIVED UNITS WHICH ARE EXPRESSED IN TERMS OF SI BASE UNITS AND SI SUPPLEMENTARY UNITS

Quantity	SI unit	
	Name	Symbol
acceleration	metre per second squared	m/s^2
angular acceleration	radian per second squared	rad/s^2
angular momentum	kilogram metre squared per second	$kg \cdot m^2/s$
angular velocity	radian per second	rad/s
area	square metre	m^2
coefficient of linear expansion	1 per kelvin	K^{-1}
concentration (of amount of substance)	mole per cubic metre	mol/m^3
density	kilogram per cubic metre	kg/m^3
diffusion coefficient	metre squared per second	m^2/s
electric current density	ampere per square metre	A/m^2
exposure rate (ionising radiation)	ampere per kilogram	A/kg
kinematic viscosity	metre squared per second	m^2/s
luminance	candela per square metre	cd/m^2
magnetic field strength	ampere per metre	A/m
magnetic moment	ampere metre squared	$A \cdot m^2$
mass flow rate	kilogram per second	kg/s
mass per unit area	kilogram per square metre	kg/m^2
mass per unit length	kilogram per metre	kg/m
molality	mole per kilogram	mol/kg
molar mass	kilogram per mole	kg/mol
molar volume	cubic metre per mole	m^3/mol
moment of inertia	kilogram metre squared	$kg \cdot m^2$
moment of momentum	kilogram metre squared per second	$kg \cdot m^2/s$
momentum	kilogram metre per second	$kg \cdot m/s$
radioactivity (disintegration rate)	1 per second	s^{-1}
rotational frequency	1 per second	s^{-1}
specific volume	cubic metre per kilogram	m^3/kg
speed	metre per second	m/s
velocity	metre per second	m/s
volume	cubic metre	m^3
wave number	1 per metre	m^{-1}

2.3.2. **TABLE 3**

SI DERIVED UNITS WITH SPECIAL NAMES

Quantity	SI unit			
	Name	Symbol	Expression in terms of other SI units and definition of unit	Expression in terms of SI base units
admittance	siemens	S	Ω^{-1}	$m^{-2} \cdot kg^{-1} \cdot s^3 \cdot A^2$
capacitance	farad	F	C/V	$m^{-2} \cdot kg^{-1} \cdot s^4 \cdot A^2$
conductance	siemens	S	Ω^{-1}	$m^{-2} \cdot kg^{-1} \cdot s^3 \cdot A^2$
electrical resistance	ohm	Ω	V/A	$m^2 \cdot kg \cdot s^{-3} \cdot A^{-2}$
electric charge	coulomb	C	A·s	s·A
electric flux	coulomb	C	A·s	s·A
electric potential	volt	V	W/A	$m^2 \cdot kg \cdot s^{-3} \cdot A^{-1}$
electromotive force	volt	V	W/A	$m^2 \cdot kg \cdot s^{-3} \cdot A^{-1}$
energy	joule	J	N·m	$m^2 \cdot kg \cdot s^{-2}$
energy flux	watt	W	J/s	$m^2 \cdot kg \cdot s^{-3}$
flux of displacement	coulomb	C	A·s	s·A
force	newton	N	$kg \cdot m/s^2$	$m \cdot kg \cdot s^{-2}$
frequency	hertz	Hz	s^{-1}	s^{-1}
illuminance	lux	lx	lm/m^2	$m^{-2} \cdot cd \cdot sr$
impedance	ohm	Ω	V/A	$m^2 \cdot kg \cdot s^{-3} \cdot A^{-2}$
inductance	henry	H	Wb/A (V·s/A)	$m^2 \cdot kg \cdot s^{-2} \cdot A^{-2}$
luminous flux	lumen	lm	cd·sr	cd·sr
magnetic flux	weber	Wb	V·s	$m^2 \cdot kg \cdot s^{-2} \cdot A^{-1}$
magnetic flux density	tesla	T	Wb/m^2	$kg \cdot s^{-2} \cdot A^{-1}$
magnetic induction	tesla	T	Wb/m^2	$kg \cdot s^{-2} \cdot A^{-1}$
magnetic polarization	tesla	T	Wb/m^2	$kg \cdot s^{-2} \cdot A^{-1}$
permeance	henry	H	Wb/A (V·s/A)	$m^2 \cdot kg \cdot s^{-2} \cdot A^{-2}$
potential difference	volt	V	W/A	$m^2 \cdot kg \cdot s^{-3} \cdot A^{-1}$
power	watt	W	J/s	$m^2 \cdot kg \cdot s^{-3}$
pressure	pascal	Pa	N/m^2	$m^{-1} \cdot kg \cdot s^{-2}$
quantity of electricity	coulomb	C	A·s	s·A
quantity of heat	joule	J	N·m	$m^2 \cdot kg \cdot s^{-2}$
reactance	ohm	Ω	V/A	$m^2 \cdot kg \cdot s^{-3} \cdot A^{-2}$
stress	pascal	Pa	N/m^2	$m^{-1} \cdot {}^{.} \cdot g \cdot s^{-2}$
susceptance	siemens	S	Ω^{-1}	$m^{-2} \cdot kg^{-1} \cdot s^3 \cdot A^2$
weight	newton	N	$kg \cdot m/s^2$	$m \cdot kg \cdot s^{-2}$
work	joule	J	N·m	$m^2 \cdot kg \cdot s^{-2}$

Notes:

(i) The expressions in the fourth column represent the definitions of the respective units in symbolic form and were obtained in accordance with the rule in 2.1. For instance, the quantity force is defined as the product of mass and acceleration ($F = m \cdot a$) so the definition of the unit of force, the newton (N) is given by 1 N = 1 $kg \cdot m/s^2$.

Where more than one algebraic relationship exists between applicable units, for example $V = I \cdot R$ (potential difference equals current multiplied by resistance) or $V = P/I$ (potential difference equals power divided by current) then the definition of the corresponding unit in the fourth column is the one which is officially accepted by the CGPM.

(ii) Mechanical energy must not be expressed in newton meters (N·m) but only in joules (J). The former unit is used only for torque or moment of force.

(iii) In the expressions for the lumen (lm) and lux (lx) in the fifth column, the steradian (sr) is treated as a base unit.

2.3.3.

TABLE 4

EXAMPLES OF SI DERIVED UNITS WHICH ARE EXPRESSED IN TERMS OF SI DERIVED UNITS WITH SPECIAL NAMES AS WELL AS SI BASE UNITS AND SI SUPPLEMENTARY UNITS

Quantity	SI unit		Expression in terms of SI base units and SI supplementary units
	Name	Symbol	
absorbed dose	joule per kilogram	J/kg	$m^2 \cdot s^{-2}$
coefficient of heat transfer	watt per metre squared kelvin	$W/m^2 \cdot K$	$kg \cdot s^{-3} \cdot K^{-1}$
conductivity	siemens per metre	S/m	$m^{-3} \cdot kg^{-1} \cdot s^3 \cdot A^2$
dielectric polarization	coulomb per square metre	C/m^2	$m^{-2} \cdot s \cdot A$
displacement	coulomb per square metre	C/m^2	$m^{-2} \cdot s \cdot A$
dynamic viscosity	pascal second	Pa·s	$m^{-1} \cdot kg \cdot s^{-1}$
electric charge density	coulomb per cubic metre	C/m^3	$m^{-3} \cdot s \cdot A$
electric dipole moment	coulomb metre	C·m	$m \cdot s \cdot A$
electric field strength	volt per metre	V/m	$m \cdot kg \cdot s^{-3} \cdot A^{-1}$
energy density	joule per cubic metre	J/m^3	$m^{-1} \cdot kg \cdot s^{-2}$
entropy	joule per kelvin	J/K	$m^2 \cdot kg \cdot s^{-2} \cdot K^{-1}$
exposure (ionizing radiation)	coulomb per kilogram	C/kg	$kg^{-1} \cdot s \cdot A$
heat capacity	joule per kelvin	J/K	$m^2 \cdot kg \cdot s^{-2} \cdot K^{-1}$
heat flux density	watt per square metre	W/m^2	$kg \cdot s^{-3}$
magnetic dipole moment	weber metre	Wb·m	$m^3 \cdot kg \cdot s^{-2} \cdot A^{-1}$
molar energy	joule per mole	J/mol	$m^2 \cdot kg \cdot s^{-2} \cdot mol^{-1}$
molar entropy	joule per mole kelvin	J/mol·K	$m^2 \cdot kg \cdot s^{-2} \cdot K^{-1} \cdot mol^{-1}$
molar heat capacity	joule per mole kelvin	J/mol·K	$m^2 \cdot kg \cdot s^{-2} \cdot K^{-1} \cdot mol^{-1}$
moment of force	newton metre	N·m	$m^2 \cdot kg \cdot s^{-2}$
permeability	henry per metre	H/m	$m \cdot kg \cdot s^{-2} \cdot A^{-2}$
permittivity	farad per metre	F/m	$m^{-3} \cdot kg^{-1} \cdot s^4 \cdot A^2$
radiant intensity	watt per steradian	W/sr	$m^2 \cdot kg \cdot s^{-3} \cdot sr^{-1}$
reluctance	1 per henry	H^{-1}	$m^{-2} \cdot kg^{-1} \cdot s^2 \cdot A^2$
resistivity	ohm metre	$\Omega \cdot m$	$m^3 \cdot kg \cdot s^{-3} \cdot A^{-2}$
specific energy	joule per kilogram	J/kg	$m^2 \cdot s^{-2}$
specific entropy	joule per kilogram kelvin	J/kg·K	$m^2 \cdot s^{-2} \cdot K^{-1}$
specific heat capacity	joule per kilogram kelvin	J/kg·K	$m^2 \cdot s^{-2} \cdot K^{-1}$
specific latent heat	joule per kilogram	J/kg	$m^2 \cdot s^{-2}$
surface charge density	coulomb per square metre	C/m^2	$m^{-2} \cdot s \cdot A$
surface tension	newton per metre	N/m	$kg \cdot s^{-2}$
thermal conductivity	watt per metre kelvin	W/m·K	$m \cdot kg \cdot s^{-3} \cdot K^{-1}$
torque	newton metre	N·m	$m^2 \cdot kg \cdot s^{-2}$

Notes:

(i) In the interests of uniformity it is preferable to define, as far as possible, the SI derived units in accordance with the combinations given in the above tables. This does not, however, exclude the possibility of using other equivalent combinations in special cases. In education for example, it may be convenient to define electric field strength initially in terms of the force experienced by unit charge and to use the corresponding unit newton per coulomb (N/C) instead of volt per metre (V/m).
Note that: 1 V/m = 1 W/A·m = 1 J/s·A·m = 1 N·m/s·A·m = 1 N/C .

(ii) Torque or moment of force should not be expressed in joules (J) but only in newton metres (N·m) .

(iii) The values of certain so-called dimensionless quantities such as index of refraction, relative permeability and relative permittivity are expressed as pure numbers. Each of these quantities does have an SI unit but this consists of the ratio of two identical SI units and so may be expressed by the number 1.

2.4. SI supplementary units

TABLE 5

SI SUPPLEMENTARY UNITS

Quantity	SI unit		
	Name	Symbol	Definition
plane angle	radian	rad	The radian is the plane angle between two radii of a circle which cut off on the circumference an arc equal in length to the radius.
solid angle	steradian	sr	The steradian is the solid angle which, having its vertex in the centre of a sphere, cuts off an area of the surface of the sphere equal to that of a square with sides of length equal to the radius of the sphere.

2.5. Method of writing SI units and symbols

2.5.1. Symbols

2.5.1.1. Symbols are typed or printed in roman (upright) letters and are always lower case letters except if the name of the corresponding unit is derived from the name of a person, in which case the symbol, or the first letter thereof if it consists of more than one letter, is a capital letter. Examples: metre (m), second (s), but watt (W), hertz (Hz), etc. These rules apply always, even if the rest of the subject matter is printed in upper case or other letter types as in headings of tables, paragraphs, etc.

Examples:

LENGTH IN m   or *Length in* m
FREQUENCY IN Hz or *Frequency in* Hz

2.5.1.2. Symbols have no plural, e.g. 1 m, 2 m, etc.

2.5.1.3. Note that it is incorrect to refer to the symbols as abbreviations. Symbols are therefore not followed by a fullstop unless they occur at the end of a sentence, in which case it is recommended that a space be left between the symbol and the fullstop to stress that the fullstop is not part of the symbol, e.g. The length of an object is 2,5 m .

2.5.1.4. The product of two or more symbols is preferably indicated by means of a point. This point is preferably raised above the line as in N·m but may be also printed on the line as in N.m if the former position is not easily reproduced, for example in typed work. If there is no risk of confusion with other symbols then the point may be replaced by a space (N m).

2.5.1.5. A solidus, horizontal line, or negative powers may be used to indicate division of symbols, e.g. m/s, $\frac{m}{s}$ or $m \cdot s^{-1}$. Only one solidus may be used, e.g. J/mol·K or m/s² but *not* J/mol/K or m/s/s. It is recommended that negative powers be used in more complicated cases which may lack clarity in other notation. Brackets may be also used.

Example:

$m \cdot kg \cdot s^{-3} \cdot A^{-1}$ or $m \cdot kg/(s^3 \cdot A)$.

2.5.2. Units written in full

2.5.2.1. When written out in full the name of a unit is written in lower case letters irrespective of whether it is derived from the name of a person or not. Exceptions are if the unit appears at the beginning of a sentence in which case the first letter is a capital letter, and if the whole of the subject matter is printed in capital letters, e.g. LENGTH IN METRES.

3. MULTIPLES AND SUBMULTIPLES OF SI UNITS

3.1 SI prefixes

The use of only SI units would sometimes lead to inconveniently large or small values.
To avoid cumbersome notation a series of international prefixes is used to form decimal multiples and submultiples of SI units.

3.1.1.

TABLE 6

PREFERRED SI PREFIXES

Factor		Factor in words	SI prefix	SI symbol
1 000 000 000 000	or 10^{12}	billion	tera-	T
1 000 000 000	or 10^9	milliard	giga-	G
1 000 000	or 10^6	million	mega-	M
1 000	or 10^3	thousand	kilo-	k
0,001	or 10^{-3}	thousandth	milli-	m
0,000 001	or 10^{-6}	millionth	micro-	μ
0,000 000 001	or 10^{-9}	milliardth	nano-	n
0,000 000 000 001	or 10^{-12}	billionth	pico-	p
0,000 000 000 000 001	or 10^{-15}	billiardth	femto-	f
0,000 000 000 000 000 001	or 10^{-18}	trillionth	atto-	a

3.1.2.

TABLE 7

OTHER SI PREFIXES

Factor		Factor in words	SI prefix	SI symbol
100	or 10^2	hundred	hecto-	h
10	or 10^1	ten	deca-	da
0,1	or 10^{-1}	tenth	deci-	d
0,01	or 10^{-2}	hundredth	centi-	c

3.2. Style and use of SI prefixes and their symbols

3.2.1. Base units, derived units with special names, and supplementary units

3.2.1.1. All of these SI units have single names and symbols i.e. they are not written as combinations of other units or their respective symbols. Multiples and submultiples of these SI units are formed by writing the prefixes and their symbols directly in front of the names of the relevant units or their symbols respectively, without a space, point or other mark of separation. In this manner new names and symbols are obtained, e.g. millimetre (mm), megagram (Mg), picofarad (pF), etc.

3.2.1.2. Combinations of prefixes must not be used, e.g.:

nanometre (nm) but *not* millimicrometre (mμm)
picofarad (pF) but *not* micromicrofarad ($\mu\mu$F)

3.2.1.3. As mentioned in 3.2.1.1, the combination of a unit and a prefix (or their symbols) is a new entity, consequently raising to a power has bearing on the combination as a whole and not merely on the unit which carries the exponent.

Examples:

$1 \ \mu s^{-1} = (10^{-6}s)^{-1} = 10^6 s^{-1}$ but not $10^{-6}s^{-1}$
$1 \ mm^2 = 1 \ (mm)^2 = (10^{-3}m)^2 = 10^{-6}m^2$
and not $10^{-3}m^2$, i.e. mm^2 stands for square millimetre and *not* milli (square metre).

Note that multiples and submultiples of units which represent other units raised to powers (e.g. area: m^2, volume: m^3, etc.) can therefore not be formed by using rule 3.2.1.1. Multiples and submultiples of the SI units of area and volume are thus in effect powers of multiples and submultiples of the SI unit of length.

3.2.1.4. The kilogram (kg) represents a second exception to rule 3.2.1.1. This unit, although it is an SI unit, contains the prefix kilo- for historical reasons. It has thus far not been possible to remove this anomaly because agreement on a suitable name for the kilogram could as yet not be reached at an international level.

On account of rule 3.2.1.2, no prefixes may be attached to the word kilogram and multiples and submultiples of this unit are therefore formed by attaching the prefixes to the word gram (g), e.g. gram (g) and not a millikilogram (mkg) and milligram (mg) and not a microkilogram (μkg).

Note that the gram (g) is not an SI unit but that it is a submultiple of an SI unit.

3.2.2. Other derived units

3.2.2.1. If multiples and submultiples of units in this category (i.e. SI derived units which are written as combinations of other SI units) are formed in accordance with rule 3.2.1.1, they may be regarded as 'true' multiples and submultiples of SI units. The prefixes or their symbols are then written directly before the first unit or symbol of the combination respectively, e.g. millimetre per second (mm/s); micro-ohm metre ($\mu\Omega$·m); kilowatt per square metre (kW/m²).

In this form, the prefix may be regarded as applying to the combination (an SI unit) which follows it as a whole, i.e. kW/m² = k(W/m²) and no further rules or exceptions other than those given in 3.2.1 are necessary.

3.2.2.2. In practice it is sometimes convenient to form combinations of multiples and submultiples of SI base units and SI supplementary units, or SI derived units with special names, e.g. micrometre per millisecond (μm/ms) or milliohm millimetre (mΩ·mm). Some experts are of the opinion that these forms are not true multiples and submultiples of SI units but only combinations of multiples and/or submultiples. It is recommended that they should be converted to forms such as in 3.2.2.1, e.g.

$1\,\mu\text{m/ms} = 10^{-6}\,\text{m}/10^{-3}\,\text{s} = 10^{-3}\,\text{m/s} = 1\,\text{mm/s}$
$1\,\text{m}\Omega\text{·mm} = 10^{-3}\Omega\cdot10^{-3}\,\text{m} = 10^{-6}\Omega\text{·m} = 1\,\mu\Omega\text{·m}$

This is recommended because the use of the combinations referred to can often lead to complications (see 3.2.3.4).

Note:

The use of prefixes in the denominator of combination units which consist of the quotients of SI units is particularly deprecated and must be avoided wherever possible [e.g. kilonewton per meter (kN/m) and not newton per millimetre (N/mm)], except of course in the case of the kilogram.

3.2.3. Preferred multiples and submultiples

3.2.3.1. One of the most important aims of the SI is the simplification and rationalization of units for measuring and calculations. (See for example the remarks on units of energy in the introduction). The number of multiples and submultiples is accordingly restricted by giving preference to the use of prefixes which represent steps of 1 000 (Table 6). Wherever possible, preference must be given to these prefixes and the other prefixes (Table 7) should be avoided. The latter are given merely for completeness and because they are still sometimes required in specialized fields. For example the centimetre (cm) is used in the clothing and textile industries and therefore also for the related dimensions of the human body. It should preferably not be introduced elsewhere.

3.2.3.2. Unfortunately it is not possible to apply the above preference consistently because SI units which are raised to the second or higher powers [e.g. area (m²), volume (m³), etc.] do not have special names and the preferred usage, because of 3.2.1.3, results in unpractically large steps, e.g.

Area:

$1\,\text{km}^2 = 10^6\,\text{m}^2$
$1\,\text{m}^2 = 10^6\,\text{mm}^2$, etc.

Volume:

$1\,\text{km}^3 = 10^9\,\text{m}^3$
$1\,\text{m}^3 = 10^9\,\text{mm}^3$, etc.

It is therefore sometimes necessary to use prefixes from Table 7, usually only centi- (c) and deci- (d). The other two are seldom required and should be avoided.

Note that in the case of volume the use of centi- (c) and deci- (d) again leads to steps of 1 000.

$1\,\text{m}^3 = 1\,000\,\text{dm}^3$
$1\,\text{dm}^3 = 1\,000\,\text{cm}^3$
$1\,\text{cm}^3 = 1\,000\,\text{mm}^3$

It is in particular, where multiples and sub-multiples of SI units are raised to powers of 2 or higher (area, volume, etc.) and are formed with non-preferred prefixes in combinations such as those in 3.2.2.2, that the complications which are mentioned there occur. If such combinations are used then additional factors of 10 and 100 are necessary to bring the data into a suitable form for calculations. ($1 \text{ g/dm}^2 = 10^{-1} \text{kg/m}^2 = 100 \times 10^{-3} \text{ kg/m}^2$; $1 \text{ g·cm}^2 = 10^{-7} \text{ kg·m}^2$). Inevitably the chance of error is considerably greater than it would be if only factors of 1 000; 1 000 000; 1/1 000 etc. are used.

3.2.3.3. Although the above use does solve the problem of too big steps to a certain extent, it is never the less recommended that such data be given in terms of SI units where possible. The slight inconvenience brought about by the resulting small or large values is compensated for by the uniformity and simplicity of calculations (see 6.4).

Examples:

Write (a) 350 cm^2 as $0,035 \text{ m}^2$ or $3,5 \times 10^{-2} \text{ m}^2$
 (b) 75 dm^3 as $0,075 \text{ m}^3$ or $7,5 \times 10^{-2} \text{ m}^3$

3.2.3.4. Because the consistent use of only SI units offers considerable advantages in calculations, it is preferable to express data in SI units or at least in terms of preferred multiples and submultiples of SI units. It is then only necessary to multiply by integral powers of 1 000 to bring the data into a suitable form for calculations.

4. UNITS WHICH DO NOT FORM PART OF THE SI BUT WHICH MAY BE USED WITH THE SI SUBJECT TO CERTAIN RESTRICTIONS

4.1. At this stage it is unfortunately not yet possible to use only SI units and multiples and submultiples of SI units. This chapter contains units which may be used with the SI as follows:

(a) Units which will probably be used with the SI for a long time yet;

(b) units which for the time being may be used with the SI in special fields;

(c) units which may be used together with the SI only temporarily.

Nevertheless, it is strongly recommended that where possible, and in particular where scientific and technological calculations are under consideration, such units be avoided in favour of the corresponding SI units, or where data are provided in such units that these data be first converted to the correct SI units before being used in calculations.

4.2. Units for general use together with the SI

The following units (Table 8) have attained such wide general usage that there is little hope of eliminating them within the foreseeable future. The CGPM recognises that they play such an important part that they must be retained for general use together with the SI. The CGPM does not list the gon in this table (see however note vii).

TABLE 8

UNITS WHICH ARE USED TOGETHER WITH THE SI

Quantity	Name and symbol	Value in terms of the SI	Note
volume fluid	litre (ℓ)	$1\,\ell$ = 1 dm^3 = 0,001 m^3	(v)
mass	metric ton (t)	$1\,t$ = 1 Mg = 1 000 kg	(iv)
plane angle	degree ($^\circ$)	1° = $\pi/180$ rad	(i), (ii)
plane angle	minute (')	$1'$ = $\pi/10\,800$ rad	(i)
plane angle	second (")	$1''$ = $\pi/648\,000$ rad	(i)
plane angle	gon (gon)	1 gon = $\pi/200$ rad	(iii), (vii)
time	minute (min)	1 min = 60 s	(i)
time	hour (h)	1 h = 3,6 ks = 3 600 s	(i)
time	day (d)	1 d = 86,4 ks = 86 400 s	(i)
time	week	1 week = 604,8 ks = 604 800 s	(i), (vi)
volume fluid	litre (ℓ)	$1\,\ell$ = 1 dm^3 = 0,001 m^3	(v)

Notes:

(i) SI prefixes are not used with the minute, hour, day, week, degree, minute and second (plane angle).

(ii) When the degree ($^\circ$) is used it is recommended that where possible decimal subdivisions be used in place of minutes (') and seconds (").

(iii) Note that there are 400 gon in a circle, i.e. 100 gon in a right angle.

(iv) The metric ton is a 'commercial' unit, i.e. it is intended for everyday use but not for use in scientific and technological calculations. Only the SI prefixes kilo-, mega-, giga-, and tera- are used with the metric ton.

(v) The litre is likewise a 'commercial' unit. Only SI prefixes from Table 6 and deca- and hecto- may be used with the litre. The litre is by definiton [Resolution 6, 12th CGPM, (1964)] exactly equal to 1 dm^3. The international symbol for the litre is a lower case l. This can however sometimes be confused with the number 1 in typed and printed matter and it is therefore recommended that a 'script' ℓ such as shown here be used for this purpose. Suppliers of typewriters supply this symbol and in addition also the degree- (^{0}), second power- (^{2}), and third power- (^{3}) symbols.

(vi) The month and year of the Gregorian calendar are also used with the SI although they are variable and therefore strictly speaking cannot be classified as units.

(vii) The gon enjoys equal status with the degree in the EEC directive. ISO refers to it under the following remark: The units degree and grade (or gon), with their decimal subdivisions, are recommended for use when the unit radian is not suitable. Note that ISO recognises both names (grade and gon) in English.

4.3. Units for use with SI in specialised fields

The following units (Table 9) may be used with the SI in specialized fields of scientific research.

TABLE 9

UNITS WHICH MAY BE USED TOGETHER WITH THE SI IN SPECIALISED FIELDS

Quantity	Name	Symbol	*Approximate value in terms of the SI	Restriction
distance	astronomical unit	AU	1 AU = 149,6 Gm = $1,496 \times 10^{11}$ m	Only in astronomy
distance	parsec	pc	1 pc = 30 857 Tm = $3,085\ 7 \times 10^{16}$ m	Only in astronomy
energy	electronvolt	eV	1 eV = 0,160 219 aJ = $1,602\ 19 \times 10^{-19}$ J	Only in the atomic and nuclear sciences
mass	atomic mass unit (unified)	u	1 u = $1,660\ 53 \times 10^{-27}$ kg	Only in the natural sciences

*The values of these units in terms of the SI have to be determined experimentally and are therefore not known exactly.

Definitions of units in Table 9:

(i) 1 eV is the energy acquired by an electron in passing through a potential difference of 1 V in vacuum.

(ii) 1 u is equal to the fraction $\frac{1}{12}$ of the mass of an atom of the nuclide carbon-12.

(iii) 1 AU is the length of the radius of the unperturbed circular orbit of a body of negligible mass moving around the sun with a sidereal angular velocity of 17,202 098 950 mrad/d of 86 400 ephemeris seconds.

(iv) 1 pc is the distance at which 1 AU subtends an angle of 1″.

4.4. Units which are only recognised temporarily

TABLE 10

UNITS WHICH MAY ONLY BE USED WITH SI FOR A LIMITED TIME

Quantity	Name	Symbol	Value in terms of the SI	Restriction
absorbed dose	rad	rad,rd	1 rad = 10 mJ/kg = 10^{-2} J/kg	Only in radiation dosimetry
acceleration	gal	Gal	1 Gal = 10 mm/s^2 = 0,01 m/s^2	Only in geodesy and geophysics
apparent power	volt ampere	VA		Only in electrical engineering
area	hectare	ha	1 ha = 10 000 m^2	Only in surveying and mapping
area	barn	b	1 b = 100 fm^2 = 10^{-28} m^2	Only in nuclear and atomic physics
distance	nautical mile (international)		1 nautical mile = 1,852 km = 1 852 m	Only in nautical and aeronautical navigation
exposure	röntgen	R	1 R = 258 μC/kg = 2,58 x 10^{-4} C/kg	Only in radiation dosimetry
length	ångström	Å	1 Å = 0,1 nm = 10^{-10} m	
mass per unit length	tex	tex	1 tex = 1 mg/m = 10^{-6} kg/m	Only in the textile industry
pressure*	bar	bar	1 bar = 100 kPa = 10^5 Pa	
radioactivity	curie	Ci	1 Ci = 37 ns^{-1} = 3,7 x 10^{10} s^{-1}	Only in connection with radioactive radiation
reactive power	volt ampere reactive	var		Only in electrical engineering
refractive power	dioptre	δ	1 δ = 1 m^{-1}	Only in optics
rotational frequency	revolution per minute	r/min	1 r/min = 16,666 667 ks^{-1} = 16,666 667 x 10^{-3} s^{-1}	
speed, velocity	knot (international)		1 knot = 1 nautical mile per hour = 0,514 444 m/s	Only in nautical and aeronautical navigation

Notes:

* The name pascal, symbol Pa, was given to the SI unit for pressure and stress (the newton per square metre) by the CGPM in October 1971 and the bar was classified amongst the units which may only be used with the SI for a limited time. The CGPM took this decision with the motivation that it should contribute to the elimination of the bar. It is therefore strongly recommended that from now on all new instruments for measuring pressure be ordered with pascal calibrations (or suitable multiples and submultiples thereof). Existing instruments which are already calibrated in bars can easily be changed by simply replacing the word bar on the dial with x 100 kPa without altering any of the calibrations.

TABLE 11

DEFINITIONS OF DERIVED SI UNITS HAVING SPECIAL NAMES

Quantity	SI unit and -symbol	Definition
frequency	hertz, Hz	The hertz is the frequency of a periodic phenomenon of which the period is 1 s.
force	newton, N	The newton is that force which, when applied to a body having a mass of 1 kg, gives it an acceleration of 1 m/s^2.
pressure, stress	pascal, Pa	The pascal is the pressure or stress which results when a force of 1 N is applied evenly and perpendicularly to an area of 1 m^2.
energy, work	joule, J	The joule is the work done when the point of application of a force of 1 N is displaced through a distance of 1 m in the direction of the force.
power	watt, W	The watt is the power which results in the production of energy at the rate of 1 J/s.
electric charge	coulomb, C	The coulomb is the quantity of electric charge transported in 1 s by a current of 1 A.
electric potential difference (electromotive force)	volt, V	The volt is the potential difference between two points of a conducting wire carrying a constant current of 1 A, when the power dissipated between these points is equal to 1 W.
capacitance	farad, F	The farad is the capacitance of a capacitor between the plates of which there appears a potential difference of 1 V when it is charged with an electric charge equal to 1 C.
electric resistance	ohm, Ω	The ohm is the electric resistance between two points of a conductor when a constant potential difference of 1 V, applied between these two points, produces a current of 1 A, the conductor not being the source of any electromotive force.
conductance	siemens, S	The siemens is the conductance of a conductor of resistance 1 Ω and it is numerically equal to 1 Ω^{-1}.
magnetic flux	weber, Wb	The weber is the magnetic flux which, linking a circuit of one turn, produces in it an electromotive force of 1 V if it is reduced to zero at a uniform rate in 1 s.
magnetic flux density	tesla, T	The tesla is a magnetic flux density of 1 Wb/m^2.
inductance	henry, H	The henry is the inductance of a closed circuit in which an electromotive force of 1 V is produced if the electric current in the circuit varies uniformly at the rate of 1 A/s.
luminous flux	lumen, lm	The lumen is the luminous flux emitted within a solid angle of 1 sr by a point source having a uniform intensity of 1 cd.
illumination	lux, lx	The lux is an illumination of 1 lm/m^2.

CONVERSION FACTORS

TABLE 12

ALPHABETICAL LIST OF CONVERSIONS TO SI UNITS
(SI SYMBOLS ARE GIVEN IN BRACKETS)

To convert from	to	multiply by
abampere (biot)	ampere (A)	*1×10^1
abcoulomb	coulomb (C)	*1×10^1
abfarad	farad (F)	*1×10^9
abhenry	henry (H)	*1×10^{-9}
abmho	siemens (S)	*1×10^9
abohm	ohm (Ω)	*1×10^{-9}
abvolt	volt (V)	*1×10^{-8}
acre	square metre (m^2)	*$4{,}046\ 86 \times 10^3$
acre foot	cubic metre (m^3)	$1{,}233\ 482 \times 10^3$
ampere (international of 1948)	ampere (A)	$9{,}998\ 35 \times 10^{-1}$
ampere hour	coulomb (C)	*$3{,}6 \times 10^3$
ångström	metre (m)	*1×10^{-10}
are	square metre (m^2)	*1×10^2
astronomical unit	metre (m)	$1{,}496 \times 10^{11}$
atmosphere (standard)	pascal (Pa)	*$1{,}013\ 25 \times 10^5$
atmosphere (technical) (= 1 kgf/cm^2)	pascal (Pa)	$9{,}806\ 65 \times 10^4$
atomic mass unit (unified)	kilogram (kg)	$1{,}660\ 531 \times 10^{-27}$
bar	pascal (Pa)	*1×10^5
barn	square metre (m^2)	*1×10^{-28}
barrel (petroleum; 42 gallons (USA); liquid)	cubic metre (m^2)	$1{,}589\ 873 \times 10^{-1}$
biot (abampere)	ampere (A)	*1×10^1
British thermal unit (mean)	joule (J)	$1{,}055\ 87 \times 10^3$
British thermal unit (39°F)	joule (J)	$1{,}059\ 67 \times 10^3$
British thermal unit (60°F)	joule (J)	$1{,}054\ 68 \times 10^3$

Note: Conversion factors preceded by an asterisk are exact.

To convert from	to	multiply by
British thermal unit (international table)	joule (J)	$1{,}055\ 056 \times 10^3$
British thermal unit (thermochemical)	joule (J)	$1{,}054\ 35 \times 10^3$
[1] British thermal unit (international table) inch per hour square foot degree Fahrenheit	watt per metre kelvin (W/m·K)	$1{,}442\ 279 \times 10^{-1}$
[1] British thermal unit (thermochemical) inch per hour square foot degree Fahrenheit	watt per metre kelvin (W/m·K)	$1{,}441\ 314 \times 10^{-1}$
British thermal unit (international table) per cubic foot	joule per cubic metre (J/m³)	$3{,}725\ 89 \times 10^4$
British thermal unit (thermochemical) per cubic foot	joule per cubic metre (J/m³)	$3{,}723\ 402 \times 10^4$
[1] British thermal unit (international table) per cubic foot degree Fahrenheit	joule per cubic metre kelvin (J/m³·K)	$6{,}706\ 607 \times 10^4$
[1] British thermal unit (thermochemical) per cubic foot degree Fahrenheit	joule per cubic metre kelvin (J/m³·K)	$6{,}702\ 118 \times 10^4$
British thermal unit (international table) per hour	watt (W)	$2{,}930\ 711 \times 10^{-1}$
British thermal unit (thermochemical) per hour	watt (W)	$2{,}928\ 751 \times 10^{-1}$
[1] British thermal unit (international table) per hour square foot degree Fahrenheit	watt per square metre kelvin (W/m²·K)	$5{,}678\ 263 \times 10^0$
[1] British thermal unit (thermochemical) per hour square foot degree Fahrenheit	watt per square metre kelvin (W/m²·K)	$5{,}674\ 466 \times 10^0$
British thermal unit (international table) per pound	joule per kilogram (J/kg)	$*2{,}326 \times 10^3$
British thermal unit (thermochemical) per pound	joule per kilogram (J/kg)	$2{,}324\ 444 \times 10^3$
[1] British thermal unit (international table) per pound degree Fahrenheit	joule per kilogram kelvin (J/kg·K)	$*4{,}186\ 8 \times 10^3$

[1] Because the degree Fahrenheit in the denominator represents a temperature interval it follows from 2.2 note (i) that precisely the same conversion factor applies if the kelvin (K) in the SI unit is replaced by the degree Celsius (°C).

To convert from	to	multiply by
[1] British thermal unit (thermochemical) per pound degree Fahrenheit	joule per kilogram kelvin (J/kg·K)	$4,184 \times 10^3$
British thermal unit (international table) per square foot	joule per square metre (J/m²)	$1,135\ 653 \times 10^4$
British thermal unit (thermochemical) per square foot	joule per square metre (J/m²)	$1,134\ 893 \times 10^4$
British thermal unit (international table) per square foot hour	watt per square metre (W/m²)	$3,154\ 592 \times 10^0$
British thermal unit (thermochemical) per square foot hour	watt per square metre (W/m²)	$3,152\ 481 \times 10^0$
bushel (UK)	cubic metre (m³)	$3,636\ 872 \times 10^{-2}$
bushel (USA)	cubic metre (m³)	$3,523\ 907 \times 10^{-2}$
[2] calorie (15°C)	joule (J)	$4,185\ 5 \times 10^0$
[2] calorie (20°C)	joule (J)	$4,181\ 9 \times 10^0$
[2] calorie (mean)	joule (J)	$4,190\ 02 \times 10^0$
[2] calorie (international table)	joule (J)	$*4,186\ 8 \times 10^0$
[2] calorie (thermochemical)	joule (J)	$*4,184 \times 10^0$
[2] calorie (international table) per hour	watt (W)	$*1,163 \times 10^{-3}$
[2] calorie (thermochemical) per square centimetre minute	watt per square metre (W/m²)	$6,973\ 333 \times 10^2$
candela per square foot	candela per square metre (cd/m²)	$1,076\ 39 \times 10^1$
carat (metric)	kilogram (kg)	$*2 \times 10^{-4}$
centimetre of mercury (0°C)	pascal (Pa)	$1,333\ 223\ 9 \times 10^3$
centimetre of water (4°C)	pascal (Pa)	$9,806\ 38 \times 10^1$
centipoise	pascal second (Pa·s)	$*1 \times 10^{-3}$
centistokes	metre squared per second (m²/s)	$*1 \times 10^{-6}$
chain (Gunter's or surveyors')	metre (m)	$*2,011\ 68 \times 10^1$
chain (Ramden's or engineers')	metre (m)	$*3,048 \times 10^1$
cheval vapeur or metric horsepower	watt (W)	$7,354\ 99 \times 10^2$
clo	kelvin square metre per watt (K·m²/W)	$2,003\ 712 \times 10^-$

[1] Because the degree Fahrenheit in the denominator represents a temperature interval it follows from 2.2 note (i) that precisely the same conversion factor applies if the kelvin (K) in the SI unit is replaced by the degree Celsius (°C).

[2] Note that reference is often made to the calorie when in actual fact the kilocalorie (also called Calorie, large calorie, or kilogram calorie) is meant. (1 kilocalorie = 1 000 calories).

To convert from	to	multiply by
clusec	pascal cubic metre per second ($Pa \cdot m^3/s$)	$1,333\ 224 \times 10^{-6}$
coulomb (international of 1948)	coulomb (C)	$9,998\ 35 \times 10^{-1}$
cubic foot	cubic metre (m^3)	$2,831\ 685 \times 10^{-2}$
cubic foot per minute	cubic metre per second (m^3/s)	$4,719\ 474 \times 10^{-4}$
cubic foot per second	cubic metre per second (m^3/s)	$2,831\ 685 \times 10^{-2}$
cubic inch	cubic metre (m^3)	$*1,638\ 706\ 4 \times 10^{-5}$
cubic inch per minute	cubic metre per second (m^3/s)	$2,731\ 177 \times 10^{-7}$
cubic inch per pound	cubic metre per kilogram (m^3/kg)	$3,612\ 729 \times 10^{-5}$
cubic yard	cubic metre (m^3)	$7,645\ 549 \times 10^{-1}$
cubic yard per minute	cubic metre per second (m^3/s)	$1,274\ 258 \times 10^{-2}$
cup (UK)	cubic metre (m^3)	$2,841\ 306 \times 10^{-4}$
cup (USA)	cubic metre (m^3)	$2,365\ 882 \times 10^{-4}$
curie	per second (s^{-1})	$*3,7 \times 10^{10}$
cusec (see cubic foot per second)		
cusec hour	cubic metre (m^3)	$1,019\ 407 \times 10^2$
cycle per second	hertz (Hz)	$*1 \times 10^0$
day (mean solar)	second (s)	$8,64 \times 10^4$
day (sidereal)	second (s)	$8,616\ 409 \times 10^4$
debye	coulomb metre ($C \cdot m$)	$3,335\ 64 \times 10^{-30}$
degree (angle)	radian (rad)	$1,745\ 329 \times 10^{-2}\ (= *\pi/180)$
degree Celsius (particular temperature)	kelvin (K)	use $T = t_C + 273,15$
degree Celsius (temperature interval)	kelvin (K)	$*1 \times 10^0$
degree Fahrenheit (particular temperature)	kelvin (K)	use $T = (t_F + 459,67)/1,8$
degree Fahrenheit (temperature interval)	kelvin (K)	$0,555\ 556\ (= *1/1,8)$
degree Rankine (particular temperature and temperature interval)	kelvin (K)	$0,555\ 556\ (= *1/1,8)$
dioptre	per metre (m^{-1})	$*1 \times 10^0$
drachm (fluid) (UK)	cubic metre (m^3)	$3,551\ 633 \times 10^{-6}$
drachm (60 grains) (apothecaries)	kilogram (kg)	$3,887\ 93 \times 10^{-3}$
dram ($\frac{1}{256}$ pound) (avoirdupois)	kilogram (kg)	$1,771\ 85 \times 10^{-3}$

To convert from	to	multiply by
dyne	newton (N)	*1 x 10⁻⁵
dyne centimetre	newton metre (N·m)	*1 x 10⁻⁷
dyne per square centimetre	pascal (Pa)	*1 x 10⁻¹
electromagnetic unit of capacitance	farad (F)	*1 x 10⁹
electromagnetic unit of charge	coulomb (C)	*1 x 10¹
electromagnetic unit of current	ampere (A)	*1 x 10¹
electromagnetic unit of inductance	henry (H)	*1 x 10⁻⁹
electromagnetic unit of potential	volt (V)	*1 x 10⁻⁸
electromagnetic unit of resistance	ohm (Ω)	*1 x 10⁻⁹
electronvolt	joule (J)	1,602 191 7 x 10⁻¹⁹
electrostatic unit of capacitance	farad (F)	1,112 649 x 10⁻¹²
electrostatic unit of charge (franklin)	coulomb (C)	3,335 64 x 10⁻¹⁰
electrostatic unit of current	ampere (A)	3,335 64 x 10⁻¹⁰
electrostatic unit of inductance	henry (H)	8,987 554 31 x 10¹¹
electrostatic unit of potential	volt (V)	2,997 925 x 10²
electrostatic unit of resistance	ohm (Ω)	8,987 554 31 x 10¹¹
erg	joule (J)	*1 x 10⁻⁷
farad (international of 1948)	farad (F)	9,995 05 x 10⁻¹
faraday (based on carbon-12)	coulomb per mole (C/mol)	9,648 67 x 10⁴
faraday (chemical)	coulomb per mole (C/mol)	9,649 57 x 10⁴
faraday (physical)	coulomb per mole (C/mol)	9,652 19 x 10⁴
fathom	metre (m)	*1,828 8 x 10⁰
fermi	metre (m)	*1 x 10⁻¹⁵
fluid drachm (UK)	cubic metre (m³)	3,551 633 x 10⁻⁶
fluid ounce (UK)	cubic metre (m³)	2,841 306 x 10⁻⁵
fluid ounce (USA)	cubic metre (m³)	2,957 353 x 10⁻⁵
foot	metre (m)	*3,048 x 10⁻¹
foot (Cape)	metre (m)	*3,148 581 x 10⁻¹
foot (geodetic Cape)	metre (m)	*3,148 555 751 6 x 10⁻¹
[3] foot (South African geodetic)	metre (m)	*3,047 972 654 x 10⁻¹

[3] Land surveyors also refer to this as the 'English foot'.

To convert from	to	multiply by
foot candle (lumen per square foot)	lux (lx)	$1,076\,391 \times 10^1$
foot lambert	candela per square metre (cd/m^2)	$3,426\,259 \times 10^0$
foot of water (39,2°F)	pascal (Pa)	$2,988\,98 \times 10^3$
foot per minute	metre per second (m/s)	$^*5,08 \times 10^{-3}$
foot per second squared	metre per second squared (m/s^2)	$^*3,048 \times 10^{-1}$
foot poundal (energy)	joule (J)	$4,214\,011 \times 10^{-2}$
foot poundal (torque)	newton metre (N·m)	$4,214\,011 \times 10^{-2}$
foot pound-force (energy)	joule (J)	$1,355\,818 \times 10^0$
foot pound-force (torque)	newton metre (N·m)	$1,355\,818 \times 10^0$
foot pound-force per second	watt (W)	$1,355\,818 \times 10^0$
foot to the fourth power (second moment of area)	metre to the fourth power (m^4)	$8,630\,975 \times 10^{-3}$
foot to the third power	(see cubic foot)	
franklin (electrostatic unit of charge)	coulomb (C)	$3,335\,64 \times 10^{-10}$
frigorie	watt (W)	$1,162\,639 \times 10^0$
furlong	metre (m)	$^*2,011\,68 \times 10^2$
gal	metre per second squared (m/s^2)	$^*1 \times 10^{-2}$
gallon (Canada; liquid)	cubic metre (m^3)	$4,546\,122 \times 10^{-3}$
gallon (UK)	cubic metre (m^3)	$^*4,546\,09 \times 10^{-3}$
gallon (USA; dry)	cubic metre (m^3)	$4,404\,884 \times 10^{-3}$
gallon (USA; liquid)	cubic metre (m^3)	$3,785\,412 \times 10^{-3}$
gallon (UK) per hour	cubic metre per second (m^3/s)	$1,262\,803 \times 10^{-6}$
gallon (UK) per pound	cubic metre per kilogram (m^3/kg)	$1,002\,24 \times 10^{-2}$
gamma (magnetic induction)	tesla (T)	$^*1 \times 10^{-9}$
gamma (mass)	kilogram (kg)	$^*1 \times 10^{-9}$
gauss	tesla (T)	$^*1 \times 10^{-4}$
gill (UK)	cubic metre (m^3)	$1,420\,653 \times 10^{-4}$
gill (USA)	cubic metre (m^3)	$1,182\,941 \times 10^{-4}$
[4] gon	radian (rad)	$1,570\,796 \times 10^{-2}$ (=$^*\pi/200$)
[4] grade (see gon)		
grain	kilogram (kg)	$^*6,479\,891 \times 10^{-5}$
grain per gallon (UK)	kilogram per cubic metre (kg/m^3)	$1,425\,38 \times 10^{-2}$
grain per gallon (USA, liquid)	kilogram per cubic metre (kg/m^3)	$1,711\,806 \times 10^{-2}$

[4] See 4.2, note (vii).

To convert from	to	multiply by
hectare	square metre (m²)	*1 × 10⁴
henry (international of 1948)	henry (H)	1,000 495 × 10⁰
horsepower (boiler)	watt (W)	9,809 5 × 10³
horsepower (electrical)	watt (W)	*7,46 × 10²
horsepower (550 foot pounds-force per second)	watt (W)	7,456 999 × 10²
horsepower (metric or cheval vapeur)	watt (W)	7,345 99 × 10²
horsepower (UK)	watt (W)	7,457 × 10²
horsepower (water)	watt (W)	7,460 43 × 10²
horsepower (550 foot pounds-force per second) hour	joule (J)	2,684 52 × 10⁶
hour (mean; solar)	second (s)	3,6 × 10³
hour (sidereal)	second (s)	3,590 17 × 10³
hundredweight (112 pounds)	kilogram (kg)	5,080 235 × 10¹
hundredweight (100 pounds)	kilogram (kg)	4,535 924 × 10¹
hundredweight (112 pounds) per acre	kilogram per square metre (kg/m²)	1,255 35 × 10⁻²
inch	metre (m)	*2,54 × 10⁻²
inch of mercury (32°F)	pascal (Pa)	3,386 389 × 10³
inch of mercury (60°F)	pascal (Pa)	3,376 85 × 10³
inch of water (39,2°F)	pascal (Pa)	2,490 82 × 10²
inch of water (60°F)	pascal (Pa)	2,488 4 × 10²
inch per minute	metre per second (m/s)	4,233 333 × 10⁻⁴
inch to the fourth power	metre to the fourth power (m⁴)	4,162 314 × 10⁻⁷
inch to the third power	(see cubic inch)	
iron (shoes)	metre (m)	5,3 × 10⁻⁴
joule (international of 1948)	joule (J)	1,000 165 × 10⁰
kayser	per metre (m⁻¹)	*1 × 10²
kilocalorie (international table)	joule (J)	*4,186 8 × 10³
kilocalorie (mean)	joule (J)	4,190 02 × 10³
kilocalorie (thermochemical)	joule (J)	*4,184 × 10³
kilogram-force	newton (N)	*9,806 65 × 10⁰
kilogram-force metre (energy)	joule (J)	*9,806 65 × 10⁰
kilogram-force metre (torque)	newton metre (N·m)	*9,806 65 × 10⁰
kilogram-force per square centimetre	pascal (Pa)	*9,806 65 × 10⁴
kilometre per hour	metre per second (m/s)	2,777 778 × 10⁻¹ (=*1/3,6)

To convert from	to	multiply by
kilopond (=kgf)	newton (N)	*9,806 65 x 10^0
kilopond metre (energy)	joule (J)	*9,806 65 x 10^0
kilopond metre (torque)	newton metre (N·m)	*9,806 65 x 10^0
kilopond per square centimetre	pascal (Pa)	*9,806 65 x 10^4
kilowatt hour	joule (J)	*3,6 x 10^6
kilowatt hour (international of 1948)	joule (J)	3,600 59 x 10^6
kip (1 000 pounds-force)	newton (N)	4,448 222 x 10^3
kip (1 000 pounds-force) per square inch	pascal (Pa)	6,894 757 x 10^6
knot (international)	metre per second (m/s)	5,144 444 x 10^{-1}
knot (UK)	metre per second (m/s)	5,147 733 x 10^{-1}
knot (USA)	metre per second (m/s)	5,144 444 x 10^{-1}
lambda	cubic metre (m^3)	1 x 10^{-9}
lambert	candela per square metre (cd/m^2)	3,183 099 x 10^3 (=*$10^4/\pi$)
langley	joule per square metre (J/m^2)	*4,184 x 10^4
leaguer	cubic metre (m^3)	5,773 534 x 10^{-1}
light year	metre (m)	9,460 55 x 10^{15}
ligne (buttons) ($\frac{1}{40}$ inch)	metre (m)	*6,35 x 10^{-4}
litre	cubic metre (m^3)	*1 x 10^{-3}
litre atmosphere	joule (J)	1,013 28 x 10^2
lumen per square foot (foot candle)	lux (lx)	1,076 391 x 10^1
lusec	pascal cubic metre per second (Pa·m^3/s)	1,333 224 x 10^{-4}
maxwell	weber (Wb)	*1 x 10^{-8}
metre kilogram-force (energy)	joule (J)	*9,806 65 x 10^0
metre kilogram-force (torque)	newton metre (N·m)	*9,806 65 x 10^0
metre kilopond (energy)	joule (J)	*9,806 65 x 10^0
metre kilopond (torque)	newton metre (N·m)	*9,806 65 x 10^0
metre of water (4°C)	pascal (Pa)	9,806 38 x 10^3
metric horsepower or cheval vapeur	watt (W)	7,354 99 x 10^2
micron	metre (m)	*1 x 10^{-6}
mil (circular)	square metre (m^2)	5,067 075 x 10^{-10}
mil (thou)	metre	*2,54 x 10^{-5}
mile	metre (m)	*1,609 344 x 10^3
mile per hour	metre per second (m/s)	*4,470 4 x 10^{-1}
[5] millimetre of mercury (0°C)	pascal (Pa)	1,333 223 9 x 10^2

[5] Defined by: ρgh = 13 595,1 x 9,806 65 x 10^{-3}

To convert from	to	multiply by
minim	cubic metre (m³)	$5,919\ 39 \times 10^{-8}$
minute (mean; solar)	second (s)	6×10^1
minute (sidereal)	second (s)	$5,983\ 617 \times 10^1$
minute (plane angle)	radian (rad)	$2,908\ 882 \times 10^{-4}\ (=*\pi/10\ 800)$
month (mean; calendar)	second (s)	$2,628 \times 10^6$
morgen	square metre (m²)	$*8,565\ 32 \times 10^3$
morgen foot	cubic metre (m³)	$2,610\ 71 \times 10^3$
nautical mile (international)	metre (m)	$*1,852 \times 10^3$
nautical mile (telegraph)	metre (m)	$1,855\ 32 \times 10^3$
nautical mile (UK)	metre (m)	$*1,853\ 184 \times 10^3$
nautical mile (USA)	metre (m)	$*1,852 \times 10^3$
oersted	ampere per metre (A/m)	$7,957\ 747 \times 10^1\ (=*1\ 000/4\ \pi)$
ohm (international of 1948)	ohm (Ω)	$1,000\ 495 \times 10^0$
ohm centimetre	ohm metre (Ω·m)	$*1 \times 10^{-2}$
ounce (avoirdupois)	kilogram (kg)	$2,834\ 952 \times 10^{-2}$
ounce (troy or apothecaries)	kilogram (kg)	$3,110\ 348 \times 10^{-2}$
ounce (fluid; UK)	cubic metre (m³)	$2,841\ 306 \times 10^{-5}$
ounce (fluid; USA)	cubic metre (m³)	$2,957\ 353 \times 10^{-5}$
ounce-force	newton (N)	$2,780\ 139 \times 10^{-1}$
ounce-force inch (torque)	newton metre (N·m)	$7,061\ 552 \times 10^{-3}$
ounce (avoirdupois) per cubic inch	kilogram per cubic metre (kg/m³)	$1,729\ 994 \times 10^3$
ounce (avoirdupois) per gallon (UK)	kilogram per cubic metre (kg/m³)	$6,236\ 023 \times 10^0$
ounce (avoirdupois) per gallon (USA; liquid)	kilogram per cubic metre (kg/m³)	$7,489\ 152 \times 10^0$
ounce per inch	kilogram per metre (kg/m)	$1,116\ 12 \times 10^0$
ounce per square yard	kilogram per square metre (kg/m²)	$3,390\ 575 \times 10^{-2}$
parsec	metre (m)	$3,085\ 7 \times 10^{16}$
peck (UK)	cubic metre (m³)	$*9,092\ 18 \times 10^{-3}$
peck (USA)	cubic metre (m³)	$8,809\ 768 \times 10^{-3}$
pennyweight	kilogram (kg)	$1,555\ 174 \times 10^{-3}$
perch (area)	square metre (m²)	$2,529\ 29 \times 10^1$
perch (length)	metre (m)	$*5,029\ 2 \times 10^0$
perm (0°C)	kilogram per newton second (kg/N·s)	$5,721\ 35 \times 10^{-11}$
perm (23°C)	kilogram per newton second (kg/N·s)	$5,745\ 25 \times 10^{-11}$
perm inch (0°C)	kilogram metre per newton second (kg·m/N·s)	$1,453\ 22 \times 10^{-12}$
perm inch (23°C)	kilogram metre per newton second (kg·m/N·s)	$1,459\ 29 \times 10^{-12}$

To convert from	to	multiply by
phot	lux (lx)	*1×10^4
pica (printing)	metre (m)	$4,217\ 518 \times 10^{-3}$
pièze	pascal (Pa)	*1×10^3
pint (UK)	cubic metre (m³)	$5,682\ 613 \times 10^{-4}$
pint (UK; reputed)	cubic metre (m³)	$3,788\ 408 \times 10^{-4}$
pint (USA; dry)	cubic metre (m³)	$5,506\ 105 \times 10^{-4}$
pint (USA; liquid)	cubic metre (m³)	$4,731\ 765 \times 10^{-4}$
pint (USA; reputed)	cubic metre (m³)	$3,154\ 51 \times 10^{-4}$
point (printing)	metre (m)	*$3,514\ 598 \times 10^{-4}$
poise	pascal second (Pa·s)	*1×10^{-1}
poiseuille	pascal second (Pa·s)	*1×10^0
pole (area)	square metre (m²)	$2,529\ 29 \times 10^1$
pole (length)	metre (m)	*$5,029\ 2 \times 10^0$
pound	kilogram (kg)	*$4,535\ 923\ 7 \times 10^{-1}$
poundal	newton (N)	$1,382\ 55 \times 10^{-1}$
poundal per square foot	pascal (Pa)	$1,488\ 164 \times 10^0$
poundal per square inch	pascal (Pa)	$2,142\ 96 \times 10^2$
poundal second per square foot	pascal second (Pa·s)	$1,488\ 164 \times 10^0$
pound foot squared (moment of inertia)	kilogram metre squared (kg·m²)	$4,214\ 012 \times 10^{-2}$
pound-force	newton (N)	$4,448\ 222 \times 10^0$
pound-force foot (torque)	newton metre (N·m)	$1,355\ 818 \times 10^0$
pound-force inch (torque)	newton metre (N·m)	$1,129\ 848 \times 10^{-1}$
pound-force per foot	newton per metre (N/m)	$1,459\ 39 \times 10^1$
pound-force per square foot	pascal (Pa)	$4,788\ 026 \times 10^1$
pound-force per square inch	pascal (Pa)	$6,894\ 757 \times 10^3$
pound-force second per square foot	pascal second (Pa·s)	$4,788\ 026 \times 10^1$
pound inch squared (moment of inertia)	kilogram metre squared (kg·m²)	$2,926\ 397 \times 10^{-4}$
pound per cubic foot	kilogram per cubic metre (kg/m³)	$1,601\ 846 \times 10^1$
pound per gallon (UK)	kilogram per cubic metre (kg/m³)	$9,977\ 636 \times 10^1$
pound per gallon (USA; liquid)	kilogram per cubic metre (kg/m³)	$1,198\ 264 \times 10^2$
pound per minute	kilogram per second (kg/s)	$7,559\ 873 \times 10^{-3}$
pound per square foot	kilogram per square metre (kg/m²)	$4,882\ 428 \times 10^0$
pound per yard	kilogram per metre (kg/m)	$4,960\ 55 \times 10^{-1}$
quart (UK)	cubic metre (m³)	$1,136\ 523 \times 10^{-3}$
quart (UK; reputed)	cubic metre (m³)	$7,576\ 817 \times 10^{-4}$

To convert from	to	multiply by
quart (USA; dry)	cubic metre (m³)	1,101 221 x 10⁻³
quart (USA; liquid)	cubic metre (m³)	9,463 529 x 10⁻⁴
quart (USA; reputed)	cubic metre (m³)	6,309 02 x 10⁻⁴
quarter (2 stone)	kilogram (kg)	1,270 059 x 10¹
quintal	kilogram (kg)	*1 x 10²
rad (absorbed dose; ionising radiation)	joule per kilogram (J/kg)	*1 x 10⁻²
register ton	cubic metre (m³)	2,831 685 x 10⁰
revolution per minute	per second (s⁻¹)	1,666 667 x 10⁻²
rhe	per pascal second (Pa⁻¹·s⁻¹)	*1 x 10¹
rod (UK and USA)	metre (m)	*5,029 2 x 10⁰
röntgen	coulomb per kilogram (C/kg)	*2,58 x 10⁻⁴
rood (Cape)	metre (m)	*3,778 297 2 x 10⁰
rood (geodetic Cape)	metre (m)	3,778 266 9 x 10⁰
rood (UK)	square metre (m²)	*1,011 715 x 10³
scruple	kilogram (kg)	1,295 978 x 10⁻³
second (plane angle)	radian (rad)	4,848 137 x 10⁻⁶ (= *π/648 000)
second (sidereal)	second (s)	9,972 696 x 10⁻¹
shake	second (s)	*1 x 10⁻⁸
slug	kilogram (kg)	1,459 39 x 10¹
slug per cubic foot	kilogram per cubic metre (kg/m³)	5,153 79 x 10²
slug per foot second	pascal second (Pa·s)	4,788 026 x 10¹
square foot	square metre (m²)	*9,290 304 x 10⁻²
[1] square foot hour degree Fahrenheit per British thermal unit (international table) inch	metre kelvin per watt (m·K/W)	6,933 471 x 10⁰
[1] square foot hour degree Fahrenheit per British thermal unit (thermochemical) inch	metre kelvin per watt (m·K/W)	6,938 113 x 10⁰
square foot per hour	square metre per second (m²/s)	*2,580 64 x 10⁻⁵
square inch	square metre (m²)	*6,451 6 x 10⁻⁴
square mile	square metre (m²)	2,589 988 x 10⁶
square mile per ton (2 240 pounds)	square metre per kilogram (m² kg)	2,549 08 x 10³
square yard	square metre (m²)	*8,361 273 6 x 10⁻¹
square yard per ton (2 240 pounds)	square metre per kilogram (m²/kg)	8,229 22 x 10⁻⁴
statampere	ampere (A)	3,335 64 x 10⁻¹⁰

---

[1] Because the degree Fahrenheit in the denominator represents a temperature interval it follows from 2.2 note (i) that precisely the same conversion factor applies if the kelvin (K) in the SI unit is replaced by the degree Celsius (°C).

To convert from	to	multiply by
statcoulomb	coulomb (C)	$3{,}335\ 64 \times 10^{-10}$
statfarad	farad (F)	$1{,}112\ 649 \times 10^{-12}$
stathenry	henry (H)	$8{,}987\ 554\ 31 \times 10^{11}$
statmho	siemens (S)	$1{,}112\ 649 \times 10^{-12}$
statohm	ohm (Ω)	$8{,}987\ 554\ 31 \times 10^{11}$
statvolt	volt (V)	$2{,}997\ 925 \times 10^2$
stere	cubic metre (m^3)	$*1 \times 10^0$
sthène	newton (N)	$*1 \times 10^3$
stilb	candela per square metre (cd/m^2)	$*1 \times 10^4$
stokes	metre squared per second (m^2/s)	$*1 \times 10^{-4}$
stone	kilogram (kg)	$6{,}350\ 293 \times 10^0$
tablespoon (UK)	cubic metre (m^3)	$1{,}420\ 653 \times 10^{-5}$
tablespoon (USA)	cubic metre (m^3)	$1{,}478\ 676 \times 10^{-5}$
teaspoon (UK)	cubic metre (m^3)	$4{,}735\ 51 \times 10^{-6}$
teaspoon (USA)	cubic metre (m^3)	$4{,}928\ 922 \times 10^{-6}$
tex	kilogram per metre (kg/m)	$*1 \times 10^{-6}$
therm	joule J)	$1{,}055\ 06 \times 10^8$
thermie	joule (J)	$4{,}185\ 5 \times 10^6$
therm per gallon (UK)	joule per cubic metre (J/m^3)	$2{,}320\ 8 \times 10^{10}$
thou (mil)	metre (m)	$*2{,}54 \times 10^{-5}$
ton (2 240 pounds)	kilogram (kg)	$1{,}016\ 047 \times 10^3$
ton (2 000 pounds)	kilogram (kg)	$9{,}071\ 847 \times 10^2$
[6] ton (metric)	kilogram (kg)	$*1 \times 10^3$
ton (nuclear equivalent of TNT)	joule (J)	$4{,}2 \times 10^9$
ton (refrigeration) (12 000 British thermal units per hour)	watt (W)	$3{,}516\ 853 \times 10^3$
ton (refrigeration) (13 440 British thermal units per hour)	watt (W)	$3{,}938\ 876 \times 10^3$
ton-force (2 240 pounds-force)	newton (N)	$9{,}964\ 02 \times 10^3$
ton-force (2 000 pounds-force)	newton (N)	$8{,}896\ 44 \times 10^3$
ton-force (metric)	newton (N)	$*9{,}806\ 65 \times 10^3$
ton-force (2 240 pounds-force) per foot	newton per metre (N/m)	$3{,}269\ 03 \times 10^4$
ton-force (2 240 pounds-force) per square foot	pascal (Pa)	$1{,}072\ 52 \times 10^5$

[6] Also referred to overseas as 'tonne'.

To convert from	to	multiply by
ton-force (2 240 pounds-force) per square inch	pascal (Pa)	$1{,}544\ 43 \times 10^7$
ton-force (2 000 pounds-force) per square inch	pascal (Pa)	$1{,}378\ 95 \times 10^7$
ton (2 240 pound) mile	kilogram metre (kg·m)	$1{,}635\ 17 \times 10^6$
ton (2 240 pounds) per acre	kilogram per square metre (kg/m²)	$2{,}510\ 71 \times 10^{-1}$
ton (2 000 pounds) per acre	kilogram per square metre (kg/m²)	$2{,}241\ 7 \times 10^{-1}$
ton (2 240 pounds) per cubic yard	kilogram per cubic metre (kg/m³)	$1{,}328\ 939 \times 10^3$
ton (2 000 pounds) per cubic yard	kilogram per cubic metre (kg/m³)	$1{,}186\ 55 \times 10^3$
ton (2 240 pounds) per mile	kilogram per metre (kg/m)	$6{,}313\ 42 \times 10^{-1}$
ton (2 000 pounds) per mile	kilogram per metre (kg/m)	$5{,}636\ 98 \times 10^{-1}$
ton (2 000 pounds) per morgen	kilogram per square metre (kg/m²)	$1{,}059\ 14 \times 10^{-1}$
ton (2 240 pounds) per square mile	kilogram per square metre (kg/m²)	$3{,}922\ 98 \times 10^{-4}$
ton (2 240 pounds) per 1 000 yards	kilogram per metre (kg/m)	$1{,}111\ 16 \times 10^0$
ton (2 000 pounds) per 1 000 yards	kilogram per metre (kg/m)	$9{,}921\ 09 \times 10^{-1}$
torr	pascal (Pa)	[7] $1{,}333\ 223\ 7 \times 10^2$
unit pole	weber (Wb)	$1{,}256\ 637 \times 10^{-7}$
volt (international of 1948)	volt (V)	$1{,}000\ 33 \times 10^0$
watt (international of 1948)	watt (W)	$1{,}000\ 165 \times 10^0$
watt hour	joule (J)	*$3{,}6 \times 10^3$
yard	metre (m)	*$9{,}144 \times 10^{-1}$
yard per pound	metre per kilogram (m/kg)	$2{,}015\ 91 \times 10^0$
year (calendar)	second (s)	$3{,}153\ 6 \times 10^7$
year (sidereal)	second (s)	$3{,}155\ 815 \times 10^7$
year (tropical)	second (s)	$3{,}155\ 693 \times 10^7$

[7] The exact value is 101 325/760 Pa .

TABLE 13

ALPHABETICAL LIST OF CONVERSIONS TO NON-SI UNITS
WHICH ARE STILL USED WITH THE SI

(INTERNATIONAL AND ONLY CORRECT SYMBOLS ARE GIVEN IN BRACKETS)

To convert from	to	multiply by
acre	hectare (ha)	*0,404 686
are	hectare (ha)	*0,01
barrel (petroleum; 42 gallons (USA); liquid)	litre (ℓ)	158,987 3
bushel (UK)	litre (ℓ)	36,368 72
bushel (USA)	litre (ℓ)	35,239 07
cup (UK)	millilitre (mℓ)	284,130 6
cup (USA)	millilitre (mℓ)	236,588 2
degree Fahrenheit (particular temperature)	degree Celsius (°C)	Use $t_C = (t_F - 32)/1,8$
degree Fahrenheit (temperature interval)	degree Celsius (°C)	0,555 556 (=*1/1,8)
degree Rankine (particular temperature	degree Celsius (°C)	Use $t_C = (t_R - 491,67)/1,8$
degree Rankine (temperature interval	degree Celsius (°C)	0,555 556 (=*1/1,8)
fluid drachm (UK)	millilitre (mℓ)	3,551 633
fluid ounce (UK)	millilitre (mℓ)	28,413 06
fluid ounce (USA)	millilitre (mℓ)	29,573 53
gallon (Canada; liquid)	litre (ℓ)	4,546 122
gallon (UK)	litre (ℓ)	*4,546 09
gallon (USA; dry)	litre (ℓ)	4,404 884
gallon (USA; liquid)	litre (ℓ)	3,785 412
gallon (UK) per hour	litre per hour (ℓ/h)	4,546 087
gallon (UK) per pound	litre per kilogram (ℓ/kg)	10,022 4
gill (UK)	millilitre (mℓ)	142,065 3
gill (USA)	millilitre (mℓ)	118,294 1
gon	degree (angle) (...°)	*0,9
grain per gallon (UK)	milligram per litre (mg/ℓ)	14,253 8
grain per gallon (USA; liquid)	milligram per litre (mg/ℓ)	17,118 06
hundredweight (112 pounds) per acre	kilogram per hectare (kg/ha)	125,535
knot (international)	kilometre per hour (km/h)	*1,852
knot (UK)	kilometre per hour (km/h)	*1,853 184
knot (USA)	kilometre per hour (km/h)	*1,852
lambda	microlitre ($\mu\ell$)	1
leaguer	litre (ℓ)	577,353 4
mile per gallon	litre per hundred kilometres (ℓ/100 km)	Divide 282,481 by the value in miles per gallon

To convert from	to	multiply by
mile per hour	kilometre per hour (km/h)	*1,609 344
minim	microlitre ($\mu \ell$)	59,193 9
morgen	hectare (ha)	*0,856 532
ounce (avoirdupois) per gallon (UK)	gram per litre (g/ℓ)	6,236 027
ounce (avoirdupois) per gallon (USA; liquid)	gram per litre (g/ℓ)	7,489 152
peck (UK)	litre (ℓ)	*9,092 18
peck (USA)	litre (ℓ)	8,809 768
pint (UK)	millilitre (mℓ)	568,261 3
pint (UK; reputed)	millilitre (mℓ)	378,840 8
pint (USA; dry)	millilitre (mℓ)	550,610 5
pint (USA; liquid)	millilitre (mℓ)	473,176 5
pint (USA; reputed)	millilitre (mℓ)	315,451
pound per gallon (UK)	gram per litre (g/ℓ)	99,776 36
pound per gallon (USA; liquid)	gram per litre (g/ℓ)	119,826 4
quart (UK)	litre (ℓ)	1,136 523
quart (UK; reputed)	millilitre (mℓ)	757,681 7
quart (USA; dry)	litre (ℓ)	1,101 221
quart (USA; liquid)	millilitre (mℓ)	946,352 9
quart (USA; reputed)	millilitre (mℓ)	630,902
square mile per ton (2 240 pounds)	square kilometre per metric ton (km^2/t)	2,549 08
square yard per ton (2 240 pounds)	square metre per metric ton (m^2/t)	0,822 922
tablespoon (UK)	millilitre (mℓ)	14,206 53
tablespoon (USA)	millilitre (mℓ)	14,786 76
teaspoon (UK)	millilitre (mℓ)	4,735 51
teaspoon (USA)	millilitre (mℓ)	4,928 922
ton (2 240 pounds)	metric ton (t)	1,016 047
ton (2 000 pounds)	metric ton (t)	0,907 184 7
ton (2 240 pounds) mile	metric ton kilometre (t·km)	1,635 17
ton (2 240 pounds) per acre	metric ton per hectare (t/ha)	2,510 71
ton (2 000 pounds) per acre	metric ton per hectare (t/ha)	2,241 7
ton (2 240 pounds) per cubic yard	metric ton per cubic metre (t/m^3)	1,328 939
ton (2 000 pounds) per cubic yard	metric ton per cubic metre (t/m^3)	1,186 55
ton (2 000 pounds) per morgen	metric ton per hectare (t/ha)	1,059 14
ton (2 240 pounds) per mile	metric ton per kilometre (t/km)	0,631 342
ton (2 000 pounds) per mile	metric ton per kilometre (t/km)	0,563 698
ton (2 240 pounds) per square mile	metric ton per square kilometre (t/km^2)	0,392 298

II. DEFINITIONS OF UNITS

1. Length

Fundamental Units

A metre (m) is a unit of length equal to 1 650 763.73 wave lengths in a vacuum of orange-red radiation of krypton 86.

Multiples and Submultiples

1 kilometre (km)	=	1 000 metres.
1 hectometre (hm)	=	100 metres.
1 dekametre (dam)	=	10 metres.
1 decimetre (dm)	=	0.1 metre.
1 centimetre (cm)	=	0.01 metre.
1 millimetre (mm)	=	0.001 metre.
1 micrometre (μm)	=	0.000 001 metre
	=	0.001 millimetre.
1 nanometre (nm)	=	0.000 000 001 metre
	=	0.001 micrometre.
	=	0.000 000 1 millimetre.
1 angstrom (A)	=	0.000 1 micrometre.
	=	0.1 nanometre

DEFINITIONS OF UNITS **(continued)**

2. **Area**

Fundamental Units

A square metre (m^2) is a unit of area equal to the area of a square the sides of which are 1 metre.

Multiples and Submultiples

1 square kilometre (km^2)	=	1 000 000 square metres.
1 hectare (ha), or square hectometre (hm^2)	=	10 000 square metres.
1 are (a), or square dekametre (dam^2)	=	100 square metres.
1 centare (ca)	=	1 square metre.
1 square decimetre (dm^2)	=	0.01 square metre.
1 square centimetre (cm^2)	=	0.000 1 square metre.
1 square millimetre (mm^2)	=	0.000 001 square metre.

DEFINITIONS OF UNITS (continued)

3. Volume

Fundamental Units

A cubic metre (m³) is a unit of volume equal to a cube the edges of which are 1 metre.

Multiples and Submultiples

1 cubic kilometre (km³)	= 1 000 000 000 cubic metres.
1 cubic hectometre (hm³)	= 1 000 000 cubic metres.
1 cubic dekametre (dam³)	= 1 000 cubic metres.
1 cubic decimetre (dm³)	= 0.001 cubic metre.
1 cubic centimetre (cm³)	= 0.000 001 cubic metre
	= 0.001 cubic decimetre.
1 cubic millimetre (mm³)	= 0.000 000 001 cubic metre
	= 0.001 cubic centimetre.

4. Capacity

Fundamental Units

A litre (l) is a unit of capacity equal to 1 cubic decimetre (dm³).

Multiples and Submultiples

1 hectolitre (hl)	= 100 litres.
1 dekalitre (dal)	= 10 litres.
1 decilitre (dl)	= 0.1 litre.
1 centilitre (cl)	= 0.01 litre.
1 millilitre (ml)	= 0.001 litre
	= 1 cubic centimetre (cm³)

DEFINITIONS OF UNITS (continued)

5. Mass

Fundamental Units

A kilogram (kg) is a unit of mass equal to the mass of the International Prototype Kilogram.
A gram (g) is a unit of mass equal to one-thousandth of the mass of the International Prototype Kilogram.

Multiples and Submultiples

1 metric ton (t)	=	1 000 kilograms.
1 hectogram (hg)	=	100 grams.
1 dekagram (dag)	=	10 grams.
1 decigram (dg)	=	0.1 gram.
1 centigram (cg)	=	0.01 gram.
1 milligram (mg)	=	0.001 gram.

III. LENGTH

Length is a measure of extent or distance. The metre (m) with its recommended multiples and submultiples, the kilometre (km), and millimetre (mm) will be used as units of length in trade, industry, science, and other fields. However, there are some exceptions where owing to practical considerations the centimetre (cm) will be used, such as, textiles, clothing, body measurements, and many other things.

Units

The units of length which are of primary importance are:

SI principal unit	Recommended SI multiples and submultiples	Other SI multiples and submultiples
metre (m)	kilometre (km) 1 km = 1 000 m	centimetre (cm) 1 cm = $\frac{1}{100}$ m
	millimetre (mm) 1 mm = $\frac{1}{1\,000}$ m = 0.001 m	

Measure of Length

10 millimetres (mm)	= 1 centimetre (cm)
10 centimetres (cm)	= 1 decimetre (dm)
10 decimetres (dm)	= 1 metre (m)
10 metres (m)	= 1 dekametre (dam)
10 dekametres (dam)	= 1 hectometre (hm)
10 hectometres (hm)	= 1 kilometre (km)

1 centimetre (cm)	= 10 millimetres (mm)
1 metre (m)	= 100 centimetres (cm)
	= 1 000 millimetres (mm)
1 kilometre (km)	= 1 000 metres (m)

The above table shows that each unit of length is 10 times larger than its next smaller unit, and inversely, it is 1/10 of its next larger unit.

We can change from one unit to another by multiplying or dividing by 10, 100, 1 000 or other power of 10 according to the conversion desired, up or down.

Rule 1.

To change from any given unit to any smaller unit **multiply** the given unit by the proper conversion factor or factors shown in the table above.

Example:

Rule: Given unit x conversion factor = smaller unit
Problem: Change 5 metres to decimetres.
Method: The given unit is metres.
         The conversion factor is 10 because 10 dm = 1 m
thus,
         5 m × 10 = 50 dm

Rule 2.

To change from any given unit to any larger unit **divide** the given unit by the proper conversion factor or factors shown in the table above.

Example:

Rule:
Given unit ÷ conversion factor = larger unit.

Problem:
Change 50 decimetres to metres.

Method:
The given unit is decimetres.

The conversion factor is 10 because 10 dm = 1 m thus,

50 dm ÷ 10 = 5 m

Units of Measurement—Conversion Factors*

Units of Length

To Convert from Centimeters	
To	Multiply by
Inches	0.393 700 8
Feet	0.032 808 40
Yards	0.010 936 13
Meters	**0.01**

To Convert from Meters	
To	Multiply by
Inches	39.370 08
Feet	3.280 840
Yards	1.093 613
Miles	0.000 621 37
Millimeters	**1 000**
Centimeters	**100**
Kilometers	**0.001**

To Convert from Inches	
To	Multiply by
Feet	0.083 333 33
Yards	0.027 777 78
Centimeters	**2.54**
Meters	**0.025 4**

To Convert from Feet	
To	Multiply by
Inches	**12**
Yards	0.333 333 3
Miles	0.000 189 39
Centimeters	**30.48**
Meters	**0.304 8**
Kilometers	**0.000 304 8**

* All boldface figures are exact; the others generally are given to seven significant figures.

In using conversion factors, it is possible to perform division as well as the multiplication process shown here. Division may be particularly advantageous where more than the significant figures published here are required. Division may be performed in lieu of multiplication by using the reciprocal of any indicated multiplier as divisor. For example, to convert from centimeters to inches by division, refer to the table headed "To Convert from *Inches*" and use the factor listed at "centimeters" (*2.54*) as divisor.

To Convert from Yards	
To	Multiply by
Inches	**36**
Feet	**3**
Miles	0.000 568 18
Centimeters	**91.44**
Meters	**0.914 4**

To Convert from Miles	
To	Multiply by
Inches	**63 360**
Feet	**5 280**
Yards	**1 760**
Centimeters	**160 934.4**
Meters	**1 609.344**
Kilometers	**1.609 344**

IV. AREA

Area is the surface contents of any figure determined by measuring the number of units of square measure contained within its perimeter. The area of a rectangle is equal to its length times its width.

When computing area the linear units of measure used should be in the same denomination, i.e. millimetres × millimetres; centimetres × centimetres; decimetres × decimetres, etc. There are various formulae for computing areas of geometric figures. These formulae remain the same when used with metric measurements.

Units

The units of area which are of primary importance are:

SI principal unit	SI multiples and submultiples	Decimal multiples of SI units with special names
	square kilometre (km²) $1 \text{ km}^2 = 1\,000\,000 \text{ m}^2$	
		hectare (ha) $1 \text{ ha} = 10\,000 \text{ m}^2$
square metre (m²)		
	square centimetre (cm²) $1 \text{ cm}^2 = 0.000\,1 \text{ m}^2$ $= 1/10\,000 \text{ m}^2$ square millimetre (mm²) $1 \text{ mm}^2 = 0\,000\,001 \text{ m}^2$ $= 1/1\,000\,000 \text{ m}^2$	

Measure of Area

100 square millimetres (mm²)	=	1 square centimetre (cm²)
100 square centimetres	=	1 square decimetre (dm²)
100 square decimetres	=	1 square metre (m²)
100 square metres	=	1 square dekametre (dam²)
		or 1 are (a)
100 square dekametres	=	1 square hectometre (hm²)
		or 1 hectare (ha)
		= 10 000 m²
100 square hectometres	=	1 square kilometre (km²)
(or 100 hectares)		= 1 000 000 m²)

It is obvious from the table above that each unit of area is 100 times larger than its next smaller unit, and inversely, it is 1/100 of its next larger unit. It follows therefore, that we can change from one unit of area to another by multiplying or dividing by 100, 1 000, 10 000 or other power, according to the conversion desired, up or down, as stated in Rules 1 and 2 on pages 18 and 19.

Units of Area

To Convert from **Square Centimeters**	
To	Multiply by
Square Inches	0.155 000 3
Square Feet	0.001 076 39
Square Yards	0.000 119 599
Square Meters	**0.000 1**

To Convert from **Square Meters**	
To	Multiply by
Square Inches	1 550.003
Square Feet	10.763 91
Square Yards	1.195 990
Acres	0.000 247 105
Square Centimeters	**10 000**
Hectares	**0.000 1**

To Convert from **Hectares**	
To	Multiply by
Square Feet	107 639.1
Square Yards	11 959.90
Acres	2.471 054
Square Miles	0.003 861 02
Square Meters	**10 000**

To Convert from **Square Inches**	
To	Multiply by
Square Feet	0.006 944 44
Square Yards	0.000 771 605
Square Centimeters	**6.451 6**
Square Meters	**0.000 645 16**

To Convert from **Square Feet**	
To	Multiply by
Square Inches	**144**
Square Yards	0.111 111 1
Acres	0.000 022 957
Square Centimeters	**929.030 4**
Square Meters	**0.092 903 04**

To Convert from **Square Yards**	
To	Multiply by
Square Inches	**1 296**
Square Feet	**9**
Acres	0.000 206 611 6
Square Miles	0.000 000 322 830 6
Square Centimeters	**8 361.273 6**
Square Meters	**0.836 127 36**
Hectares	**0.000 083 612 736**

To Convert from **Acres**	
To	Multiply by
Square Feet	**43 560**
Square Yards	**4 840**
Square Miles	**0.001 562 5**
Square Meters	**4 046.856 422 4**
Hectares	**0.404 685 642 24**

To Convert from **Square Miles**	
To	Multiply by
Square Feet	**27 878 400**
Square Yards	**3 097 600**
Acres	**640**
Square Meters	**2 589 988.110 336**
Hectares	**258.998 811 033 6**

V. VOLUME

The concept of volume is the space occupied by a quantity of matter as measured by cubic units. The cubic metre (m^3) is a unit of volume equal to a cube the edges of which are 1 metre. The numerical quantity values between units of volume derived from the millimetre, the metre, and the kilometre are very large, for instance,

$$1 \, m^3 = 1 \, 000 \, mm \times 1 \, 000 \, mm \times 1 \, 000 \, mm =$$
$$1 \, 000 \, 000 \, 000 \, mm^3.$$

As a result, other submultiples, such as the cubic centimetre (cm^3) have to be used in order to avoid unmanageably large numbers.

The litre was defined as being precisely equal to one cubic decimetre (dm^3) (1 000 cubic centimetres).

The correct symbol for cubic centimetres is cm^3 and not cc or c.c. In the SI cc would stand for centi-centi, which is meaningless.

Units

The units of volume which are of primary importance are:

SI principal unit	SI multiples and submultiples	Decimal multiples of SI units with special names
cubic metre (m^3)	cubic centimetre (cm^3) $1 \, cm^3 = 0 \, 000 \, 001 \, m^3$ $= \dfrac{1}{1 \, 000 \, 000} \, m^3$ cubic millimetre (mm^3) $1 \, mm^3 = 0.000 \, 000 \, 001 \, m^3$ $= \dfrac{1}{1 \, 000 \, 000 \, 000} \, m^3$	kilolitre (kl) $1 \, kl = 1 \, 000 \, litres$ $= 1 \, m^3$ litre (l) $1 \, litre = 1 \, 000 \, cm^3$ $(= 1 \, dm^3)$ millilitre (ml) $1 \, ml = 0,001 \, litres$ $= 1 \, cm^3$

Measure of Volume

1 000 cubic millimetres (mm³)	=	1 cubic centimetre (cm³)
1 000 cubic centimetres (cm³)	=	1 cubic decimetre (dm³)
1 000 cubic decimetres (dm³)	=	1 cubic metre (m³)
1 000 cubic metres (m³)	=	1 cubic dekametre (dam³)
1 000 cubic dekametres (dam³)	=	1 cubic hectometre (hm³)
1 000 cubic hectometres (hm³)	=	1 cubic kilometre (km³)

It is obvious from the above table that each unit of volume (cubic measure) is 1 000 times larger than its next smaller unit, and inversely, it is 1/1 000 of its next larger unit. It follows therefore, that we can change from one unit of volume to another by multiplying or dividing by 1 000, 10 000, 100 000 or other power, according to the conversion desired, up or down. (See Rules 1 and 2 on pages 41 and 42.

Metric units of volume differ by 1 000 for this reason: 1 centimetre (cm) = 10 millimetres (mm). When these are cubed by multiplying length by width by height to get the measure of volume or cubic space occupied, we get 1 cm × 1 cm × 1 cm equals 1 cubic centimetre (cm³) which is the same as 10 mm × 10 mm × 10 mm equal to 1 000 cubic millimetres (mm³).

Units of Capacity, or Volume, Liquid Measure

To Convert from Milliliters

To	Multiply by
Minims	16.230 73
Liquid Ounces	0.033 814 02
Gills	0.008 453 5
Liquid Pints	0.002 113 4
Liquid Quarts	0.001 056 7
Gallons	0.000 264 17
Cubic Inches	0.061 023 74
Liters	**0.001**

To Convert from Liters

To	Multiply by
Liquid Ounces	33.814 02
Gills	8.453 506
Liquid Pints	2.113 376
Liquid Quarts	1.056 688
Gallons	0.264 172 05
Cubic Inches	61.023 74
Cubic Feet	0.035 314 67
Milliliters	**1 000**
Cubic Meters	**0.001**
Cubic Yards	0.001 307 95

To Convert from Cubic Meters

To	Multiply by
Gallons	264.172 05
Cubic Inches	61 023.74
Cubic Feet	35.314 67
Liters	**1 000**
Cubic Yards	1.307 950 6

To Convert from Minims

To	Multiply by
Liquid Ounces	0.002 083 33
Gills	0.000 520 83
Cubic Inches	0.003 759 77
Milliliters	0.061 611 52

To Convert from Gills

To	Multiply by
Minims	**1 920**
Liquid Ounces	**4**
Liquid Pints	**0.25**
Liquid Quarts	**0.125**
Gallons	**0.031 25**
Cubic Inches	**7.218 75**
Cubic Feet	0.004 177 517
Milliliters	118.294 118 25
Liters	**0.118 294 118 25**

To Convert from Liquid Pints

To	Multiply by
Minims	**7 680**
Liquid Ounces	**16**
Gills	**4**
Liquid Quarts	**0.5**
Gallons	**0.125**
Cubic Inches	**28.875**
Cubic Feet	0.016 710 07
Milliliters	**473.176 473**
Liters	**0.473 176 473**

To Convert from **Liquid Ounces**	
To	Multiply by
Minims	480
Gills	0.25
Liquid Pints	0.062 5
Liquid Quarts	0.031 25
Gallons	0.007 812 5
Cubic Inches	1.804 687 5
Cubic Feet	0.001 044 38
Milliliters	29.573 53
Liters	0.029 573 53

To Convert from **Cubic Feet**	
To	Multiply by
Liquid Ounces	957.506 5
Gills	239.376 6
Liquid Pints	59.844 16
Liquid Quarts	29.922 08
Gallons	7.480 519
Cubic Inches	1 728
Liters	28.316 846 592
Cubic Meters	0.028 316 846 592
Cubic Yards	0.037 037 04

To Convert from **Cubic Inches**	
To	Multiply by
Minims	265.974 0
Liquid Ounces	0.554 112 6
Gills	0.138 528 1
Liquid Pints	0.034 632 03
Liquid Quarts	0.017 316 02
Gallons	0.004 329 0
Cubic Feet	0.000 578 7
Milliliters	16.387 064
Liters	0.016 387 064
Cubic Meters	0.000 016 387 064
Cubic Yards	0.000 021 43

To Convert from **Cubic Yards**	
To	Multiply by
Gallons	201.974 0
Cubic Inches	46 656
Cubic Feet	27
Liters	764.554 857 984
Cubic Meters	0.764 554 857 984

To Convert from **Liquid Quarts**	
To	Multiply by
Minims	15 360
Liquid Ounces	32
Gills	8
Liquid Pints	2
Gallons	0.25
Cubic Inches	57.75
Cubic Feet	0.033 420 14
Milliliters	946.352 946
Liters	0.946 352 946

To Convert from **Gallons**	
To	Multiply by
Minims	61 440
Liquid Ounces	128
Gills	32
Liquid Pints	8
Liquid Quarts	4
Cubic Inches	231
Cubic Feet	0.133 680 6
Milliliters	3 785.411 784
Liters	3.785 411 784
Cubic Meters	0.003 785 411 784
Cubic Yards	0.004 951 13

VI. CAPACITY

The litre (l) is a unit of liquid capacity equal in volume to exactly 1 cubic decimetre (dm^3).

Measure of Capacity

10 millilitres (ml)	= 1 centilitre (cl)
10 centilitres (cl)	= 1 decilitre (dl)
10 decilitres (dl)	= 1 litre
10 litres	= 1 dekalitre (dal)
10 dekalitres (dal)	= 1 hectolitre (hl)
10 hectolitres (hl)	= 1 kilolitre (kl)

It is obvious from the above table that each unit of capacity is 10 times larger than its next lower unit, and inversely, it is 1/10 of its next larger unit. It follows therefore, that we can change from one unit to another by multiplying or dividing by 10, 100, 1 000 or any other power of 10 according to the conversion desired, up or down, as stated in Rules 1 and 2 on pages 41 and 42.

Units of Capacity, or Volume, Dry Measure

To Convert from Liters	
To	Multiply by
Dry Pints	1.816 166
Dry Quarts	0.908 082 98
Pecks	0.113 510 4
Bushels	0.028 377 59
Dekaliters	0.1

To Convert from Cubic Meters	
To	Multiply by
Pecks	113.510 4
Bushels	28.377 59

To Convert from Dekaliters	
To	Multiply by
Dry Pints	18.161 66
Dry Quarts	9.080 829 8
Pecks	1.135 104
Bushels	0.283 775 9
Cubic Inches	610.237 4
Cubic Feet	0.353 146 7
Liters	10

To Convert from Dry Pints	
To	Multiply by
Dry Quarts	0.5
Pecks	0.062 5
Bushels	0.015 625
Cubic Inches	33.600 312 5
Cubic Feet	0.019 444 63
Liters	0.550 610 47
Dekaliters	0.055 061 05

To Convert from Dry Quarts	
To	Multiply by
Dry Pints	2
Pecks	0.125
Bushels	0.031 25
Cubic Inches	67.200 625
Cubic Feet	0.038 889 25
Liters	1.101 221
Dekaliters	0.110 122 1

To Convert from Pecks	
To	Multiply by
Dry Pints	16
Dry Quarts	8
Bushels	0.25
Cubic Inches	537.605
Cubic Feet	0.311 114
Liters	8.809 767 5
Dekaliters	0.880 976 75
Cubic Meters	0.008 809 77
Cubic Yards	0.011 522 74

To Convert from Bushels	
To	Multiply by
Dry Pints	64
Dry Quarts	32
Pecks	4
Cubic Inches	2 150.42
Cubic Feet	1.244 456
Liters	35.239 07
Dekaliters	3.523 907
Cubic Meters	0.035 239 07
Cubic Yards	0.046 090 96

To Convert from Cubic Inches	
To	Multiply by
Dry Pints	0.029 761 6
Dry Quarts	0.014 880 8
Pecks	0.001 860 10
Bushels	0.000 465 025

To Convert from Cubic Yards	
To	Multiply by
Pecks	86.784 91
Bushels	21.696 227

To Convert from Cubic Feet	
To	Multiply by
Dry Pints	51.428 09
Dry Quarts	25.714 05
Pecks	3.214 256
Bushels	0.803 563 95

Note:

1 peck (pk) = 1/4 bushel = 537.605 cubic inches.

1 dry quart (dry qt) = 1/32 bushel = 1/8 peck = 67.200 625 cubic inches.

1 dry pint (dry pt) = 1/64 bushel = 1/2 dry quart = 33.600 312 5 cubic inches

1 barrel, for fruits, vegetables, and other dry commodities, other than cranberries = 7 056 cubic inches = 105 dry quarts.

1 barrel for cranberries = 5 826 cubic inches.

VII. MASS, FORCE, AND WEIGHT

The term weight has been used in many ways, resulting in confusion. In our everyday lives it is used as being synonymous with mass. In this usage it is measured in kilograms or grams. In physics and technology, however, it has been used as a force related to gravity. In that usage, the weight of an object stationary on the earth was defined as being equal to the force of gravity on the object and was measured in newtons. That use of the term weight is now falling into disfavor.

In the study of physics you will learn more about force. For now remember that it is measured in newtons and **not** in kilograms. Because weight was in the past often used as a force, a brief explanation of that usage will be of interest to you. The weight as a force of a body can be visualized as being the force of reaction that the body exerts on all forces that are in contact with it. This type of visualization will better enable you to see why it is that an astronaut when he is in space "falling" toward the earth or during his long voyage in skylab is said to be "weightless"; i.e., that his weight is zero. This obviously does not mean that his mass is zero. It means only that except for gravitation there are no forces acting on him against which to react. He thus feels "weightless" even though he is not "massless."

Because of this confusion, the term weight will more and more be avoided in science and technology.

MASS

Mass is related to heaviness. The principal unit, the kilogram (kg), already uses a prefix in contrast to all other principal units. This is specifically mentioned to emphasize the fact that, in spite of the prefix, the kilogram is the principal unit of more common usage than the gram.

The term "megagram" will not be used very much as in most cases the term "metric ton" will be used instead. The old imperial ton we have used heretofore will be gradually supplanted by metric ton.

Units

The important units of mass are the following:

SI principal unit	Recommended SI multiples and submultiples	Other units
kilogram (kg)	megagram (Mg) 1 Mg = 1 000 kg gram (g) $1 g = \frac{1}{1\,000} (kg)$ $= 0.001 \text{ kg}$ milligram (mg) $1 mg = \frac{1}{1\,000\,000} \text{ kg}$ $= 0.000\,001 \text{ kg}$	metric ton(t) 1 t = 1 000 kg

Measure of Mass

10 milligrams (mg)	=	1 centigram (cg)
10 centigrams (cg)	=	1 decigram (dg)
10 decigrams (dg)	=	1 gram (g)
10 grams (g)	=	1 dekagram (dag)
10 dekagrams (dag)	=	1 hectogram (hg)
10 hectograms (hg)	=	1 kilogram (kg)
1 000 kilograms (kg)	=	1 metric ton (t)

It is obvious from the above table that each unit of mass is 10 times larger than its next smaller unit, and inversely, it is 1/10 of its next larger unit. It follows therefore, that we can change from one unit of mass to another by multiplying or dividing by 10, 100, 1 000 or other power of 10, according to the conversion desired, up or down, as stated in Rules 1 and 2 on pages 41 and 42.

Units of Mass

To Convert from **Grams**	
To	Multiply by
Grains--------------------	15.432 36
Avoirdupois Drams--------	0.564 383 4
Avoirdupois Ounces--------	0.035 273 96
Troy Ounces--------------	0.032 150 75
Troy Pounds--------------	0.002 679 23
Avoirdupois Pounds--------	0.002 204 62
Milligrams--------------- **1 000**	
Kilograms---------------	**0.001**

To Convert from **Kilograms**	
To	Multiply by
Grains--------------------	15 432.36
Avoirdupois Drams--------	564.383 4
Avoirdupois Ounces--------	35.273 96
Troy Ounces--------------	32.150 75
Troy Pounds--------------	2.679 229
Avoirdupois Pounds--------	2.204 623
Grams-------------------- **1 000**	
Short Hundredweights------	0.022 046 23
Short Tons---------------	0.001 102 31
Long Tons---------------	0.000 984 2
Metric Tons--------------	**0.001**

To Convert from **Metric Tons**	
To	Multiply by
Avoirdupois Pounds---------	2 204.623
Short Hundredweights-------	22.046 23
Short Tons----------------	1.102 311 3
Long Tons----------------	0.984 206 5
Kilograms---------------- **1 000**	

To Convert from **Grains**	
To	Multiply by
Avoirdupois Drams--------	0.036 571 43
Avoirdupois Ounces--------	0.002 285 71
Troy Ounces--------------	0.002 083 33
Troy Pounds-------------	0.000 173 61
Avoirdupois Pounds--------	0.000 142 86
Milligrams-------------- **64.798 91**	
Grams------------------ **0.064 798 91**	
Kilograms-------------- **0.000 064 798 91**	

To Convert from **Avoirdupois Ounces**	
To	Multiply by
Grains-----------------	**437.5**
Avoirdupois Drams-----	**16**
Troy Ounces-----------	0.911 458 3
Troy Pounds-----------	0.075 954 86
Avoirdupois Pounds-----	**0.062 5**
Grams-----------------	**28.349 523 125**
Kilograms-------------	**0.028 349 523 125**

To Convert from
Avoirdupois Pounds

To	Multiply by
Grains	**7 000**
Avoirdupois Drams	**256**
Avoirdupois Ounces	**16**
Troy Ounces	14.583 33
Troy Pounds	1.215 278
Grams	**453.592 37**
Kilograms	**0.453 592 37**
Short Hundredweights	**0.01**
Short Tons	**0.000 5**
Long Tons	0.000 446 428 6
Metric Tons	**0.000 453 592 37**

To Convert from
Short Hundredweights

To	Multiply by
Avoirdupois Pounds	**100**
Short Tons	**0.05**
Long Tons	0.044 642 86
Kilograms	**45.359 237**
Metric Tons	**0.045 359 237**

To Convert from
Short Tons

To	Multiply by
Avoirdupois Pounds	**2 000**
Short Hundredweights	**20**
Long Tons	0.892 857 1
Kilograms	907.184 74
Metric Tons	**0.907 184 74**

To Convert from
Long Tons

To	Multiply by
Avoirdupois Ounces	**35 840**
Avoirdupois Pounds	**2 240**
Short Hundredweights	**22.4**
Short Tons	**1.12**
Kilograms	**1 016.046 908 8**
Metric Tons	**1.016 046 908 8**

To Convert from
Troy Ounces

To	Multiply by
Grains	**480**
Avoirdupois Drams	17.554 29
Avoirdupois Ounces	1.097 143
Troy Pounds	0.083 333 3
Avoirdupois Pounds	0.068 571 43
Grams	**31.103 476 8**

To Convert from
Troy Pounds

To	Multiply by
Grains	**5 760**
Avoirdupois Drams	210.651 4
Avoirdupois Ounces	13.165 71
Troy Ounces	**12**
Avoirdupois Pounds	0.822 857 1
Grams	**373.241 721 6**

VIII. VOLUME, CAPACITY, MASS

The relationship between some units of volume, capacity, and mass is given hereunder.

> 1 cubic centimetre (cm³) of water has a mass equivalent of 1 gram (g).
> 1 millilitre (ml) of water has a mass equivalent of 1 gram (g).
> 1 cubic decimetre (dm³) of water has a mass equivalent of 1 kilogram (kg).
> 1 litre (l) of water has a mass equivalent of 1 kilogram (kg).

MISCELLANEOUS EQUIVALENTS

1 litre = 1 cubic decimetre (dm³) = 1 000 cubic centimetres (cm³)
1 millilitre (ml) = 1 cubic centimetre (cm³)
1 litre of water weighs 1 kilogram (kg)
1 millilitre (ml) or cubic centimetre (cm³) of water weighs 1 gram (g)

IX. TEMPERATURE

In practice temperature is expressed in **degrees Celsius** (^{o}C). The zero point on this scale is the temperature at which water freezes, while the boiling point of water is 100 ^{o}C.

Practical Application

Celsius: Replaces Fahrenheit. Atmospheric and body temperatures are expressed in ^{o}C. Oven temperatures for baking purposes will also be given in ^{o}C.

10 ^{o}C = 50 ^{o} F. For every increase or decrease of 5 degrees on the Celsius scale, 9 degrees are added or subtracted from the Fahrenheit scale.

or   Number of degrees Celsius
= (Number of degrees Fahrenheit — 32) $\times \dfrac{5}{9}$
Number of degrees Fahrenheit
= (Number of degrees Celsius $\times \dfrac{9}{5}$) + 32

X. CONDENSED TABULATION OF METRIC MEASURES

LIST OF PREFIXES

mega   means a million times
kilo   means a thousand times
hecto   means a hundred times
deka   means ten times
deci   means a tenth part of
centi   means a hundredth part of
milli   means a thousandth part of
micro means a millionth part of

LENGTH

10 millimetres (mm) = 1 centimetre (cm)
10 centimetres   = 1 decimetre (dm) = 100 millimetres
10 decimetres   = 1 metre (m) = 1 000 millimetres
10 metres   = 1 dekametre (dam)
10 dekametres   = 1 hectometre (hm) = 100 metres
10 hectometres   = 1 kilometre (km) = 1 000 metres

1 centimetre (cm)   = 10 millimetres (mm)
1 metre (m)   = 100 centimetres (cm)
                   = 1 000 millimetres (mm)
1 kilometre (km)   = 1 000 metres (m)

AREA

100 square millimetres (mm^2)   = 1 square centimetre (cm^2)
100 square centimetres (cm^2)   = 1 square decimetre (dm^2)
100 square decimetres (dm^2)   = 1 square metre (m^2)
1 000 000 square metres (m^2)   = 1 square kilometre (km^2)

CONDENSED TABULATION OF METRIC MEASURES
(continued)

CAPACITY (Liquid)

10 millilitres (ml)	= 1 centilitre (cl)
10 centilitres	= 1 decilitre (dl) = 100 millilitres
10 decilitres	= 1 litre (l) = 1 000 millilitres
10 litres	= 1 dekalitre (dal)
10 dekalitres	= 1 hectolitre (hl) = 100 litres
10 hectolitres	= 1 kilolitre (kl) = 1 000 litres

MISCELLANEOUS EQUIVALENTS

1 litre = 1 cubic decimetre (dm^3) = 1 000 cubic centimetres (cm^3)

1 millilitre (ml) = 1 cubic centimetre (cm^3)

1 litre of water weighs 1 kilogram (kg)

1 millilitre (ml) or cubic centimetre (cm^3) of water weighs 1 gram (g)

VOLUME (Dry)

1 000 cubic millimetres (mm^3)	= 1 cubic centimetre (cm^3)
1 000 cubic centimetres	= 1 cubic decimetre (dm^3)
	= 1 000 000 cubic millimetres
1 000 cubic decimetres	= 1 cubic metre (m^3)
	= 1 000 000 cubic centimetres
	= 1 000 000 000 cubic millimetres

CONDENSED TABULATION OF METRIC MEASURES
(continued)

MASS

10 milligrams (mg)	= 1 centigram (cg)	
10 centigrams	= 1 decigram (dg)	= 100 milligrams
10 decigrams	= 1 gram (g)	= 1 000 milligrams
10 grams	= 1 dekagram (dag)	
10 dekagrams	= 1 hectogram (hg)	= 100 grams
10 hectograms	= 1 kilogram (kg)	= 1 000 grams
1 000 kilograms	= 1 metric ton (t)	

Linear Measure Equivalents

1 inch	= 2.54 centimetres, or 25.4 millimetres.
1 foot	= 30.4799 centimetres, 304.799 millimetres, or 0.3047 metre
1 yard	= 0.914399 metre
1 mile	= 1.6093 kilometres = 5280 feet
1 millimetre	= 0.03937 inch
1 centimetre	= 0.3937 inch
1 decimetre	= 3.937 inches
1 metre	= 39.370113 inches
	= 3.28084 feet
	= 1.093614 yards
1 kilometre	= 0.62137 mile
1 dekametre (10 m)	= 10.936 yards
1 hectometre (100 m)	= 328.084 feet

CONDENSED TABULATION OF METRIC MEASURES
(continued)

Metric Conversion Factors

To convert—

millimetres to inches	× 0.03937 or ÷ 25.4
centimetres to inches	× 0.3937 or ÷ 2.54
metres to inches	× 39.37
metres to feet	× 3.281
metres per second to feet per minute	× 197
kilometres to miles	× 0.6214 or ÷ 1.6093
kilometres to feet	× 3280.8693
square millimetres to square inches	× 0.00155 or ÷ 645.1
square centimetres to square inches	× 0.155 or ÷ 6.451
square metres to square feet	× 10.764
square metres to square yards	× 1.2
square kilometres to acres	× 247.1
hectares to acres	× 2.471
cubic centimetres to cubic inches	× 0.06 or ÷ 16.383
cubic metres to cubic feet	× 35.315
cubic metres to cubic yards	× 1.308
cubic metres to gallons (231 cu. in.)	× 164.2
litres to cubic inches	÷ 61.022
litres to gallons	× 0.2642 or ÷ 3.78
litres to cubic feet	× 28.316
hectolitres to cubic feet	× 3.531
hectolitres to bushels (2150.42 cu. in.)	× 2.84
hectolitres to cubic yards	× 0.131

CONDENSED TABULATION OF METRIC MEASURES
(continued)

Metric Conversion Factors

hectolitres to gallons	÷ 26.42
grams to ounces (avoirdupois)	× 0.035 or ÷ 28.35
grams per cubic centimetre to pounds per cubic inch.	÷ 27.7
joules to foot-pounds	× 0.7373
kilograms to ounces	× 35.3
kilograms to pounds	× 2.2046
kilograms to tons	× 0.001
kilograms per square centimetre to pounds per square inch	× 14.223

CONDENSED TABULATION OF METRIC MEASURES
(continued)

Compound Conversion Factors

U.S. - Metric

pounds per lineal foot	×	1.488
	=	kilos per lineal metre
pounds per lineal yard	×	0.496
	=	kilos per lineal metre
tons per lineal foot	×	3333.33
	=	kilos per lineal metre
tons per lineal yard	×	1111.11
	=	kilos per lineal metre
pounds per mile	×	0.2818
	=	kilos per kilometre
pounds per square inch	×	0.0703
	=	kilos per square centimetre
tons per square inch	×	1.575
	=	kilos per square millimetre
pounds per square foot	×	4.883
	=	kilos per square metre
tons per square foot	×	10.936
	=	tons per square metre
tons per square yard	×	1.215
	=	tons per square metre
pounds per cubic yard	×	0.5933
	=	kilos per cubic metre
pounds per cubic foot	×	16.020
	=	kilos per cubic metre
tons per cubic yard	×	1.329
	=	tons per cubic metre
grains per gallon	×	0.01426
	=	grams per litre
pounds per gallon	×	0.09983
	=	kilos per litre

CONDENSED TABULATION OF METRIC MEASURES
(continued)

Compound Conversion Factors ·

Metric - U.S.

kilos per lineal metre	× 0.672	= pounds per lineal foot
kilos per lineal metre	× 2.016	= pounds per lineal yard
kilos per lineal metre	× 0.0003	= tons per lineal foot
kilos per lineal metre	× 0.0009	= tons per lineal yard
kilos per kilometre	× 3.548	= pounds per mile
kilos per square centimetre	× 14.223	= pounds per square inch
kilos per square millimetre	× 0.635	= tons per square inch
kilos per square metre	× 0.2048	= pounds per square foot
tons per square metre	× 0.0914	= tons per square foot
tons per square metre	× 0.823	= tons per square yard
kilos per cubic metre	× 1.686	= pounds per cubic yard
kilos per cubic metre	× 0.0624	= pounds per cubic foot
tons per cubic metre	× 0.752	= tons per cubic yard
grams per litre	× 70.12	= grains per gallon
kilos per litre	× 10.438	= pounds per gallon

CONDENSED TABULATION OF METRIC MEASURES

(continued)

Table 1 — Linear Measure

Conversion of price per foot to price per metre

Cents per ft	Cents per m	Cents per ft	Cents per m
1	3.281	51	167.323
2	6.562	52	170.604
3	9.843	53	173.885
4	13.123	54	177.165
5	16.404	55	180.446
6	19.685	56	183.727
7	22.966	57	187.008
8	26.247	58	190.289
9	29.528	59	193.570
10	32.808	60	196.850
11	36.089	61	200.131
12	39.370	62	203.412
13	42.651	63	206.693
14	45.932	64	909.974
15	49.213	65	213.255
16	52.493	66	216.535
17	55.774	67	219.816
18	59.055	68	223.097
19	62.336	69	226.378
20	65.617	70	229.659
21	68.898	71	232.940
22	72.179	72	236.220
23	75.459	73	239.501
24	78.740	74	242.782
25	82.021	75	246.063
26	85.302	76	249.344
27	88.583	77	252.625
28	91.864	78	255.906
29	95.144	79	259.186
30	98.425	80	262.467
31	101.706	81	265.748
32	104.987	82	269.029
33	108.268	83	272.310
34	111.549	84	275.591
35	114.829	85	278.871
36	118.110	86	282.152
37	121.391	87	284.433
38	124.672	88	288.714
39	127.953	89	291.995
40	131.234	90	295.276
41	134.514	91	298.556
42	137.795	92	301.837
43	141.076	93	305.118
44	144.357	94	308.399
45	147.638	95	311.680
46	150.919	96	314.961
47	154.199	97	318.241
48	157.480	98	321.522
49	160.761	99	324.803
50	164.042	100	328.084

CONDENSED TABULATION OF METRIC MEASURES

(continued)

Table 2 — Area (square Measure)

Conversion of price per square foot to price per square metre

Cents per ft²	Cents per m²	Cents per ft²	Cents per m²
1	10.764	51	548.959
2	21.528	52	559.723
3	32.292	53	570.487
4	43.056	54	581.251
5	53.820	55	592.015
6	64.583	56	602.779
7	75.347	57	613.543
8	86.111	58	624.307
9	96.875	59	635.071
10	107.639	60	645.835
11	118.403	61	656.599
12	129.167	62	667.362
13	139.931	63	678.126
14	150.695	64	688.890
15	161.459	65	699.654
16	172.223	66	710.418
17	182.986	67	721.182
18	193.750	68	731.946
19	204.514	69	742.710
20	215.278	70	753.474
21	226.042	71	764.238
22	236.806	72	775.002
23	247.570	73	785.765
24	258.334	74	796.529
25	269.098	75	807.293
26	279.862	76	818.057
27	290.626	77	828.821
28	301.389	78	839.585
29	312.153	79	850.349
30	322.917	80	861.113
31	333.681	81	871.877
32	344.445	82	882.641
33	355.209	83	893.405
34	365.973	84	904.168
35	376.737	85	914.932
36	387.501	86	925.696
37	398.265	87	936.460
38	409.029	88	947.224
39	419.793	89	957.988
40	430.556	90	968.752
41	441.320	91	979.516
42	452.084	92	990.280
43	462.848	93	1 001.04
44	473.612	94	1 011.81
45	484.376	95	1 022.57
46	495.140	96	1 033.34
47	505.904	97	1 044.10
48	516.668	98	1 054.86
49	527.432	99	1 065.63
50	538.196	100	1 076.39

CONDENSED TABULATION OF METRIC MEASURES
(continued)

Table 3 — Area (Square Measure)
Conversion of price per square yard to price per square metre

Cents per yd²	Cents per m²	Cents per yd²	Cents per m²
1	1.196	s51	60.996
2	2.392	52	62.192
3	3.588	53	63.388
4	4.784	54	64.584
5	5.980	55	65.780
6	7.176	56	66.975
7	8.372	57	68.171
8	9.568	58	69.367
9	10.764	59	70.563
10	11.960	60	71.759
11	13.156	61	72.955
12	14.352	62	74.151
13	15.548	63	75.347
14	16.744	64	76.543
15	17.940	65	77.739
16	19.136	66	78.935
17	20.332	67	80.131
18	21.528	68	81.327
19	22.724	69	82.523
20	23.920	70	83.719
21	25.116	71	84.915
22	26.312	72	86.111
23	27.508	73	87.307
24	28.704	74	88.503
25	29.900	75	89.699
26	31.096	76	90.895
27	32.292	77	92.091
28	33.488	78	93.287
29	34.684	79	94.483
30	35.880	80	95.679
31	37.076	81	96.875
32	38.272	82	98.071
33	39.468	83	99.267
34	40.664	84	100.463
35	41.860	85	101.659
36	43.056	86	102.855
37	44.252	87	104.051
38	45.448	88	105.247
39	46.644	89	106.443
40	47.840	90	107.639
41	49.036	91	108.835
42	50.232	92	110.031
43	51.428	93	111.227
44	52.624	94	112.423
45	53.820	95	113.619
46	55.016	96	114.815
47	56.212	97	116.011
48	57.408	98	117.207
49	58.604	99	118.403
50	59.800	100	119.599

CONDENSED TABULATION OF METRIC MEASURES
(continued)

Table 4 — Volume (Cubic Measure)
Conversion of price per cubic yard to price per cubic metre

Cents per yd³	Cents per m³	Cents per yd³	Cents per m³
1	1.308	51	66.706
2	2.616	52	68.013
3	3.924	53	69.321
4	5.232	54	70.629
5	6.540	55	71.937
6	7.848	56	73.245
7	9.156	57	74.553
8	10.464	58	75.861
9	11.772	59	77.169
10	13.080	60	78.477
11	14.388	61	79.785
12	15.695	62	81.093
13	17.003	63	82.401
14	18.311	64	83.709
15	19.619	65	85.017
16	20.927	66	86.325
17	22.235	67	87.633
18	23.543	68	88.941
19	24.851	69	90.249
20	26.159	70	91.557
21	27.467	71	92.865
22	28.775	72	94.172
23	30.083	73	95.480
24	31.391	74	96.788
25	32.699	75	98.096
26	34.007	76	99.404
27	35.315	77	100.712
28	36.623	78	102.020
29	37.931	79	103.328
30	39.239	80	104.636
31	40.547	81	105.944
32	41.854	82	107.252
33	43.162	83	108.560
34	44.470	84	109.868
35	45.778	85	111.176
36	47.086	86	112.484
37	48.394	87	113.792
38	49.702	88	115.100
39	51.010	89	116.408
40	52.318	90	117.716
41	53.626	91	119.024
42	54.934	92	120.331
43	56.242	93	121.639
44	57.550	94	122.947
45	58.858	95	124.255
46	60.166	96	125.563
47	61.474	97	126.871
48	62.782	98	128.179
49	64.090	99	129.487
50	65.398	100	130.795

CONDENSED TABULATION OF METRIC MEASURES

(continued)

Table 5 — Mass

Conversion of price per pound to price per kilogram

Cents per lb	Cents per kg	Cents per lb	Cents per kg
1	2.205	51	112.436
2	4.409	52	114.640
3	6.614	53	116.845
4	8.819	54	119.050
5	11.023	55	121.254
6	13.228	56	123.459
7	15.432	57	125.663
8	17.637	58	127.868
9	19.842	59	130.073
10	22.046	60	132.277
11	24.251	61	134.482
12	26.456	62	136.687
13	28.660	63	138.891
14	30.865	64	141.096
15	33.069	65	143.300
16	35.274	66	145.505
17	37.479	67	147.710
18	39.683	68	149.914
19	41.888	69	152.119
20	44.093	70	154.324
21	46.297	71	156.528
22	48.502	72	158.733
23	50.706	73	160.937
24	52.911	74	163.142
25	55.116	75	165.347
26	57.320	76	167.551
27	59.525	77	169.756
28	61.729	78	171.961
29	63.934	79	174.165
30	66.139	80	176.370
31	68.343	81	178.574
32	70.548	82	180.779
33	72.753	83	182.984
34	74.957	84	185.188
35	77.162	85	187.393
36	79.366	86	189.598
37	81.571	87	191.802
38	83.776	88	194.007
39	85.980	89	196.211
40	88.185	90	198.416
41	90.390	91	200.621
42	92.594	92	202.825
43	94.799	93	205.030
44	97.003	94	207.235
45	99.208	95	209.439
46	101.413	96	211.644
47	103.617	97	213.848
48	105.822	98	216.053
49	108.027	99	218.258
50	110.231	100	220.462

ALPHABETICAL CONVERSION TABLE

The fundamental purpose of this chart is to furnish a source of reference for units, standards, and conversion factors

1 acre $\begin{cases} =160 \text{ square rods.} \\ =4,840 \text{ square yards.} \\ =43,560 \text{ square feet.} \end{cases}$

1 barrel=7,056 cubic inches.

1 board foot $\begin{cases} =144 \text{ cubic inches.} \\ =2,360 \text{ cubic centimetres.} \end{cases}$

1 B. t. u. (British thermal unit) $\begin{cases} =778 \text{ foot pounds.} \\ =0.2930 \text{ international watt hour.} \\ =0.252 \text{ calorie (I. T.).} \end{cases}$

1 bushel $\begin{cases} =2,150.42 \text{ cubic inches.} \\ =1\frac{1}{4} \text{ cubic feet, approx.} \end{cases}$

1 calorie (I. T.) $\begin{cases} =1/860 \text{ international watt hours.} \\ =3.97 \times 10^{-3} \text{ B. t. u.} \end{cases}$

1 carat, metric $\begin{cases} =200 \text{ metric milligrams.} \\ =3.0865 \text{ grains.} \end{cases}$

1 centare (square metre) $\begin{cases} =10.764 \text{ square feet.} \\ =1.196 \text{ square yards.} \end{cases}$

1 centimetre=0.3937 inch.

1 chain (engineers) $\begin{cases} =100 \text{ links of 1 foot each.} \\ =30.48 \text{ metres.} \end{cases}$

1 chain (surveyors or Gunters) $\begin{cases} =4 \text{ rods.} \\ =100 \text{ links.} \\ =66 \text{ feet.} \\ =20.1 \text{ metres.} \end{cases}$

1 cheval (French horsepower)=0.986 horsepower.

1 circular mil $\begin{cases} =\text{Area of circle whose diameter is 1 mil, or} \\ \quad 1/1000 \text{ inch.} \\ =0.000000785 \text{ square inch.} \end{cases}$

1 cord $\begin{cases} =128 \text{ cubic feet.} \\ =3.625 \text{ cubic metres.} \end{cases}$

1 cubic foot $\begin{cases} =1,728 \text{ cubic inches.} \\ =60 \text{ pints.} \\ =0.8 \text{ bushel.} \\ =1,000 \text{ ounces of water, approx.} \\ =0.028 \text{ cubic metre.} \\ =28.32 \text{ litres.} \end{cases}$

1 cubic foot of water $\begin{cases} =62.4 \text{ pounds.} \\ =1,000 \text{ ounces, approx.} \end{cases}$

1 cubic inch=16.39 cubic centimetres.

1 cubic metre $\begin{cases} =35.314 \text{ cubic feet.} \\ =1.308 \text{ cubic yards.} \end{cases}$

1 cubic yard $\begin{cases} =27 \text{ cubic feet.} \\ =0.765 \text{ cubic metre.} \end{cases}$

1 decimetre=3.937 inches.

ALPHABETICAL CONVERSION TABLE—continued

1 dram (fluid) $\begin{cases} =60 \text{ minims.} \\ =3.697 \text{ millilitres.} \\ =4 \text{ cubic centimetres, approx.} \end{cases}$

1 em, 1 pica (printing industry)=1/6 of an inch.

1 fathom (nautical) $\begin{cases} =6 \text{ feet.} \\ =1.83 \text{ metres.} \end{cases}$

1 fluid ounce $\begin{cases} =8 \text{ fluid drams.} \\ =29.573 \text{ millilitres.} \end{cases}$

1 foot $\begin{cases} =12 \text{ inches.} \\ =0.305 \text{ metre.} \end{cases}$

1 foot pound=0.1383 kilogrammetre.

1 furlong (British) $\begin{cases} =220 \text{ yards.} \\ =201.2 \text{ metres.} \end{cases}$

1 gallon (U.S.) $\begin{cases} =231 \text{ cubic inches.} \\ =4 \text{ quarts.} \\ =8 \text{ pints.} \\ =3.875 \text{ litres.} \\ =128 \text{ fluid ounces.} \end{cases}$

1 gallon of water=8.33 pounds at 62° F. (16.67° C.) in air.

1 gallon per cubic foot=133.7 litres per cubic metre.

Gallon (British Imperial and Canadian). $\begin{cases} =277.4 \text{ cubic inches.} \\ =1.201 \text{ U.S. gallons.} \\ =\text{volume of 10 pounds water at 62°} \\ \quad \text{F. (16.67° C.).} \\ =4.546 \text{ litres.} \end{cases}$

1 gill=¼ pint.

1 grain $\begin{cases} =1/7000 \text{ pound avoirdupois.} \\ =0.0648 \text{ gram.} \end{cases}$

1 gram $\begin{cases} =15.43 \text{ grains.} \\ =0.0353 \text{ ounce.} \\ =0.0022 \text{ pound.} \end{cases}$

1 hand=4 inches.

1 hectare (square hectometre)=2.47 acres.

1 horsepower $\begin{cases} =33,000 \text{ foot-pounds per minute.} \\ =42.41 \text{ B. t. u. per minute.} \\ =1.014 \text{ chevals.} \\ =746 \text{ watts.} \end{cases}$

1 hundredweight (British) $\begin{cases} =112 \text{ pounds.} \\ =50.80 \text{ kilograms.} \end{cases}$

1 inch=25.4 millimetres.

1 kilogram $\begin{cases} =2.2046 \text{ pounds.} \\ =35.274 \text{ ounces.} \\ =15432.36 \text{ grains.} \\ =0.0011 \text{ short ton.} \\ =0.00098 \text{ long ton.} \end{cases}$

1 kilometre $\begin{cases} =1000 \text{ metres.} \\ =0.621 \text{ mile.} \end{cases}$

1 kilowatt $\begin{cases} =1.34 \text{ horsepower.} \\ =56.9 \text{ B. t. u. per minute.} \end{cases}$

1 knot (nautical, speed) $\begin{cases} =6080.20 \text{ feet per hour.} \\ =1.85 \text{ kilometres per hour.} \end{cases}$

1 light year $\begin{cases} =5.9 \times 10^{12} \text{ miles.} \\ =9.5 \times 10^{12} \text{ kilometres.} \end{cases}$

1 link (surveyors measure) $\begin{cases} =0.66 \text{ foot.} \\ =0.201 \text{ metre.} \end{cases}$

1 litre $\begin{cases} =1.000028 \text{ cubic decimetres.} \\ =0.264 \text{ gallon.} \\ =1.057 \text{ quarts.} \\ =61.03 \text{ cubic inches.} \\ =0.035 \text{ cubic feet.} \\ =33.8148 \text{ fluid ounces.} \\ =270.518 \text{ fluid drams.} \end{cases}$

1 metre $\begin{cases} =39.37 \text{ inches.} \\ =3.28 \text{ feet.} \\ =1.09 \text{ yards.} \\ =1\ 650\ 763.73 \text{ wave lengths in a vacuum of} \\ \quad \text{orange-red radiation of krypton 86.} \end{cases}$

1 metric ton $\begin{cases} =2204.6 \text{ pounds.} \\ =1.1023 \text{ short tons.} \end{cases}$

1 microgram=1/1000 milligram.

1 mil $\begin{cases} =0.001 \text{ inch.} \\ =25.4 \text{ microns.} \\ =0.0254 \text{ millimetre.} \end{cases}$

1 mile $\begin{cases} =1760 \text{ yards.} \\ =5280 \text{ feet.} \\ =320 \text{ rods.} \\ =1.61 \text{ kilometres.} \end{cases}$

1 milligram=0.0154 grain.

1 millilitre (see litre above) $\begin{cases} =1.000028 \text{ cubic centimetres.} \\ =0.0610 \text{ cubic inch.} \end{cases}$

1 minim (fluid) $\begin{cases} =1/60 \text{ fluid dram.} \\ =1/480 \text{ fluid ounce.} \end{cases}$

1 ounce (avoirdupois, ordinary) $\begin{cases} =437.5 \text{ grains.} \\ =0.911 \text{ troy ounce.} \\ =0.0000279 \text{ long ton.} \\ =28.35 \text{ grams.} \end{cases}$

1 ounce, fluid $\begin{cases} =1.805 \text{ cubic inches.} \\ =29.573 \text{ millilitres.} \end{cases}$

1 ounce, troy $\begin{cases} =480 \text{ grains.} \\ =31.103 \text{ grams.} \end{cases}$

1 perch (British) $\begin{cases} =30.25 \text{ square yards.} \\ =1/160 \text{ acre.} \end{cases}$

1 pied (French foot) $\begin{cases} =12 \text{ Paris inches.} \\ =0.325 \text{ metre.} \end{cases}$

1 pint=0.4732 litre.

1 point (printers type)=1/72 inch.

1 pole (British) $\begin{cases} =5\tfrac{1}{2} \text{ yards.} \\ =5.03 \text{ metre.} \\ =1 \text{ rod.} \end{cases}$

ALPHABETICAL CONVERSION TABLE—continued

1 pouce (Paris inch)=2.71 centimetre.

1 pound (avoirdupois, ordinary)
{
=16 ounces.
=7000 grains.
=454 grams.
=0.454 kilogram.
=14.58 troy ounces.
}

1 pound per cubic foot=16.02 kilogram per cubic metre.

1 pound per square inch=0.433×head of water (in feet).

1 pound per square inch=0.0703 kilogram per square centi-metre.

1 pound per square foot=4.88 kilogram per square metre.

1 quart
{
=2 pints.
=¼ gallon.
=0.946 litre.
}

1 quarter (British quarter hundredweight)
{
=28 pounds.
=12.70 kilograms.
}

1 rod (surveyor's measure)
{
=16.5 feet.
=25 links.
=5.03 metres.
}

1 rood (British)
{
=40 perches.
=¼ acre.
}

1 square centimetre=0.155 square inch.

1 square foot=0.093 square metre.

1 square inch=6.452 square centimetres.

1 square kilometre=0.386 square mile.

1 square metre (centare)
{
=10.764 square feet.
=1.196 square yards.
}

1 square mil
{
=0.000001 square inch.
=0.00000645 square centimetre.
}

1 square mile
{
=640 acres.
=3,097,600 square yards.
=2.59 square kilometres.
}

1 square millimetre=0.00155 square inch.

1 square rod=25.29 square metres.

1 square yard=0.836 square metre.

1 stone (British)
{
=14 pounds.
=6.35 kilograms.
}

1 ton (short)
{
=2,000 pounds.
=907 kilograms.
}

1 ton (long)
{
=2,240 pounds.
=1,016 kilograms.
}

1 ton (metric)
{
=1,000 kilograms.
=2,204.62 pounds.
}

1 yard
{
=3 feet.
=36 inches.
=0.914 metre.
=1 508 798.05 wave lengths in a vacuum of
  orange-red radiation of krypton 86.
}

SPELLING AND ABBREVIATION OF UNITS

The spelling of the names of units as adopted by the National Bureau of Standards is that given in the list below. The spelling of the metric units is in accordance with that given in the law of July 28, 1866, legalizing the metric system in the United States.

Following the name of each unit in the list below is given the abbreviation which the Bureau has adopted. Attention is particularly called to the following principles:

1. The period is omitted after all abbreviations of units, except where the abbreviation forms an English word.

2. The exponents "^{2}" and "^{3}" are used to signify "square" and "cubic", respectively, in the case of the metric units, instead of the abbreviations "sq" or "cu". In conformity with this principle the abbreviation for cubic centimetre is "cm^3" (instead of "cc" or "c cm"). The term "cubic centimetre", as used in chemical work, is, in fact, a misnomer, since the unit actually used is the "millilitre", of which the correct abbreviation is "ml".

3. The use of the same abbreviation for both singular and plural is recommended. This practice is already established in expressing metric units and is in accordance with the spirit and chief purpose of abbreviations.

4. It is also suggested that, unless all the text is printed in capital letters, only small letters be used for abbreviations, except in such case as A for angstrom, etc., where the use of capital letters is general.

SI UNITS, MULTIPLES, SUBMULTIPLES AND PREFIXES

ampere	A	are	a
ampere metre squared	$A.m^2$	atto-	a
ampere per metre	A/m	bar	bar
ampere per millimetre	A/mm	candela	cd
ampere per square centimetre	A/cm^2	candela per square metre	cd/m^2
		centi-	c
ampere per square metre	A/m^2	centimetre	cm
		centipoise	cP
ampere per square millimetre	A/mm^2	centistokes	cSt
		coulomb	C

coulomb metre	C.m
coulomb per cubic centimetre	C/cm^3
coulomb per cubic metre	C/m^3
coulomb per cubic millimetre	C/mm^3
coulomb per square centimetre	C/cm^2
coulomb per square metre	C/m^2
coulomb per square millimetre	C/mm^2
cubic centimetre	cm^3
cubic decimetre	dm^3
cubic metre	m^3
cubic millimetre	mm^3
cubic metre per kilomole	$m^3/kmol$
cubic metre per mole	m^3/mol
day	d
deca-	da
decanewton	daN
deci-	d
decimetre	dm
degree (angles)	$\overset{...}{°}$
degree celsius	°C
farad	F
farad per metre	F/m
femto-	f
giga-	G
gigahertz	GHz
gigajoule	GJ
giganewton per square metre	GN/m^2
gigaohm	GΩ
gigaohm metre	GΩ.m
gigawatt	GW
gigawatt hour	GW.h
gram	g

gram per cubic centimetre	g/cm^3
gram per litre	g/l
gram per millilitre	g/ml
gram per mole	g/mol
hectare	ha
hecto-	h
hectobar	hbar
henry	H
henry per metre	H/m
hertz	Hz
hour	hr
joule	J
joule per degree celsius	J/°C
joule per kelvin	J/K
joule per kilogram	J/kg
joule per kilogram degree celsius	J/kg.°C
joule per kilogram kelvin	J/kg.K
joule per kilomole	$J/kmol$
joule per kilomole degree celsius	$J/kmol.°C$
joule per kilomole kelvin	J/kmol.K
joule per mole	J/mol
joule per mole degree celsius	$J/mol.°C$
joule per mole kelvin	J/mol.K
joule per square centimetre	J/cm^2
joule per square metre	J/m^2
kelvin	K
kilo-	k
kiloampere	kA
kiloampere per metre	kA/m
kiloampere per square metre	kA/m^2

kilocoulomb	kC	kilonewton per square metre	kN/m²
kilocoulomb per cubic metre	kC/m³	kilo-ohm	kΩ
kilocoulomb per square metre	kC/m²	kilo-ohm metre	kΩ.m
kilogram	kg	kilosecond	ks
kilogram metre per second	kg.m/s	kilosiemens	kS
		kilosiemens per metre	kS/m
kilogram metre squared per second	kg.m²/s	kilovolt	kV
		kilovolt per metre	kV/m
kilogram per cubic decimetre	kg/dm³	kilowatt	kW
		kilowatt hour	kW.h
kilogram per cubic metre	kg/m³	kilowatt per square metre	kW/m²
kilogram per litre	kg/l	kiloweber per metre	kWb/m
kilogram per mole	kg/mol	litre	l
kilohertz	kHz	lumen	lm
kilojoule	kJ	lumen hour	lm.h
kilojoule per degree celsius	kJ/°C	lumen second	lm.s
		lux	lx
kilojoule per kelvin	kJ/K	mega-	M
kilojoule per kilogram	kJ/kg	mega-ampere per square metre	MA/m²
		megacoulomb	MC
kilojoule per kilogram degree celsius	kJ/kg.°C	megacoulomb per cubic metre	MC/m³
kilojoule per kilogram kelvin	kJ/kg.K	megacoulomb per square metre	MC/m²
		megagram	Mg
kilojoule per square metre	kJ/m²	megagram per cubic metre	Mg/m³
kilolitre	kl	megahertz	MHz
kilometre	km	megajoule	MJ
kilometre per hour	km/h	megajoule per kilogram	MJ/kg
kilomole	kmol	meganewton	MN
kilomole per cubic metre	kmol/m³	meganewton metre	MN.m
kilomole per kilogram	kmol/kg	meganewton per square metre	MN/m²
kilomole per litre	kmol/l	megaohm	MΩ
kilonewton	kN	megaohm metre	MΩ.m
kilonewton metre	kN.m	megasiemens per metre	MS/m

megavolt	MV
megavolt per metre	MV/m
megawatt	MW
megawatt hour	MW.h
megawatt per square metre	MW/m²
metre	m
metre per second	m/s
metre per second squared	m/s²
metre raised to the fourth power	m⁴
metre squared per second	m²/s
metric ton	t
metric ton per cubic metre	t/m³
micro-	μ
microampere	μA
microbar	μbar
microcoulomb	μC
microfarad	μF
microfarad per metre	μF/m
microgram	μg
microhenry	μH
microhenry per metre	μH/m
micrometre	μm
micronewton	μN
micronewton metre	μN.m
micronewton per square metre	μN/m²
micro-ohm	μΩ
micro-ohm metre	μΩ.m
microradian	μrad
microsecond	μs
microsiemens	μS
microtesla	μT
microvolt	μV
microvolt per metre	μV/m
microwatt	μW
milli-	m

milliampere	mA
millibar	mbar
millicoulomb	mC
millifarad	mF
millifarad per metre	mF/m
milligram	mg
millihenry	mH
millijoule	mJ
millilitre	ml
millimetre	mm
millimetre squared per second	mm²/s
millinewton	mN
millinewton per metre	mN/m
millinewton per square metre	mN/m²
millinewton second per metre squared	mN.s/m²
milliohm	mΩ
milliohm metre	mΩ.m
milliradian	mrad
millisecond	ms
millisiemens	mS
millitesla	mT
millivolt	mV
millivolt per metre	mV/m
milliwatt	mW
milliweber	mWb
minute (angles)	...´
minute	min
mole	mol
mole per cubic metre	mol/m³
mole per kilogram	mol/kg
mole per litre	mol/l
nano-	n
nanoampere	nA
nanocoulomb	nC
nanofarad	nF
nanofarad per metre	nF/m

nanohenry	nH	second (angles)	$\ldots''$
nanohenry per metre	nH/m	siemens	S
nanometre	nm	siemens per metre	S/m
nano-ohm metre	$n\Omega.m$	square centimetre	cm^2
nanosecond	ns	square decimetre	dm^2
nanotesla	nT	square kilometre	km^2
nanowatt	nW	square metre	m^2
newton	N	square millimetre	mm^2
newton metre	N.m	steradian	sr
newton metre squared per ampere	$N.m^2/A$	tera-	T
		terahertz	THz
		terajoule	TJ
newton per metre	N/m	terawatt	TW
newton per square metre	N/m^2	tesla	T
		volt	V
newton per square millimetre	N/mm^2	volt ampere	V.A
		volt per centimetre	V/cm
newton second per metre squared	$N.s/m^2$	volt per metre	V/m
		volt per millimetre	V/mm
ohm	Ω	volt second	V.s
ohm metre	$\Omega.m$	watt	W
ohm millimetre	$\Omega.mm$	watt hour	W.h
pascal	Pa	watt per metre degree celsius	$W/m.°C$
per degree celsius	$°C^{-1}$		
per henry	H^{-1}	watt per metre kelvin	W/m.K
per kelvin	K^{-1}		
per ohm	Ω^{-1}	watt per square metre	W/m^2
per ohm metre	$\Omega^{-1}.m^{-1}$		
per second	s^{-1}	watt per square metre degree celsius	$W/m^2.°C$
pico-	p		
picoampere	pA		
picocoulomb	pC		
picofarad	pF	watt per square metre kelvin	$W/m.^2K$
picofarad per metre	pF/m		
picohenry	pH	watt per steradian	W/sr
radian	rad	weber	Wb
radian per second	rad/s	weber metre	Wb.m
radian per second squared	rad/s^2	weber per metre	Wb/m
second	s	weber per millimetre	Wb/mm

TABLES OF INTERRELATION
1. UNITS OF

Units	Inches	Links	Feet	Yards	Rods
1 inch =	1	0. 126 263	0. 083 333 3	0. 027 777 8	0. 005 050 51
1 link =	7.92	1	0.66	0.22	0.04
1 foot =	12	1. 515 152	1	0. 333 333	0. 060 606 1
1 yard =	36	4. 545 45	3	1	0. 181 818
1 rod =	198	25	16.5	5.5	1
1 chain =	792	100	66	22	4
1 mile =	63 360	8000	5280	1760	320
1 centimetre=	0.3937	0. 049 709 60	0. 032 808 33	0. 010 936 111	0. 001 988 384
1 metre =	39.37	4. 970 960	3. 280 833	1. 093 611 1	0. 198 838 4

2. UNITS OF

Units	Square inches	Square links	Square feet	Square yards	Square rods	Square chains
1 square inch =	1	0. 015 942 3	0. 006 944 44	0.000 771 605	0. 000 025 507 6	0. 000 001 594 23
1 square link =	62.7264	1	0.4356	0.0484	0.0016	0.0001
1 square foot =	144	2. 295 684	1	0. 111 111 1	0. 003 673 09	0. 000 229 568
1 square yard =	1296	20. 6612	9	1	0. 033 057 85	0. 002 066 12
1 square rod =	39 204	625	272.25	30.25	1	0.0625
1 square chain =	627 264	10 000	4356	484	16	1
1 acre =	6 272 640	100 000	43 560	4840	160	10
1 square mile =	4 014 489 600	64 000 000	27 878 400	3 097 600	102 400	6400
1 square centimetre=	0. 154 999 69	0. 002 471 04	0. 001 076 387	0. 000 119 598 5	0. 000 003 953 67	0. 000 000 247 104
1 square metre =	1549.9969	24. 7104	10. 763 87	1. 195 985	0. 039 536 7	0. 002 471 04
1 hectare =	15 499 969	247 104	107 638. 7	11 959. 85	395. 367	24. 7104

3. UNITS OF

Units	Cubic inches	Cubic feet	Cubic yards
1 cubic inch =	1	0. 000 578 704	0. 000 021 433 47
1 cubic foot =	1728	1	0. 037 037 0
1 cubic yard =	46 656	27	1
1 cubic centimetre =	0. 061 023 38	0. 000 035 314 45	0. 000 001 307 94
1 cubic decimetre =	61. 023·38	0. 035 314 45	0. 001 307 943
1 cubic metre =	61 023. 38	35. 314 45	1. 307 942 8

4. UNITS OF CAPACITY

Units	Minims	Fluid drams	Fluid ounces	Gills	Liquid pints
1 minim =	1	0. 016 666 7	0. 002 083 33	0. 000 520 833	0. 000 130 208
1 fluid dram =	60	1	0.125	0.031 25	0. 007 812 5
1 fluid ounce=	480	8	1	0.25	0.0625
1 gill =	1920	32	4	1	0.25
1 liquid pint =	7680	128	16	4	1
1 liquid quart=	15 360	256	32	8	2
1 gallon =	61 440	1024	128	32	8
1 millilitres =	16. 2311	0. 270 518	0. 033 814 7	0. 008 453 68	0. 002 113 42
1 liter =	16 231. 1	270. 518	33. 8147	8. 453 68	2. 113 42
1 cubic inch =	265. 974	4. 432 90	0. 554 113	0. 138 528	0. 034 632 0

OF UNITS OF MEASUREMENT

LENGTH

Chains	Miles	Centimetres	Metres	Units
0.001 262 63	0.000 015 782 8	2.540 005	0.025 400 05	=1 inch
0.01	0.000 125	20.116 84	0.201 168 4	=1 link
0.015 151 5	0.000 189 393 9	30.480 06	0.304 800 6	=1 foot
0.045 454 5	0.000 568 182	91.440 18	0.914 401 8	=1 yard
0.25	0.003 125	502.9210	5.029 210	=1 rod
1	0.0125	2011.684	20.116 84	=1 chain
80	1	160 934.72	1609.3472	=1 mile
0.000 497 096 0	0.000 006 213 699	1	0.01	=1 centimetre
0.049 709 60	0.000 621 369 9	100	1	=1 metre

AREA

Acres	Square miles	Square centimetres	Square metres	Hectares	Units
0.000 000 159 423	0.000 000 000 249 1	6.451 626	0.000 645 162 6	0.000 000 064 516	=1 square inch
0.000 01	0.000 000 015 625	404.6873	0.040 468 73	0.000 004 046 87	=1 square link
0.000 022 956 8	0.000 000 035 870 1	929.0341	0.092 903 41	0.000 009 290 34	=1 square foot
0.000 206 612	0.000 000 322 831	8361.307	0.836 130 7	0.000 083 613 1	=1 square yard
0.006 25	0.000 009 765 625	252 929.5	25.292 95	0.002 529 295	=1 square rod
0.1	0.000 156 25	4 046 873	404.6873	0.040 468 7	=1 square chain
1	0.001 562 5	40 468 726	4046.873	0.404 687	=1 acre
640	1	25 899 984 703	2 589 998	258.9998	=1 square mile
0.000 000 024 710 4	0.000 000 000 038 610 06	1	0.0001	0.000 000 01	=1 square centimetre
0.000 247 104	0.000 000 386 100 6	10 000	1	0.0001	=1 square metre
2.471 04	0.003 861 006	100 000 000	10 000	1	=1 hectare

VOLUME

Cubic centimetres	Cubic decimetres	Cubic metres	Units
16.387 162	0.016 387 16	0.000 016 387 16	=1 cubic inch
28 317.016	28.317 016	0.028 317 016	=1 cubic foot
764 559.4	764.5594	0.764 559 4	=1 cubic yard
1	0.001	0.000 001	=1 cubic centimetre
1 000	1	0.001	=1 cubic decimetre
1 000 000	1000	1	=1 cubic metre

LIQUID MEASURE

Liquid quarts	Gallons	Milliliters	Liters	Cubic inches	Units
0.000 065 104	0.000 016 276	0.061 610 2	0.000 061 610 2	0.003 759 77	=1 minim
0.003 906 25	0.000 976 562	3.696 61	0.003 696 61	0.225 586	=1 fluid dram
0.031 25	0.007 812 5	29.5729	0.029 572 9	1.804 69	=1 fluid ounce
0.125	0.031 25	118.292	0.118 292	7.218 75	=1 gill
0.5	0.125	473.167	0.473 167	28.875	=1 liquid pint
1	0.25	946.333	0.946 333	57.75	=1 liquid quart
4	1	3785.332	3.785 332	231	=1 gallon
0.001 056 71	0.000 264 178	1	0.001	0.061 025 0	=1 milliliter
1.056 71	0.264 178	1000	1	61.0250	=1 liter
0.017 316 0	0.004 329 00	16.3867	0.016 386 7	1	=1 cubic inch

TABLES OF INTERRELATION
5. UNITS OF CAPACITY

Units	Dry pints	Dry quarts	Pecks	Bushels
1 dry pint =	1	0.5	0.0625	0.015 625
1 dry quart =	2	1	0.125	0.031 25
1 peck =	16	8	1	0.25
1 bushel =	64	32	4	1
1 liter =	1.816 20	0.908 102	0.113 513	0.028 378
1 dekalitre =	18.1620	9.081 02	1.135 13	0.283 78
1 cubic inch =	0.029 761 6	0.014 880 8	0.001 860 10	0.000 465 025

6. UNITS OF MASS LESS

Units *	Grains	Apothecaries' scruples	Pennyweights	Avoirdupois drams	Apothecaries' drams	Avoirdupois ounces
1 grain =	1	0.05	0.041 666 67	0.036 571 43	0.016 666 7	0.002 285 71
1 apoth. scruple =	20	1	0.833 333 3	0.731 428 6	0.333 333	0.045 714 3
1 pennyweight =	24	1.2	1	0.877 714 3	0.4	0.054 857 1
1 avoir. dram =	27.343 75	1.367 187 5	1.139 323	1	0.455 729 2	0.0625
1 apoth. dram =	60	3	2.5	2.194 286	1	0.137 142 9
1 avoir. ounce =	437.5	21.875	18.229 17	16	7.291 67	1
1 apoth. or troy ounce=	480	24	20	17.554 28	8	1.097 142 9
1 apoth. or troy pound=	5760	288	240	210.6514	96	13.165 714
1 avoir. pound =	7000	350	291.6667	256	116.6667	16
1 milligram =	0.015 432 356	0.000 771 618	0.000 643 014 8	0.000 564 383 3	0.000 257 205 9	0.000 035 273 96
1 gram =	15.432 356	0.771 618	0.643 014 85	0.564 383 3	0.257 205 9	0.035 273 96
1 kilogram =	15 432.356	771.6178	643.014 85	564.383 32	257.205 94	35.273 96

7. UNITS OF MASS

Units	Avoirdupois ounces	Avoirdupois pounds	Short hundred-weights	Short tons
1 avoirdupois ounce =	1	0.0625	0.000 625	0.000 031 25
1 avoirdupois pound =	16	1	0.01	0.0005
1 short hundredweight =	1600	100	1	0.05
1 short ton =	32 000	2000	20	1
1 long ton =	35 840	2240	22.4	1.12
1 kilogram =	35.273 957	2.204 622 34	0.022 046 223	0.001 102 311.2
1 metric ton =	35 273.957	2204.622 34	22.046 223	1.102 311 2

* "Avoir." is now abbreviated "avdp".

Note:

The U. S. stricken bushel = 2 150.42 cubic inches. It is used to measure dry commodities only.

The U. S. heaped bushel for apples of 2 747.175 cubic inches was established by the U. S. Court of Customs Appeals on February 15, 1912, in United States v. Weber (no. 757). A heaped bushel, equivalent to 1-1/4 stricken bushel, is also recognized.

The British bushel is equal to the volume of 2 219.36 cubic inches, 3% larger than a U. S. bushel.

OF UNITS OF MEASUREMENT
DRY MEASURE

Litres	Dekalitres	Cubic inches	Units
0.550 599	0.055 060	33.600 312 5	—1 dry pint
1.101 198	0.110 120	67.200 625	—1 dry quart
8.809 58	0.880 958	537.605	—1 peck
35.2383	3.523 83	2150.42	—1 bushel
1	0.1	61.0250	—1 liter
10	1	610.250	—1 dekalitre
0.016 386 7	0.001 638 67	1	—1 cubic inch

THAN POUNDS AND KILOGRAMS

Apothecaries' or troy ounces	Apothecaries' or troy pounds	Avoirdupois pounds	Milligrams	Grams	Kilograms	Units
0.002 083 33	0.000 173 611 1	0.000 142 857 1	64.798 918	0.064 798 918	0.000 064 798 9	—1 grain
0.041 666 7	0.003 472 222	0.002 857 143	1295.9784	1.295 978 4	0.001 295 978	—1 apoth. scruple
0.05	0.004 166 667	0.003 428 571	1555.1740	1.555 174 0	0.001 555 174	—1 pennyweight
0.056 966 146	0.004 747 178 8	0.003 906 25	1771.8454	1.771 845 4	0.001 771 845	—1 avoir. dram
0.125	0.010 416 667	0.008 571 429	3887.9351	3.887 935 1	0.003 887 935	—1 apoth. dram
0.911 458 3	0.075 954 861	0.0625	28 349.527	28.349 527	0.028 349 53	—1 avoir. ounce
1	0.083 333 33	0.068 571 43	31 103.481	31.103 481	0.031 103 48	—1 apoth. or troy ounce
12	1	0.822 857 1	373 241.77	373.241 77	0.373 241 77	—1 apoth. or troy pound
14.583 333	1.215 277 8	1	453 592.4277	453.592 4277	0.453 592 427 7	—1 avoir. pound
0.000 032 150 74	0.000 002 679 23	0.000 002 204 62	1	0.001	0.000 001	—1 milligram
0.032 150 74	0.002 679 23	0.002 204 62	1000	1	0.001	—1 gram
32.150 742	2.679 228 5	2.204 622 341	1 000 000	1000	1	—1 kilogram

GREATER THAN AVOIRDUPOIS OUNCES

Long tons	Kilograms	Metric tons	Units
0.000 027 901 79	0.028 349 53	0.000 028 349 53	—1 avoirdupois ounce
0.000 446 428 6	0.453 592 427 7	0.000 453 592 43	—1 avoirdupois pound
0.044 642 86	45.359 243	0.045 359 243	—1 short hundredweight
0.892 857 1	907.184 86	0.907 184 86	—1 short ton
1	1016.047 04	1.016 047 04	—1 long ton
0.000 984 206 4	1	0.001	—1 kilogram
0.984 206 40	1000	1	—1 metric ton

COMPARISON OF METRIC AND CUSTOMARY UNITS FROM 1 TO 9

1. LENGTH

Inches (in.)	Millimetres (mm)	Feet (ft)	Metres (m)	Yards (yd)	Metres (m)	Rods (rd)	Metres (m)	U.S. miles (mi)	Kilometres (km)
1=	25.4001	1=0.304 801		1=0.914 402		1= 5.029 21		1= 1.609 347	
2=	50.8001	2=0.609 601		2=1.828 804		2=10.058 42		2= 3.218 694	
3=	76.2002	3=0.914 402		3=2.743 205		3=15.087 63		3= 4.828 042	
4=	101.6002	4=1.219 202		4=3.657 607		4=20.116 84		4= 6.437 389	
5=	127.0003	5=1.524 003		5=4.572 009		5=25.146 05		5= 8.046 736	
6=	152.4003	6=1.828 804		6=5.486 411		6=30.175 26		6= 9.656 083	
7=	177.8004	7=2.133 604		7=6.400 813		7=35.204 47		7=11.265 431	
8=	203.2004	8=2.438 405		8=7.315 215		8=40.233 68		8=12.874 778	
9=	228.6005	9=2.743 205		9=8.229 616		9=45.262 89		9=14.484 125	
0.039 37=1		3.280 83=1		1.093 611=1		0.198 838=1		0.621 370=1	
0.078 74=2		6.561 67=2		2.187 222=2		0.397 677=2		1.242 740=2	
0.118 11=3		9.842 50=3		3.280 833=3		0.596 515=3		1.864 110=3	
0.157 48=4		13.123 33=4		4.374 444=4		0.795 354=4		2.485 480=4	
0.196 85=5		16.404 17=5		5.468 056=5		0.994 192=5		3.106 850=5	
0.236 22=6		19.685 00=6		6.561 667=6		1.193 030=6		3.728 220=6	
0.275 59=7		22.965 83=7		7.655 278=7		1.391 869=7		4.349 590=7	
0.314 96=8		26.246 67=8		8.748 889=8		1.590 707=8		4.970 960=8	
0.354 33=9		29.527 50=9		9.842 500=9		1.789 545=9		5.592 330=9	

2. AREA

Square inches (sq in.)	Square centimetres (cm²)	Square feet (sq ft)	Square metres (m²)	Square yards (sq yd)	Square metres (m²)	Acres (acre)	Hectares (ha)	Square miles (sq mi)	Square Kilometres (km²)
1=	6.452	1=0.092 90		1=0.8361		1=0.4047		1= 2.5900	
2=	12.903	2=0.185 81		2=1.6723		2=0.8094		2= 5.1800	
3=	19.355	3=0.278 71		3=2.5084		3=1.2141		3= 7.7700	
4=	25.807	4=0.371 61		4=3.3445		4=1.6187		4=10.3600	
5=	32.258	5=0.464 52		5=4.1807		5=2.0234		5=12.9500	
6=	38.710	6=0.557 42		6=5.0168		6=2.4281		6=15.5400	
7=	45.161	7=0.650 32		7=5.8529		7=2.8328		7=18.1300	
8=	51.613	8=0.743 23		8=6.6890		8=3.2375		8=20.7200	
9=	58.065	9=0.836 13		9=7.5252		9=3.6422		9=23.3100	
0.155 00=1		10.764=1		1.1960=1		2.471=1		0.3861=1	
0.310 00=2		21.528=2		2.3920=2		4.942=2		0.7722=2	
0.465 00=3		32.292=3		3.5880=3		7.413=3		1.1583=3	
0.620 00=4		43.055=4		4.7839=4		9.884=4		1.5444=4	
0.775 00=5		53.819=5		5.9799=5		12.355=5		1.9305=5	
0.930 00=6		64.583=6		7.1759=6		14.826=6		2.3166=6	
1.085 00=7		75.347=7		8.3719=7		17.297=7		2.7027=7	
1.240 00=8		86.111=8		9.5679=8		19.768=8		3.0888=8	
1.395 00=9		96.875=9		10.7639=9		22.239=9		3.4749=9	

3. VOLUME

Cubic inches (cu in.)	Cubic centimetres (cm³)	Cubic feet (cu ft)	Cubic metres (m³)	Cubic yards (cu yd)	Cubic metres (m³)	Cubic inches (cu in.)	Litres (litre)	Cubic feet (cu ft)	Litres (litre)
1=	16.3872	1=0.028 317		1=0.7646		1=0.016 386 7		1= 28.316	
2=	32.7743	2=0.056 634		2=1.5291		2=0.032 773 4		2= 56.633	
3=	49.1615	3=0.084 951		3=2.2937		3=0.049 160 2		3= 84.949	
4=	65.5486	4=0.113 268		4=3.0582		4=0.065 546 9		4=113.265	
5=	81.9358	5=0.141 585		5=3.8228		5=0.081 933 6		5=141.581	
6=	98.3230	6=0.169 902		6=4.5874		6=0.098 320 3		6=169.898	
7=	114.7101	7=0.198 219		7=5.3519		7=0.114 707 0		7=198.214	
8=	131.0973	8=0.226 536		8=6.1165		8=0.131 093 8		8=226.530	
9=	147.4845	9=0.254 853		9=6.8810		9=0.147 480 5		9=254.846	
0.061 02=1		35.314=1		1.3079=1		61.025=1		0.035 315=1	
0.122 05=2		70.629=2		2.6159=2		122.050=2		0.070 631=2	
0.183 07=3		105.943=3		3.9238=3		183.075=3		0.105 946=3	
0.244 09=4		141.258=4		5.2318=4		244.100=4		0.141 262=4	
0.305 12=5		176.572=5		6.5397=5		305.125=5		0.176 577=5	
0.366 14=6		211.887=6		7.8477=6		366.150=6		0.211 892=6	
0.427 16=7		247.201=7		9.1556=7		427.175=7		0.247 208=7	
0.488 19=8		282.516=8		10.4635=8		488.200=8		0.282 523=8	
0.549 21=9		317.830=9		11.7715=9		549.225=9		0.317 839=9	

4. CAPACITY—LIQUID MEASURE

U. S. fluid drams (fl dr)	Millilitres (ml)	U. S. fluid ounces (fl oz)	Millilitres (ml)	U.S. liquid pints (pt)	Litres (litre)	U.S. liquid quarts (qt)	Litres (litre)	U. S. gallons (gal)	Litres (litre)
1= 3.6966		1= 29.573		1=0.473 17		1=0.946 33		1= 3.785 33	
2= 7.3932		2= 59.146		2=0.946 33		2=1.892 67		2= 7.570 66	
3=11.0898		3= 88.719		3=1.419 50		3=2.839 00		3=11.356 00	
4=14.7865		4=118.292		4=1.892 67		4=3.785 33		4=15.141 33	
5=18.4831		5=147.865		5=2.365 83		5=4.731 67		5=18.926 66	
6=22.1797		6=177.437		6=2.839 00		6=5.678 00		6=22.711 99	
7=25.8763		7=207.010		7=3.312 17		7=6.624 33		7=26.497 33	
8=29.5729		8=236.583		8=3.785 33		8=7.570 66		8=30.282 66	
9=33.2695		9=266.156		9=4.258 50		9=8.517 00		9=34.067 99	
0.270 52=1		0.033 815=1		2.1134=1		1.056 71=1		0.264 18=1	
0.541 04=2		0.067 629=2		4.2268=2		2.113 42=2		0.528 36=2	
0.811 55=3		0.101 444=3		6.3403=3		3.170 13=3		0.792 53=3	
1.082 07=4		0.135 259=4		8.4537=4		4.226 84=4		1.056 71=4	
1.352 59=5		0.169 074=5		10.5671=5		5.283 55=5		1.320 89=5	
1.623 11=6		0.202 888=6		12.6805=6		6.340 26=6		1.585 07=6	
1.893 63=7		0.236 703=7		14.7939=7		7.396 97=7		1.849 24=7	
2.164 14=8		0.270 518=8		16.9074=8		8.453 68=8		2.113 42=8	
2.434 66=9		0.304 333=9		19.0208=9		9.510 39=9		2.377 60=9	

5. CAPACITY—DRY MEASURE

U. S. dry quarts (qt)	Litres (litre)	U. S. pecks (pk)	Litres (litre)	U. S. pecks (pk)	Dekalitres (dkl)	U. S. bushels (bu)	Hecto-litres (hl)	U. S. bushels per acre	Hecto-litres per hectare
1=1.1012		1= 8.810		1=0.8810		1=0.352 38		1=0.8708	
2=2.2024		2=17.619		2=1.7619		2=0.704 77		2=1.7415	
3=3.3036		3=26.429		3=2.6429		3=1.057 15		3=2.6123	
4=4.4048		4=35.238		4=3.5238		4=1.409 53		4=3.4830	
5=5.5060		5=44.048		5=4.4048		5=1.761 92		5=4.3538	
6=6.6072		6=52.857		6=5.2857		6=2.114 30		6=5.2245	
7=7.7084		7=61.667		7=6.1667		7=2.466 68		7=6.0953	
8=8.8096		8=70.477		8=7.0477		8=2.819 07		8=6.9660	
9=9.9108		9=79.286		9=7.9286		9=3.171 45		9=7.8368	
0.9081=1		0.113 51=1		1.1351=1		2.8378=1		1.1484=1	
1.8162=2		0.227 03=2		2.2703=2		5.6756=2		2.2969=2	
2.7243=3		0.340 54=3		3.4054=3		8.5135=3		3.4453=3	
3.6324=4		0.454 05=4		4.5405=4		11.3513=4		4.5937=4	
4.5405=5		0.567 56=5		5.6756=5		14.1891=5		5.7421=5	
5.4486=6		0.681 08=6		6.8108=6		17.0269=6		6.8906=6	
6.3567=7		0.794 59=7		7.9459=7		19.8647=7		8.0390=7	
7.2648=8		0.908 10=8		9.0810=8		22.7026=8		9.1874=8	
8.1729=9		1.021 61=9		10.2161=9		25.5404=9		10.3359=9	

6. MASS

Grains (grain)	Grams (g)	Apothecaries' drams (dr ap or ʒ)	Grams (g)	Troy ounces (oz t)	Grams (g)	Avoirdupois ounces (oz avdp)	Grams (g)	Avoirdupois pounds (lb avdp)	Kilograms (kg)
1=0.064 799		1= 3.8879		1= 31.103		1= 28.350		1=0.453 59	
2=0.129 598		2= 7.7759		2= 62.207		2= 56.699		2=0.907 18	
3=0.194 397		3=11.6638		3= 93.310		3= 85.049		3=1.360 78	
4=0.259 196		4=15.5517		4=124.414		4=113.398		4=1.814 37	
5=0.323 995		5=19.4397		5=155.517		5=141.748		5=2.267 96	
6=0.388 794		6=23.3276		6=186.621		6=170.097		6=2.721 55	
7=0.453 592		7=27.2155		7=217.724		7=198.447		7=3.175 15	
8=0.518 391		8=31.1035		8=248.828		8=226.796		8=3.628 74	
9=0.583 190		9=34.9914		9=279.931		9=255.146		9=4.082 33	
15.4324=1		0.257 21=1		0.032 151=1		0.035 274=1		2.204 62=1	
30.8647=2		0.514 41=2		0.064 301=2		0.070 548=2		4.409 24=2	
46.2971=3		0.771 62=3		0.096 452=3		0.105 822=3		6.613 87=3	
61.7294=4		1.028 82=4		0.128 603=4		0.141 096=4		8.818 49=4	
77.1618=5		1.286 03=5		0.160 754=5		0.176 370=5		11.023 11=5	
92.5941=6		1.543 24=6		0.192 904=6		0.211 644=6		13.227 73=6	
108.0265=7		1.800 44=7		0.225 055=7		0.246 918=7		15.432 36=7	
123.4589=8		2.057 65=8		0.257 206=8		0.282 192=8		17.636 98=8	
138.8912=9		2.314 85=9		0.289 357=9		0.317 466=9		19.841 60=9	

COMPARISON OF THE VARIOUS TONS AND POUNDS IN USE IN THE UNITED STATES (FROM 1 TO 9 UNITS)

Troy pounds	Avoirdupois pounds	Kilograms	Short tons	Long tons	Metric tons
1	0.822 857	0.373 24	0.000 411 43	0.000 367 35	0.000 373 24
2	1.645 71	0.746 48	0.000 822 86	0.000 734 69	0.000 746 48
3	2.468 57	1.119 73	0.001 234 29	0.001 102 04	0.001 119 73
4	3.291 43	1.492 97	0.001 645 71	0.001 469 39	0.001 492 97
5	4.114 29	1.866 21	0.002 057 14	0.001 836 73	0.001 866 21
6	4.937 14	2.239 45	0.002 468 57	0.002 204 08	0.002 239 45
7	5.760 00	2.612 69	0.002 880 00	0.002 571 43	0.002 612 69
8	6.582 86	2.985 93	0.003 291 43	0.002 938 78	0.002 985 93
9	7.405 71	3.359 18	0.003 702 86	0.003 306 12	0.003 359 18
1.215 28	1	0.453 59	0.0005	0.000 446 43	0.000 453 59
2.430 56	2	0.907 18	0.0010	0.000 892 86	0.000 907 18
3.645 83	3	1.360 78	0.0015	0.001 339 29	0.001 360 78
4.861 11	4	1.814 37	0.0020	0.001 785 71	0.001 814 37
6.076 39	5	2.267 96	0.0025	0.002 232 14	0.002 267 96
7.291 67	6	2.721 55	0.0030	0.002 678 57	0.002 721 55
8.506 94	7	3.175 15	0.0035	0.003 125 00	0.003 175 15
9.722 22	8	3.628 74	0.0040	0.003 571 43	0.003 628 74
10.937 50	9	4.082 33	0.0045	0.004 017 86	0.004 082 33
2.679 23	2.204 62	1	0.001 102 31	0.000 984 21	0.001
5.358 46	4.409 24	2	0.002 204 62	0.001 968 41	0.002
8.037 69	6.613 87	3	0.003 306 93	0.002 952 62	0.003
10.716 91	8.818 49	4	0.004 409 24	0.003 936 83	0.004
13.396 14	11.023 11	5	0.005 511 56	0.004 921 03	0.005
16.075 37	13.227 73	6	0.006 613 87	0.005 905 24	0.006
18.754 60	15.432 36	7	0.007 716 18	0.006 889 44	0.007
21.433 83	17.636 98	8	0.008 818 49	0.007 873 65	0.008
24.113 06	19.841 60	9	0.009 920 80	0.008 857 86	0.009

Troy pounds	Avoirdupois pounds	Kilograms	Short tons	Long tons	Metric tons
2430.56	2000	907.18	1	0.892 86	0.907 18
4861.11	4000	1814.37	2	1.785 71	1.814 37
7291.67	6000	2721.55	3	2.678 57	2.721 55
9722.22	8000	3628.74	4	3.571 43	3.628 74
12 152.78	10 000	4535.92	5	4.464 29	4.535 92
14 583.33	12 000	5443.11	6	5.357 14	5.443 11
17 013.89	14 000	6350.29	7	6.250 00	6.350 29
19 444.44	16 000	7257.48	8	7.142 86	7.257 48
21 875.00	18 000	8164.66	9	8.035 71	8.164 66
2722.22	2240	1016.05	1.12	1	1.016 05
5444.44	4480	2032.09	2.24	2	2.032 09
8166.67	6720	3048.14	3.36	3	3.048 14
10 888.89	8960	4064.19	4.48	4	4.064 19
13 611.11	11 200	5080.24	5.60	5	5.080 24
16 333.33	13 440	6096.28	6.72	6	6.096 28
19 055.56	15 680	7112.32	7.84	7	7.112 32
21 777.78	17 920	8128.38	8.96	8	8.128 38
24 500.00	20 160	9144.42	10.08	9	9.144 42
2679.23	2204.62	1000	1.102 31	0.984 21	1
5358.46	4409.24	2000	2.204 62	1.968 41	2
8037.69	6613.87	3000	3.306 93	2.952 62	3
10 716.91	8818.49	4000	4.409 24	3.936 83	4
13 396.14	11 023.11	5000	5.511 56	4.921 03	5
16 075.37	13 227.73	6000	6.613 87	5.905 24	6
18 754.60	15 432.36	7000	7.716 18	6.889 44	7
21 433.83	17 636.98	8000	8.818 49	7.873 65	8
24 113.06	19 841.60	9000	9.920 80	8.857 86	9

LENGTH—INCHES AND MILLIMETRES—EQUIVALENTS OF DECIMAL AND BINARY FRACTIONS OF AN INCH IN MILLIMETRES

From 1/64 to 1 Inch

½'s	¼'s	8ths	16ths	32ds	64ths	Milli-metres	Decimals of an inch
					1	= 0.397	0.015625
				1	2	= .794	.03125
					3	= 1.191	.046875
			1	2	4	= 1.588	.0625
					5	= 1.984	.078125
				3	6	= 2.381	.09375
					7	= 2.778	.109375
		1	2	4	8	= 3.175	.1250
					9	= 3.572	.140625
				5	10	= 3.969	.15625
					11	= 4.366	.171875
			3	6	12	= 4.763	.1875
					13	= 5.159	.203125
				7	14	= 5.556	.21875
					15	= 5.953	.234375
	1	2	4	8	16	= 6.350	.2500
					17	= 6.747	.265625
				9	18	= 7.144	.28125
					19	= 7.541	.296875
			5	10	20	= 7.938	.3125
					21	= 8.334	.328125
				11	22	= 8.731	.34375
					23	= 9.128	.359375
		3	6	12	24	= 9.525	.3750
					25	= 9.922	.390625
				13	26	= 10.319	.40625
					27	= 10.716	.421875
			7	14	28	= 11.113	.4375
					29	= 11.509	.453125
				15	30	= 11.906	.46875
					31	= 12.303	.484375
1	2	4	8	16	32	= 12.700	.5

Inch	½'s	¼'s	8ths	16ths	32ds	64ths	Milli-metres	Decimals of an inch
						33	= 13.097	0.515625
					17	34	= 13.494	.53125
						35	= 13.891	.546875
				9	18	36	= 14.288	.5625
						37	= 14.684	.578125
					19	38	= 15.081	.59375
						39	= 15.478	.609375
		5	10	20	40	= 15.875	.625	
						41	= 16.272	.640625
					21	42	= 16.669	.65625
						43	= 17.066	.671875
				11	22	44	= 17.463	.6875
						45	= 17.859	.703125
					23	46	= 18.256	.71875
						47	= 18.653	.734375
		3	6	12	24	48	= 19.050	.75
						49	= 19.447	.765625
					25	50	= 19.844	.78125
						51	= 20.241	.796875
				13	26	52	= 20.638	.8125
						53	= 21.034	.828125
					27	54	= 21.431	.84375
						55	= 21.828	.859375
			7	14	28	56	= 22.225	.875
						57	= 22.622	.890625
					29	58	= 23.019	.90625
						59	= 23.416	.921875
				15	30	60	= 23.813	.9375
						61	= 24.209	.953125
					31	62	= 24.606	.96875
						63	= 25.003	.984375
1	2	4	8	16	32	64	= 25.400	1.000

LENGTH—HUNDREDTHS OF AN INCH TO MILLIMETRES

From 1 to 99 Hundredths

Hundredths of an inch	0	1	2	3	4	5	6	7	8	9
10	0	0.254	0.508	0.762	1.016	1.270	1.524	1.778	2.032	2.286
20	2.540	2.794	3.048	3.302	3.556	3.810	4.064	4.318	4.572	4.826
30	5.080	5.334	5.588	5.842	6.096	6.350	6.604	6.858	7.112	7.366
40	7.620	7.874	8.128	8.382	8.636	8.890	9.144	9.398	9.652	9.906
50	10.160	10.414	10.668	10.922	11.176	11.430	11.684	11.938	12.192	12.446
60	12.700	12.954	13.208	13.462	13.716	13.970	14.224	14.478	14.732	14.986
70	15.240	15.494	15.748	16.002	16.256	16.510	16.764	17.018	17.272	17.526
80	17.780	18.034	18.288	18.542	18.796	19.050	19.304	19.558	19.812	20.066
90	20.320	20.574	20.828	21.082	21.336	21.590	21.844	22.098	22.352	22.606
	22.860	23.114	23.368	23.622	23.876	24.130	24.384	24.638	24.892	25.146

LENGTH—MILLIMETRES TO DECIMALS OF AN INCH

From 1 to 99 Units

Millimetres	0	1	2	3	4	5	6	7	8	9
10	0	0.03937	0.07874	0.11811	0.15748	0.19685	0.23622	0.27559	0.31496	0.35433
20	0.39370	.43307	.47244	.51181	.55118	.59055	.62992	.66929	.70866	.74803
30	.78740	.82677	.86614	.90551	.94488	.98425	1.02362	1.06299	1.10236	1.14173
40	1.18110	1.22047	1.25984	1.29921	1.33858	1.37795	1.41732	1.45669	1.49606	1.53543
50	1.57480	1.61417	1.65354	1.69291	1.73228	1.77165	1.81102	1.85039	1.88976	1.92913
60	1.96850	2.00787	2.04724	2.08661	2.12598	2.16535	2.20472	2.24409	2.28346	2.32283
70	2.36220	2.40157	2.44094	2.48031	2.51968	2.55905	2.59842	2.63779	2.67716	2.71653
80	2.75590	2.79527	2.83464	2.87401	2.91338	2.95275	2.99212	3.03149	3.07086	3.11023
90	3.14960	3.18897	3.22834	3.26771	3.30708	3.34645	3.38582	3.42519	3.46456	3.50393
	3.54330	3.58267	3.62204	3.66141	3.70078	3.74015	3.77952	3.81889	3.85826	3.89763

LENGTH—UNITED STATES NAUTICAL MILES, INTERNATIONAL NAUTICAL MILES, AND KILOMETRES

Basic relations 1 U.S. nautical mile = 1.853 248 kilometres. 1 U.S. nautical mile = 1.000 673 9 int. nautical miles. 1 International nautical mile = 1.852 kilometres.

U.S. nautical miles	Int. nautical miles	Kilometres
1	1.0007	1.8532
2	2.0013	3.7065
3	3.0020	5.5597
4	4.0027	7.4130
5	5.0034	9.2662
6	6.0040	11.1195
7	7.0047	12.9727
8	8.0054	14.8260
9	9.0061	16.6792
10	10.0067	18.5325
11	11.0074	20.3857
12	12.0081	22.2390
13	13.0088	24.0922
14	14.0094	25.9455
15	15.0101	27.7987
16	16.0108	29.6520
17	17.0115	31.5052
18	18.0121	33.3585
19	19.0128	35.2117
20	20.0135	37.0650
21	21.0142	38.9182
22	22.0148	40.7715
23	23.0155	42.6247
24	24.0162	44.4780
25	25.0168	46.3312
26	26.0175	48.1844
27	27.0182	50.0377
28	28.0189	51.8909
29	29.0195	53.7442
30	30.0202	55.5974
31	31.0209	57.4507
32	32.0216	59.3039
33	33.0222	61.1572
34	34.0229	63.0104
35	35.0236	64.8637
36	36.0243	66.7169
37	37.0249	68.5702
38	38.0256	70.4234
39	39.0263	72.2767
40	40.0270	74.1299
41	41.0276	75.9832
42	42.0283	77.8364
43	43.0290	79.6897
44	44.0297	81.5429
45	45.0303	83.3962
46	46.0310	85.2494
47	47.0317	87.1027
48	48.0323	88.9559
49	49.0330	90.8092

Int. nautical miles	U.S. nautical miles	Kilometres
1	0.9993	1.8520
2	1.9987	3.7040
3	2.9980	5.5560
4	3.9973	7.4080
5	4.9966	9.2600
6	5.9960	11.1120
7	6.9953	12.9640
8	7.9946	14.8160
9	8.9939	16.6680
10	9.9933	18.5200
11	10.9926	20.3720
12	11.9919	22.2240
13	12.9912	24.0760
14	13.9906	25.9280
15	14.9899	27.7800
16	15.9892	29.6320
17	16.9886	31.4840
18	17.9879	33.3360
19	18.9872	35.1880
20	19.9865	37.0400
21	20.9859	38.8920
22	21.9852	40.7440
23	22.9845	42.5960
24	23.9838	44.4480
25	24.9832	46.3000
26	25.9825	48.1520
27	26.9818	50.0040
28	27.9811	51.8560
29	28.9805	53.7080
30	29.9798	55.5600
31	30.9791	57.4120
32	31.9785	59.2640
33	32.9778	61.1160
34	33.9771	62.9680
35	34.9764	64.8200
36	35.9758	66.6720
37	36.9751	68.5240
38	37.9744	70.3760
39	38.9737	72.2280
40	39.9731	74.0800
41	40.9724	75.9320
42	41.9717	77.7840
43	42.9710	79.6360
44	43.9704	81.4880
45	44.9697	83.3400
46	45.9690	85.1920
47	46.9683	87.0440
48	47.9677	88.8960
49	48.9670	90.7480

Kilometres	U.S. nautical miles	Int. nautical miles
1	0.5396	0.5400
2	1.0792	1.0799
3	1.6188	1.6199
4	2.1584	2.1598
5	2.6980	2.6998
6	3.2376	3.2397
7	3.7772	3.7797
8	4.3167	4.3197
9	4.8563	4.8596
10	5.3959	5.3996
11	5.9355	5.9395
12	6.4751	6.4795
13	7.0147	7.0194
14	7.5543	7.5594
15	8.0939	8.0994
16	8.6335	8.6393
17	9.1731	9.1793
18	9.7127	9.7192
19	10.2523	10.2592
20	10.7919	10.7991
21	11.3315	11.3391
22	11.8711	11.8790
23	12.4106	12.4190
24	12.9502	12.9590
25	13.4898	13.4989
26	14.0294	14.0389
27	14.5690	14.5788
28	15.1086	15.1188
29	15.6482	15.6587
30	16.1878	16.1987
31	16.7274	16.7387
32	17.2670	17.2786
33	17.8066	17.8186
34	18.3462	18.3585
35	18.8858	18.8985
36	19.4254	19.4384
37	19.9649	19.9784
38	20.5045	20.5184
39	21.0441	21.0583
40	21.5837	21.5983
41	22.1233	22.1382
42	22.6629	22.6782
43	23.2025	23.2181
44	23.7421	23.7581
45	24.2817	24.2981
46	24.8213	24.8380
47	25.3609	25.3780
48	25.9005	25.9179
49	26.4401	26.4579

50	26.9978	26.9797	92.6000	49.9663	92.6624	50.0337
1	27.5378	27.5193	94.4520	50.9657	94.5156	51.0344
2	28.0778	28.0588	96.3040	51.9650	96.3689	52.0350
3	28.6177	28.5984	98.1560	52.9643	98.2221	53.0357
4	29.1577	29.1380	100.0080	53.9636	100.0754	54.0364
5	29.6976	29.6776	101.8600	54.9630	101.9286	55.0371
6	30.2376	30.2172	103.7120	55.9623	103.7819	56.0377
7	30.7775	30.7568	105.5640	56.9616	105.6351	57.0384
8	31.3175	31.2964	107.4160	57.9609	107.4884	58.0391
9	31.8575	31.8360	109.2680	58.9603	109.3416	59.0398
60	32.3974	32.3756	111.1200	59.9596	111.1949	60.0404
1	32.9374	32.9152	112.9720	60.9589	113.0481	61.0411
2	33.4773	33.4548	114.8240	61.9582	114.9014	62.0418
3	34.0173	33.9944	116.6760	62.9576	116.7546	63.0425
4	34.5572	34.5340	118.5280	63.9569	118.6079	64.0431
5	35.0972	35.0736	120.3800	64.9562	120.4611	65.0438
6	35.6371	35.6132	122.2320	65.9556	122.3144	66.0445
7	36.1771	36.1527	124.0840	66.9549	124.1676	67.0452
8	36.7171	36.6923	125.9360	67.9542	126.0209	68.0458
9	37.2570	37.2319	127.7880	68.9535	127.8741	69.0465
70	37.7970	37.7715	129.6400	69.9529	129.7274	70.0472
1	38.3369	38.3111	131.4920	70.9522	131.5806	71.0478
2	38.8769	38.8507	133.3440	71.9515	133.4339	72.0485
3	39.4168	39.3903	135.1960	72.9508	135.2871	73.0492
4	39.9568	39.9299	137.0480	73.9502	137.1404	74.0499
5	40.4968	40.4695	138.9000	74.9495	138.9936	75.0505
6	41.0367	41.0091	140.7520	75.9488	140.8468	76.0512
7	41.5767	41.5487	142.6040	76.9481	142.7001	77.0519
8	42.1166	42.0883	144.4560	77.9475	144.5533	78.0526
9	42.6566	42.6279	146.3080	78.9468	146.4066	79.0532
80	43.1965	43.1675	148.1600	79.9461	148.2598	80.0539
1	43.7365	43.7070	150.0120	80.9455	150.1131	81.0546
2	44.2765	44.2466	151.8640	81.9448	151.9663	82.0553
3	44.8164	44.7862	153.7160	82.9441	153.8196	83.0559
4	45.3564	45.3258	155.5680	83.9434	155.6728	84.0566
5	45.8963	45.8654	157.4200	84.9428	157.5261	85.0573
6	46.4363	46.4050	159.2720	85.9421	159.3793	86.0580
7	46.9762	46.9446	161.1240	86.9414	161.0326	87.0586
8	47.5162	47.4842	162.9760	87.9407	163.0858	88.0593
9	48.0562	48.0238	164.8280	88.9401	164.9391	89.0600
90	48.5961	48.5634	166.6800	89.9394	166.7923	90.0607
1	49.1361	49.1030	168.5320	90.9387	168.6456	91.0613
2	49.6760	49.6426	170.3840	91.9380	170.4988	92.0620
3	50.2160	50.1822	172.2360	92.9374	172.3521	93.0627
4	50.7559	50.7218	174.0880	93.9367	174.2053	94.0633
5	51.2959	51.2614	175.9400	94.9360	176.0586	95.0640
6	51.8359	51.8009	177.7920	95.9354	177.9118	96.0647
7	52.3758	52.3405	179.6440	96.9347	179.7651	97.0654
8	52.9158	52.8801	181.4960	97.9340	181.6183	98.0660
9	53.4557	53.4197	183.3480	98.9333	183.4716	99.0667
100	53.9957	53.9593	185.2000	99.9337	185.3248	100.0674

LENGTH—MILLIMETRES TO INCHES

[From 0.00 to 25.40 millimetres by 0.01 millimetre. 1 millimetre = 0.03937 inch.]

Milli-metres	Hundredths of millimetres				
	0.00	0.01	0.02	0.08	0.04
	Inches	Inches	Inches	Inches	Inches
0.00	0. 000000	0. 000394	0. 000787	0. 001181	0. 001575
0. 10	. 003937	. 004331	. 004724	. 005118	. 005512
0. 20	. 007874	. 008268	. 008661	. 009055	. 009449
0. 30	. 011811	. 012205	. 012598	. 012992	. 013386
0. 40	. 015748	. 016142	. 016535	. 016929	. 017323
0.50	0. 019685	0. 020079	0. 020472	0. 020866	0. 021260
0. 60	. 023622	. 024016	. 024409	. 024803	. 025197
0. 70	. 027559	. 027953	. 028346	. 028740	. 029134
0. 80	. 031496	. 031890	. 032283	. 032677	. 033071
0. 90	. 035433	. 035827	. 036220	. 036614	. 037008
1.00	0. 03937	0. 03976	0. 04016	0. 04055	0. 04094
1. 10	. 04331	. 04370	. 04409	. 04449	. 04488
1. 20	. 04724	. 04764	. 04803	. 04843	. 04882
1. 30	. 05118	. 05157	. 05197	. 05236	. 05276
1. 40	. 05512	. 05551	. 05591	. 05630	. 05669
1.50	0. 05906	0. 05945	0. 05984	0. 06024	0. 06063
1. 60	. 06299	. 06339	. 06378	. 06417	. 06457
1. 70	. 06693	. 06732	. 06772	. 06811	. 06850
1. 80	. 07087	. 07126	. 07165	. 07205	. 07244
1. 90	. 07480	. 07520	. 07559	. 07598	. 07638
2.00	0. 07874	0. 07913	0. 07953	0. 07992	0. 08031
2. 10	. 08268	. 08307	. 08346	. 08386	. 08425
2. 20	. 08661	. 08701	. 08740	. 08780	. 08819
2. 30	. 09055	. 09094	. 09134	. 09173	. 09213
2. 40	. 09449	. 09488	. 09528	. 09567	. 09606
2.50	0. 09842	0. 09882	0. 09921	0. 09961	0. 10000
2. 60	. 10236	. 10276	. 10315	. 10354	. 10394
2. 70	. 10630	. 10669	. 10709	. 10748	. 10787
2. 80	. 11024	. 11063	. 11102	. 11142	. 11181
2. 90	. 11417	. 11457	. 11496	. 11535	. 11575
8.00	0. 11811	0. 11850	0. 11890	0. 11929	0. 11968
3. 10	. 12205	. 12244	. 12283	. 12323	. 12362
3. 20	. 12598	. 12638	. 12677	. 12717	. 12756
3. 30	. 12992	. 13031	. 13071	. 13110	. 13150
3. 40	. 13386	. 13425	. 13465	. 13504	. 13543

LENGTH—MILLIMETRES TO INCHES—continued

[From 0.00 to 25.40 millimetres by 0.01 millimetre. 1 millimetre = 0.03937 inch.]

Milli-metres	Hundredths of millimetres				
	0.05	0.06	0.07	0.08	0.09
	Inches	Inches	Inches	Inches	Inches
0.00	0. 001968	0. 002362	0. 002756	0. 003150	0. 003543
0. 10	. 005906	. 006299	. 006693	. 007087	. 007480
0. 20	. 009842	. 010236	. 010630	. 011024	. 011417
0. 30	. 013780	. 014173	. 014567	. 014961	. 015354
0. 40	. 017716	. 018110	. 018504	. 018898	. 019291
0.50	0. 021654	0. 022047	0. 022441	0. 022835	0. 023228
0. 60	. 025590	. 025984	. 026378	. 026772	. 027165
0. 70	. 029528	. 029921	. 030315	. 030709	. 031102
0. 80	. 033464	. 033858	. 034252	. 034646	. 035039
0. 90	. 037402	. 037795	. 038189	. 038583	. 038976
1.00	0. 04134	0. 04173	0. 04213	0. 04252	0. 04291
1. 10	. 04528	. 04567	. 04606	. 04646	. 04685
1. 20	. 04921	. 04961	. 05000	. 05039	. 05079
1. 30	. 05315	. 05354	. 05394	. 05433	. 05472
1. 40	. 05709	. 05748	. 05787	. 05827	. 05866
1.50	0. 06102	0. 06142	0. 06181	0. 06220	0. 06260
1. 60	. 06496	. 06535	. 06575	. 06614	. 06654
1. 70	. 06890	. 06929	. 06968	. 07008	. 07047
1. 80	. 07283	. 07323	. 07362	. 07402	. 07441
1. 90	. 07677	. 07717	. 07756	. 07795	. 07835
2.00	0. 08071	0. 08110	0. 08150	0. 08189	0. 08228
2. 10	. 08465	. 08504	. 08543	. 08583	. 08622
2. 20	. 08858	. 08898	. 08937	. 08976	. 09016
2. 30	. 09252	. 09291	. 09331	. 09370	. 09409
2. 40	. 09646	. 09685	. 09724	. 09764	. 09803
2.50	0. 10039	0. 10079	0. 10118	0. 10157	0. 10197
2. 60	. 10433	. 10472	. 10512	. 10551	. 10591
2. 70	. 10827	. 10866	. 10905	. 10945	. 10984
2. 80	. 11220	. 11260	. 11299	. 11339	. 11378
2. 90	. 11614	. 11654	. 11693	. 11732	. 11772
3.00	0. 12008	0. 12047	0. 12087	0. 12126	0. 12165
3. 10	. 12402	. 12441	. 12480	. 12520	. 12559
3. 20	. 12795	. 12835	. 12874	. 12913	. 12953
3. 30	. 13189	. 13228	. 13268	. 13307	. 13346
3. 40	. 13583	. 13622	. 13661	. 13701	. 13740

LENGTH—MILLIMETRES TO INCHES—continued

[From 0.00 to 25.40 millimetres by 0.01 millimetre. 1 millimetre = 0.03937 inch.]

Milli-metres	Hundredths of millimetres				
	0.00	0.01	0.02	0.03	0.04
	Inches	Inches	Inches	Inches	Inches
3.50	0. 13780	0. 13819	0. 13858	0. 13898	0. 13937
3. 60	. 14173	. 14213	. 14252	. 14291	. 14331
3. 70	. 14567	. 14606	. 14646	. 14685	. 14724
3. 80	. 14961	. 15000	. 15039	. 15079	. 15118
3. 90	. 15354	. 15394	. 15433	. 15472	. 15512
4.00	0. 15748	0. 15787	0. 15827	0. 15866	0. 15905
4. 10	. 16142	. 16181	. 16220	. 16260	. 16299
4. 20	. 16535	. 16575	. 16614	. 16654	. 16693
4. 30	. 16929	. 16968	. 17008	. 17047	. 17087
4. 40	. 17323	. 17362	. 17402	. 17441	. 17480
4.50	0. 17716	0. 17756	0. 17795	0. 17835	0. 17874
4. 60	. 18110	. 18150	. 18189	. 18228	. 18268
4. 70	. 18504	. 18543	. 18583	. 18622	. 18661
4. 80	. 18898	. 18937	. 18976	. 19016	. 19055
4. 90	. 19291	. 19331	. 19370	. 19409	. 19449
5.00	0. 19685	0. 19724	0. 19764	0. 19803	0. 19842
5. 10	. 20079	. 20118	. 20157	. 20197	. 20236
5. 20	. 20472	. 20512	. 20551	. 20591	. 20630
5. 30	. 20866	. 20905	. 20945	. 20984	. 21024
5. 40	. 21260	. 21299	. 21339	. 21378	. 21417
5.50	0. 21654	0. 21693	0. 21732	0. 21772	0. 21811
5. 60	. 22047	. 22087	. 22126	. 22165	. 22205
5. 70	. 22441	. 22480	. 22520	. 22559	. 22598
5. 80	. 22835	. 22874	. 22913	. 22953	. 22992
5. 90	. 23228	. 23268	. 23307	. 23346	. 23386
6.00	0. 23622	0. 23661	0. 23701	0. 23740	0. 23779
6. 10	. 24016	. 24055	. 24094	. 24134	. 24173
6. 20	. 24409	. 24449	. 24488	. 24528	. 24567
6. 30	. 24803	. 24842	. 24882	. 24921	. 24961
6. 40	. 25197	. 25236	. 25276	. 25315	. 25354
6.50	0. 25590	0. 25630	0. 25669	0. 25709	0. 25748
6. 60	. 25984	. 26024	. 26063	. 26102	. 26142
6. 70	. 26378	. 26417	. 26457	. 26496	. 26535
6. 80	. 26772	. 26811	. 26850	. 26890	. 26929
6. 90	. 27165	. 27205	. 27244	. 27283	. 27323

LENGTH—MILLIMETRES TO INCHES—continued

[From 0.00 to 25.40 millimetres by 0.01 millimetre. 1 millimetre = 0.03937 inch.]

Milli-metres	Hundredths of millimetres				
	0.05	0.06	0.07	0.08	0.09
	Inches	Inches	Inches	Inches	Inches
3.50	0. 13976	0. 14016	0. 14055	0. 14094	0. 14134
3. 60	. 14370	. 14409	. 14449	. 14488	. 14528
3. 70	. 14764	. 14803	. 14842	. 14882	. 14921
3. 80	. 15157	. 15197	. 15236	. 15276	. 15315
3. 90	. 15551	. 15591	. 15630	. 15669	. 15709
4.00	0. 15945	0. 15984	0. 16024	0. 16063	0. 16102
4. 10	. 16339	. 16378	. 16417	. 16457	. 16496
4. 20	. 16732	. 16772	. 16811	. 16850	. 16890
4. 30	. 17126	. 17165	. 17205	. 17244	. 17283
4. 40	. 17520	. 17559	. 17598	. 17638	. 17677
4.50	0. 17913	0. 17953	0. 17992	0. 18031	0. 18071
4. 60	. 18307	. 18346	. 18386	. 18425	. 18465
4. 70	. 18701	. 18740	. 18779	. 18819	. 18858
4. 80	. 19094	. 19134	. 19173	. 19213	. 19252
4. 90	. 19488	. 19528	. 19567	. 19606	. 19646
5.00	0. 19882	0. 19921	0. 19961	0. 20000	0. 20039
5. 10	. 20276	. 20315	. 20354	. 20394	. 20433
5. 20	. 20669	. 20709	. 20748	. 20787	. 20827
5. 30	. 21063	. 21102	. 21142	. 21181	. 21220
5. 40	. 21457	. 21496	. 21535	. 21575	. 21614
5.50	0. 21850	0. 21890	0. 21929	0. 21968	0. 22008
5. 60	. 22244	. 22283	. 22323	. 22362	. 22402
5. 70	. 22638	. 22677	. 22716	. 22756	. 22795
5. 80	. 23031	. 23071	. 23110	. 23150	. 23189
5. 90	. 23425	. 23465	. 23504	. 23543	. 23583
6.00	0. 23819	0. 23858	0. 23898	0. 23937	0. 23976
6. 10	. 24213	. 24252	. 24291	. 24331	. 24370
6. 20	. 24606	. 24646	. 24685	. 24724	. 24764
6. 30	. 25000	. 25039	. 25079	. 25118	. 25157
6. 40	. 25394	. 25433	. 25472	. 25512	. 25551
6.50	0. 25787	0. 25827	0. 25866	0. 25905	0. 25945
6. 60	. 26181	. 26220	. 26260	. 26299	. 26339
6. 70	. 26575	. 26614	. 26653	. 26693	. 26732
6. 80	. 26968	. 27008	. 27047	. 27087	. 27126
6. 90	. 27362	. 27402	. 27441	. 27480	. 27520

LENGTH—MILLIMETRES TO INCHES—continued

[From 0.00 to 25.40 millimetres by 0.01 millimetre. 1 millimetre = 0.03937 inch.]

Milli-metres	Hundredths of millimetres				
	0.00	0.01	0.02	0.03	0.04
	Inches	Inches	Inches	Inches	Inches
7.00	0.27559	0.27598	0.27638	0.27677	0.27716
7.10	.27953	.27992	.28031	.28071	.28110
7.20	.28346	.28386	.28425	.28465	.28504
7.30	.28740	.28779	.28819	.28858	.28898
7.40	.29134	.29173	.29213	.29252	.29291
7.50	0.29528	0.29567	0.29606	0.29646	0.29685
7.60	.29921	.29961	.30000	.30039	.30079
7.70	.30315	.30354	.30394	.30433	.30472
7.80	.30709	.30748	.30787	.30827	.30866
7.90	.31102	.31142	.31181	.31220	.31260
8.00	0.31496	0.31535	0.31575	0.31614	0.31653
8.10	.31890	.31929	.31968	.32008	.32047
8.20	.32283	.32323	.32362	.32402	.32441
8.30	.32677	.32716	.32756	.32795	.32835
8.40	.33071	.33110	.33150	.33189	.33228
8.50	0.33464	0.33504	0.33543	0.33583	0.33622
8.60	.33858	.33898	.33937	.33976	.34016
8.70	.34252	.34291	.34331	.34370	.34409
8.80	.34646	.34685	.34724	.34764	.34803
8.90	.35039	.35079	.35118	.35157	.35197
9.00	0.35433	0.35472	0.35512	0.35551	0.35590
9.10	.35827	.35866	.35905	.35945	.35984
9.20	.36220	.36260	.36299	.36339	.36378
9.30	.36614	.36653	.36693	.36732	.36772
9.40	.37008	.37047	.37087	.37126	.37165
9.50	0.37402	0.37441	0.37480	0.37520	0.37559
9.60	.37795	.37835	.37874	.37913	.37953
9.70	.38189	.38228	.38268	.38307	.38346
9.80	.38583	.38622	.38661	.38701	.38740
9.90	.38976	.39016	.39055	.39094	.39134
10.00	0.39370	0.39409	0.39449	0.39488	0.39527
10.10	.39764	.39803	.39842	.39882	.39921
10.20	.40157	.40197	.40236	.40276	.40315
10.30	.40551	.40590	.40630	.40669	.40709
10.40	.40945	.40984	.41024	.41063	.41102

LENGTH—MILLIMETRES TO INCHES—continued

[From 0.00 to 25.40 millimetres by 0.01 millimetre. 1 millimetre = 0.03937 inch.]

Milli-metres	Hundredths of millimetres				
	0.05	0.06	0.07	0.08	0.09
	Inches	Inches	Inches	Inches	Inches
7.00	0. 27756	0. 27795	0. 27835	0. 27874	0. 27913
7. 10	. 28150	. 28189	. 28228	. 28268	. 28307
7. 20	. 28543	. 28583	. 28622	. 28661	. 28701
7. 30	. 28937	. 28976	. 29016	. 29055	. 29094
7. 40	. 29331	. 29370	. 29409	. 29449	. 29488
7.50	0. 29724	0. 29764	0. 29803	0. 29842	0. 29882
7. 60	. 30118	. 30157	. 30197	. 30236	. 30276
7. 70	. 30512	. 30551	. 30590	. 30630	. 30669
7. 80	. 30905	. 30945	. 30984	. 31024	. 31063
7. 90	. 31299	. 31339	. 31378	. 31417	. 31457
8.00	0. 31693	0. 31732	0. 31772	0. 31811	0. 31850
8. 10	. 32087	. 32126	. 32165	. 32205	. 32244
8. 20	. 32480	. 32520	. 32559	. 32598	. 32638
8. 30	. 32874	. 32913	. 32953	. 32992	. 33031
8. 40	. 33268	. 33307	. 33346	. 33386	. 33425
8.50	0. 33661	0. 33701	0. 33740	0. 33779	0. 33819
8. 60	. 34055	. 34094	. 34134	. 34173	. 34213
8. 70	. 34449	. 34488	. 34527	. 34567	. 34606
8. 80	. 34842	. 34882	. 34921	. 34961	. 35000
8. 90	. 35236	. 35276	. 35315	. 35354	. 35394
9.00	0. 35630	0. 35669	0. 35709	0. 35748	0. 35787
9. 10	. 36024	. 36063	. 36102	. 36142	. 36181
9. 20	. 36417	. 36457	. 36496	. 36535	. 36575
9. 30	. 36811	. 36850	. 36890	. 36929	. 36968
9. 40	. 37205	. 37244	. 37283	. 37323	. 37362
9.50	0. 37598	0. 37638	0. 37677	0. 37716	0. 37756
9. 60	. 37992	. 38031	. 38071	. 38110	. 38150
9. 70	. 38386	. 38425	. 38464	. 38504	. 38543
9. 80	. 38779	. 38819	. 38858	. 38898	. 38937
9. 90	. 39173	. 39213	. 39252	. 39291	. 39331
10.00	0. 39567	0. 39606	0. 39646	0. 39685	0. 39724
10. 10	. 39961	. 40000	. 40039	. 40079	. 40118
10. 20	. 40354	. 40394	. 40433	. 40472	. 40512
10. 30	. 40748	. 40787	. 40827	. 40866	. 40905
10. 40	. 41142	. 41181	: 41220	. 41260	. 41299

LENGTH—MILLIMETRES TO INCHES—continued

[From 0.00 to 25.40 millimetres by 0.01 millimetre. 1 millimetre = 0.03937 inch.]

Milli-metres	Hundredths of millimetres				
	0.00	0.01	0.02	0.03	0.04
	Inches	Inches	Inches	Inches	Inches
10.50	0.41338	0.41378	0.41417	0.41457	0.41496
10.60	.41732	.41772	.41811	.41850	.41890
10.70	.42126	.42165	.42205	.42244	.42283
10.80	.42520	.42559	.42598	.42638	.42677
10.90	.42913	.42953	.42992	.43031	.43071
11.00	0.43307	0.43346	0.43386	0.43425	0.43464
11.10	.43701	.43740	.43779	.43819	.43858
11.20	.44094	.44134	.44173	.44213	.44252
11.30	.44488	.44527	.44567	.44606	.44646
11.40	.44882	.44921	.44961	.45000	.45039
11.50	0.45276	0.45315	0.45354	0.45394	0.45433
11.60	.45669	.45709	.45748	.45787	.45827
11.70	.46063	.46102	.46142	.46181	.46220
11.80	.46457	.46496	.46535	.46575	.46614
11.90	.46850	.46890	.46929	.46968	.47008
12.00	0.47244	0.47283	0.47323	0.47362	0.47401
12.10	.47638	.47677	.47716	.47756	.47795
12.20	.48031	.48071	.48110	.48150	.48189
12.30	.48425	.48464	.48504	.48543	.48583
12.40	.48819	.48858	.48898	.48937	.48976
12.50	0.49212	0.49252	0.49291	0.49331	0.49370
12.60	.49606	.49646	.49685	.49724	.49764
12.70	.50000	.50039	.50079	.50118	.50157
12.80	.50394	.50433	.50472	.50512	.50551
12.90	.50787	.50827	.50866	.50905	.50945
13.00	0.51181	0.51220	0.51260	0.51299	0.51338
13.10	.51575	.51614	.51653	.51693	.51732
13.20	.51968	.52008	.52047	.52087	.52126
13.30	.52362	.52401	.52441	.52480	.52520
13.40	.52756	.52795	.52835	.52874	.52913
13.50	0.53150	0.53189	0.53228	0.53268	0.53307
13.60	.53543	.53583	.53622	.53661	.53701
13.70	.53937	.53976	.54016	.54055	.54094
13.80	.54331	.54370	.54409	.54449	.54488
13.90	.54724	.54764	.54803	.54842	.54882

LENGTH—MILLIMETRES TO INCHES—continued

[From 0.00 to 25.40 millimetres by 0.01 millimetre. 1 millimetre = 0.03937 inch.]

Milli-metres	Hundredths of millimetres				
	0.05	0.06	0.07	0.08	0.09
	Inches	Inches	Inches	Inches	Inches
10.50	0. 41535	0. 41575	0. 41614	0. 41653	0. 41693
10. 60	. 41929	. 41968	. 42008	. 42047	. 42087
10. 70	. 42323	. 42362	. 42401	. 42441	. 42480
10. 80	. 42716	. 42756	. 42795	. 42835	. 42874
10. 90	. 43110	. 43150	. 43189	. 43228	. 43268
11.00	0. 43504	0. 43543	0. 43583	0. 43622	0. 43661
11. 10	. 43898	. 43937	. 43976	. 44016	. 44055
11. 20	. 44291	. 44331	. 44370	. 44409	. 44449
11. 30	. 44685	. 44724	. 44764	. 44803	. 44842
11. 40	. 45079	. 45118	. 45157	. 45197	. 45236
11.50	0. 45472	0. 45512	0. 45551	0. 45590	0. 45630
11. 60	. 45866	. 45905	. 45945	. 45984	. 46024
11. 70	. 46260	. 46299	. 46338	. 46378	. 46417
11. 80	. 46653	. 46693	. 46732	. 46772	. 46811
11. 90	. 47047	. 47087	. 47126	. 47165	. 47205
12.00	0. 47441	0. 47480	0. 47520	0. 47559	0. 47598
12. 10	. 47835	. 47874	. 47913	. 47953	. 47992
12. 20	. 48228	. 48268	. 48307	. 48346	. 48386
12. 30	. 48622	. 48661	. 48701	. 48740	. 48779
12. 40	. 49016	. 49055	. 49094	. 49134	. 49173
12.50	0. 49409	0. 49449	0. 49488	0. 49527	0. 49567
12. 60	. 49803	. 49842	. 49882	. 49921	. 49961
12. 70	. 50197	. 50236	. 50275	. 50315	. 50354
12. 80	. 50590	. 50630	. 50669	. 50709	. 50748
12. 90	. 50984	. 51024	. 51063	. 51102	. 51142
13.00	0. 51378	0. 51417	0. 51457	0. 51496	0. 51535
13. 10	. 51772	. 51811	. 51850	. 51890	. 51929
13. 20	. 52165	. 52205	. 52244	. 52283	. 52323
13. 30	. 52559	. 52598	. 52638	. 52677	. 52716
13. 40	. 52953	. 52992	. 53031	. 53071	. 53110
13.50	0. 53346	0. 53386	0. 53425	0. 53464	0. 53504
13. 60	. 53740	. 53779	. 53819	. 53858	. 53898
13. 70	. 54134	. 54173	. 54212	. 54252	. 54291
13. 80	. 54527	. 54567	. 54606	. 54646	. 54685
13. 90	. 54921	. 54961	. 55000	. 55039	. 55079

LENGTH—MILLIMETRES TO INCHES—continued

[From 0.00 to 25.40 millimetres by 0.01 millimetre. 1 millimetre = 0.03937 inch.]

Milli-metres	Hundredths of millimetres				
	0.00	0.01	0.02	0.03	0.04
	Inches	Inches	Inches	Inches	Inches
14.00	0. 55118	0. 55157	0. 55197	0. 55236	0. 55275
14. 10	. 55512	. 55551	. 55590	. 55630	. 55669
14. 20	. 55905	. 55945	. 55984	. 56024	. 56063
14. 30	. 56299	. 56338	. 56378	. 56417	. 56457
14. 40	. 56693	. 56732	. 56772	. 56811	. 56850
14.50	0. 57086	0. 57126	0. 57165	0. 57205	0. 57244
14. 60	. 57480	. 57520	. 57559	. 57598	. 57638
14. 70	. 57874	. 57913	. 57953	. 57992	. 58031
14. 80	. 58268	. 58307	. 58346	. 58386	. 58425
14. 90	. 58661	. 58701	. 58740	. 58779	. 58819
15.00	0. 59055	0. 59094	0. 59134	0. 59173	0. 59212
15. 10	. 59449	. 59488	. 59527	. 59567	. 59606
15. 20	. 59842	. 59882	. 59921	. 59961	. 60000
15. 30	. 60236	. 60275	. 60315	. 60354	. 60394
15. 40	. 60630	. 60669	. 60709	. 60748	. 60787
15.50	0. 61024	0. 61063	0. 61102	0. 61142	0. 61181
15. 60	. 61417	. 61457	. 61496	. 61535	. 61575
15. 70	. 61811	. 61850	. 61890	. 61929	. 61968
15. 80	. 62205	. 62244	. 62283	. 62323	. 62362
15. 90	. 62598	. 62638	. 62677	. 62716	. 62756
16.00	0. 62992	0. 63031	0. 63071	0. 63110	0. 63149
16. 10	. 63386	. 63425	. 63464	. 63504	. 63543
16. 20	. 63779	. 63819	. 63858	. 63898	. 63937
16. 30	. 64173	. 64212	. 64252	. 64291	. 64331
16. 40	. 64567	. 64606	. 64646	. 64685	. 64724
16.50	0. 64960	0. 65000	0. 65039	0. 65079	0. 65118
16. 60	. 65354	. 65394	. 65433	. 65472	. 65512
16. 70	. 65748	. 65787	. 65827	. 65866	. 65905
16. 80	. 66142	. 66181	. 66220	. 66260	. 66299
16. 90	. 66535	. 66575	. 66614	. 66653	. 66693
17.00	0. 66929	0. 66968	0. 67008	0. 67047	0. 67086
17. 10	. 67323	. 67362	. 67401	. 67441	. 67480
17. 20	. 67716	. 67756	. 67795	. 67835	. 67874
17. 30	. 68110	. 68149	. 68189	. 68228	. 68268
17. 40	. 68504	. 68543	. 68583	. 68622	. 68661

LENGTH—MILLIMETRES TO INCHES—continued

[From 0.00 to 25.40 millimetres by 0.01 millimetre. 1 millimetre = 0.03937 inch.]

Milli-metres	Hundredths of millimetres				
	0.05	0.06	0.07	0.08	0.09
	Inches	Inches	Inches	Inches	Inches
14.00	0. 55315	0. 55354	0. 55394	0. 55433	0. 55472
14. 10	. 55709	. 55748	. 55787	. 55827	. 55866
14. 20	. 56102	. 56142	. 56181	. 56220	. 56260
14. 30	. 56496	. 56535	. 56575	. 56614	. 56653
14. 40	. 56890	. 56929	. 56968	. 57008	. 57047
14.50	0. 57283	0. 57323	0. 57362	0. 57401	. 57441
14. 60	. 57677	. 57716	. 57756	. 57795	. 57835
14. 70	. 58071	. 58110	. 58149	. 58189	. 58228
14. 80	. 58464	. 58504	. 58543	. 58583	. 58622
14. 90	. 58858	. 58898	. 58937	. 58976	. 59016
15.00	0. 59252	0. 59291	0. 59331	0. 59370	0. 59409
15. 10	. 59646	. 59685	. 59724	. 59764	. 59803
15. 20	. 60039	. 60079	. 60118	. 60157	. 60197
15. 30	. 60433	. 60472	. 60512	. 60551	. 60590
15. 40	. 60827	. 60866	. 60905	. 60945	. 60984
15.50	0. 61220	0. 61260	0. 61299	0. 61338	0. 61378
15. 60	. 61614	. 61653	. 61693	. 61732	. 61772
15. 70	. 62008	. 62047	. 62086	. 62126	. 62165
15. 80	. 62401	. 62441	. 62480.	. 62520	. 62559
15. 90	. 62795	. 62835	. 62874	. 62913	. 62953
16.00	0. 63189	0. 63228	0. 63268	0. 63307	0. 63346
16. 10	. 63583	. 63622	. 63661	. 63701	. 63740
16. 20	. 63976	. 64016	. 64055	. 64094	. 64134
16. 30	. 64370	. 64409	. 64449	. 64488	. 64527
16. 40	. 64764	. 64803	. 64842	. 64882	. 64921
16.50	0. 65157	0. 65197	0. 65236	0. 65275	0. 65315
16. 60	. 65551	. 65590	. 65630	. 65669	. 65709
16. 70	. 65945	. 65984	. 66023	. 66063	. 66102
16. 80	. 66338	. 66378	. 66417	. 66457	. 66496
16. 90	. 66732	. 66772	. 66811	. 66850	. 66890
17.00	0. 67126	0. 67165	0. 67205	0. 67244	0. 67283
17. 10	. 67520	. 67559	. 67598	. 67638	. 67677
17. 20	. 67913	. 67953	. 67992	. 68031	. 68071
17. 30	. 68307	. 68346	. 68386	. 68425	. 68464
17. 40	. 68701	. 68740	. 68779	. 68819	. 68858

LENGTH—MILLIMETRES TO INCHES—continued

[From 0.00 to 25.40 millimetres by 0.01 millimetre. 1 millimetre = 0.03937 inch.]

Milli-metres	Hundredths of millimetres				
	0.00	0.01	0.02	0.08	0.0ł
	Inches	Inches	Inches	Inches	Inches
17.50	0. 68898	0. 68937	0. 68976	0. 69016	0. 69055
17. 60	. 69291	. 69331	. 69370	. 69409	. 69449
17. 70	. 69685	. 69724	. 69764	. 69803	. 69842
17. 80	. 70079	. 70118	. 70157	. 70197	. 70236
17. 90	. 70472	. 70512	. 70551	. 70590	. 70630
18.00	0. 70866	0. 70905	0. 70945	0. 70984	0. 71023
18. 10	. 71260	. 71299	. 71338	. 71378	. 71417
18. 20	. 71653	. 71693	. 71732	. 71772	. 71811
18. 30	. 72047	. 72086	. 72126	. 72165	. 72205
18. 40	. 72441	. 72480	. 72520	. 72559	. 72598
18.50	0. 72834	0. 72874	0. 72913	0. 72953	0. 72992
18. 60	. 73228	. 73268	. 73307	. 73346	. 73386
18. 70	. 73622	. 73661	. 73701	. 73740	. 73779
18. 80	. 74016	. 74055	. 74094	. 74134	. 74173
18. 90	. 74409	. 74449	. 74488	. 74527	. 74567
19.00	0. 74803	0. 74842	0. 74882	0. 74921	0. 74960
19. 10	. 75197	. 75236	. 75275	. 75315	. 75354
19. 20	. 75590	. 75630	. 75669	. 75709	. 75748
19. 30	. 75984	. 76023	. 76063	. 76102	. 76142
19. 40	. 76378	. 76417	. 76457	. 76496	. 76535
19.50	0. 76772	0. 76811	0. 76850	0. 76890	0. 76929
19. 60	. 77165	. 77205	. 77244	. 77283	. 77323
19. 70	. 77559	. 77598	. 77638	. 77677	. 77716
19. 80	. 77953	. 77992	. 78031	. 78071	. 78110
19. 90	. 78346	. 78386	. 78425	. 78464	. 78504
20.00	0. 78740	0. 78779	0. 78819	0. 78858	0. 78897
20. 10	. 79134	. 79173	. 79212	. 79252	. 79291
20. 20	. 79527	. 79567	. 79606	. 79646	. 79685
20. 30	. 79921	. 79960	. 80000	. 80039	. 80079
20. 40	. 80315	. 80354	. 80394	. 80433	. 80472
20.50	0. 80708	0. 80748	0. 80787	0. 80827	0. 80866
20. 60	. 81102	. 81142	. 81181	. 81220	. 81260
20. 70	. 81496	. 81535	. 81575	. 81614	. 81653
20. 80	. 81890	. 81929	. 81968	. 82008	. 82047
20. 90	. 82283	. 82323	. 82362	. 82401	. 82441

LENGTH—MILLIMETRES TO INCHES—continued

[From 0.00 to 25.40 millimetres by 0.01 millimetre. 1 millimetre = 0.03937 inch.]

Milli-metres	Hundredths of millimetres				
	0.05	0.06	0.07	0.08	0.09
	Inches	Inches	Inches	Inches	Inches
17.50	0. 69094	0. 69134	0. 69173	0. 69212	0. 69252
17. 60	. 69488	. 69527	. 69567	. 69606	. 69646
17. 70	. 69882	. 69921	. 69960	. 70000	. 70039
17. 80	. 70275	. 70315	. 70354	. 70394	. 70433
17. 90	. 70669	. 70709	. 70748	. 70787	. 70827
18.00	0. 71063	0. 71102	0. 71142	0. 71181	0. 71220
18. 10	. 71457	. 71496	. 71535	. 71575	. 71614
18. 20	. 71850	. 71890	. 71929	. 71968	. 72008
18. 30	. 72244	. 72283	. 72323	. 72362	. 72401
18. 40	. 72638	. 72677	. 72716	. 72756	. 72795
18.50	0. 73031	0. 73071	0. 73110	0. 73149	0. 73189
18. 60	. 73425	. 73464	. 73504	. 73543	. 73583
18. 70	. 73819	. 73858	. 73897	. 73937	. 73976
18. 80	. 74212	. 74252	. 74291	. 74331	. 74370
18. 90	. 74606	. 74646	. 74685	. 74724	. 74764
19.00	0. 75000	0. 75039	0. 75079	0. 75118	0. 75157
19. 10	. 75394	. 75433	. 75472	. 75512	. 75551
19. 20	. 75787	. 75827	. 75866	. 75905	. 75945
19. 30	. 76181	. 76220	. 76260	. 76299	. 76338
19. 40	. 76575	. 76614	. 76653	. 76693	. 76732
19.50	0. 76968	0. 77008	0. 77047	0. 77086	0. 77126
19. 60	. 77362	. 77401	. 77441	. 77480	. 77520
19. 70	. 77756	. 77795	. 77834	. 77874	. 77913
19. 80	. 78149	. 78189	. 78228	. 78268	. 78307
19. 90	. 78543	. 78583	. 78622	. 78661	. 78701
20.00	0. 78937	0. 78976	0. 79016	0. 79055	0. 79094
20. 10	. 79331	. 79370	. 79409	. 79449	. 79488
20. 20	. 79724	. 79764	. 79803	. 79842	. 79882
20. 30	. 80118	. 80157	. 80197	. 80236	. 80275
20. 40	. 80512	. 80551	. 80590	. 80630	. 80669
20.50	0. 80905	0. 80945	0. 80984	0. 81023	0. 81063
20. 60	. 81299	. 81338	. 81378	. 81417	. 81457
20. 70	. 81693	. 81732	. 81771	. 81811	. 81850
20. 80	. 82086	. 82126	. 82165	. 82205	. 82244
20. 90	. 82480	. 82520	. 82559	. 82598	. 82638

LENGTH—MILLIMETRES TO INCHES—continued

[From 0.00 to 25.40 millimetres by 0.01 millimetre. 1 millimetre = 0.03937 inch.]

Milli-metres	Hundredths of millimetres				
	0.00	0.01	0.02	0.03	0.04
	Inches	Inches	Inches	Inches	Inches
21.00	0. 82677	0. 82716	0. 82756	0. 82795	0. 82834
21. 10	. 83071	. 83110	. 83149	. 83189	. 83228
21. 20	. 83464	. 83504	. 83543	. 83583	. 83622
21. 30	. 83858	. 83897	. 83937	. 83976	. 84016
21. 40	. 84252	. 84291	. 84331	. 84370	. 84409
21.50	0. 84646	0. 84685	0. 84724	0. 84764	0. 84803
21. 60	. 85039	. 85079	. 85118	. 85157	. 85197
21. 70	. 85433	. 85472	. 85512	. 85551	. 85590
21. 80	. 85827	. 85866	. 85905	. 85945	. 85984
21. 90	. 86220	. 86260	. 86299	. 86338	. 86378
22.00	0. 86614	0. 86653	0. 86693	0. 86732	0. 86771
22. 10	. 87008	. 87047	. 87086	. 87126	. 87165
22. 20	. 87401	. 87441	. 87480	. 87520	. 87559
22. 30	. 87795	. 87834	. 87874	. 87913	. 87953
22. 40	. 88189	. 88228	. 88268	. 88307	. 88346
22.50	0. 88582	0. 88622	0. 88661	0. 88701	0. 88740
22. 60	. 88976	. 89016	. 89055	. 89094	. 89134
22. 70	. 89370	. 89409	. 89449	. 89488	. 89527
22. 80	. 89764	. 89803	. 89842	. 89882	. 89921
22. 90	. 90157	. 90197	. 90236	. 90275	. 90315
23.00	0. 90551	0. 90590	0. 90630	0. 90669	0. 90708
23. 10	. 90945	. 90984	. 91023	. 91063	. 91102
23. 20	. 91338	. 91378	. 91417	. 91457	. 91496
23. 30	. 91732	. 91771	. 91811	. 91850	. 91890
23. 40	. 92126	. 92165	. 92205	. 92244	. 92283
23.50	0. 92520	0. 92559	0. 92598	0. 92638	0. 92677
23. 60	. 92913	. 92953	. 92992	. 93031	. 93071
23. 70	. 93307	. 93346	. 93386	. 93425	. 93464
23. 80	. 93701	. 93740	. 93779	. 93819	. 93858
23. 90	. 94094	. 94134	. 94173	. 94212	. 94252
24.00	0. 94488	0. 94527	0. 94567	0. 94606	0. 94645
24. 10	. 94882	. 94921	. 94960	. 95000	. 95039
24. 20	. 95275	. 95315	. 95354	. 95394	. 95433
24. 30	. 95669	. 95708	. 95748	. 95787	. 95827
24. 40	. 96063	. 96102	. 96142	. 96181	. 96220

LENGTH—MILLIMETRES TO INCHES—continued

[From 0.00 to 25.40 millimetres by 0.01 millimetre. 1 millimetre = 0.03937 inch.]

Milli-metres	Hundredths of millimetres				
	0.05	0.06	0.07	0.08	0.09
	Inches	Inches	Inches	Inches	Inches
21.00	0.82874	0.82913	0.82953	0.82992	0.83031
21.10	.83268	.83307	.83346	.83386	.83425
21.20	.83661	.83701	.83740	.83779	.83819
21.30	.84055	.84094	.84134	.84173	.84212
21.40	.84449	.84488	.84527	.84567	.84606
21.50	0.84842	0.84882	0.84921	0.84960	0.85000
21.60	.85236	.85275	.85315	.85354	.85394
21.70	.85630	.85669	.85708	.85748	.85787
21.80	.86023	.86063	.86102	.86142	.86181
21.90	.86417	.86457	.86496	.86535	.86575
22.00	0.86811	0.86850	0.86890	0.86929	0.86968
22.10	.87205	.87244	.87283	.87323	.87362
22.20	.87598	.87638	.87677	.87716	.87756
22.30	.87992	.88031	.88071	.88110	.88149
22.40	.88386	.88425	.88464	.88504	.88543
22.50	0.88779	0.88819	0.88858	0.88897	0.88937
22.60	.89173	.89212	.89252	.89291	.89331
22.70	.89567	.89606	.89645	.89685	.89724
22.80	.89960	.90000	.90039	.90079	.90118
22.90	.90354	.90394	.90433	.90472	.90512
23.00	0.90748	0.90787	0.90827	0.90866	0.90905
23.10	.91142	.91181	.91220	.91260	.91299
23.20	.91535	.91575	.91614	.91653	.91693
23.30	.91929	.91968	.92008	.92047	.92086
23.40	.92323	.92362	.92401	.92441	.92480
23.50	0.92716	0.92756	0.92795	0.92834	0.92874
23.60	.93110	.93149	.93189	.93228	.93268
23.70	.93504	.93543	.93582	.93622	.93661
23.80	.93897	.93937	.93976	.94016	.94055
23.90	.94291	.94331	.94370	.94409	.94449
24.00	0.94685	0.94724	0.94764	0.94803	0.94842
24.10	.95079	.95118	.95157	.95197	.95236
24.20	.95472	.95512	.95551	.95590	.95630
24.30	.95866	.95905	.95945	.95984	.96023
24.40	.96260	.96299	.96338	.96378	.96417

LENGTH—MILLIMETRES TO INCHES—continued

[From 0.00 to 25.40 millimetres by 0.01 millimetre. 1 millimetre = 0.03937 inch.]

Milli-metres	Hundredths of millimetres				
	0.00	0.01	0.02	0.03	0.04
	Inches	Inches	Inches	Inches	Inches
24.50	0.96456	0.96496	0.96535	0.96575	0.96614
24.60	.96850	.96890	.96929	.96968	.97008
24.70	.97244	.97283	.97323	.97362	.97401
24.80	.97638	.97677	.97716	.97756	.97795
24.90	.98031	.98071	.98110	.98149	.98189
25.00	0.98425	0.98464	0.98504	0.98543	0.98582
25.10	.98819	.98858	.98897	.98937	.98976
25.20	.99212	.99252	.99291	.99331	.99370
25.30	.99606	.99645	.99685	.99724	.99764
25.40	1.00000	....	....	....	....

```
 1 inch  = 0.02540 metre
 2 inches =  .05080 metre
 3 inches =  .07620 metre
 4 inches = 0.10160 metre
 5 inches =  .12700 metre
 6 inches =  .15240 metre
 7 inches = 0.17780 metre
 8 inches =  .20320 metre
 9 inches =  .22860 metre
10 inches = 0.25400 metre
11 inches =  .27940 metre
12 inches =  .30480 metre
```

LENGTH—MILLIMETRES TO INCHES—continued

[From 0.00 to 25.40 millimetres by 0.01 millimetre. 1 millimetre = 0.03937 inch.]

Milli-metres	Hundredths of millimetres				
	0.05	0.06	0.07	0.08	0.09
	Inches	Inches	Inches	Inches	Inches
24.50	0.96653	0.96693	0.96732	0.96771	0.96811
24.60	.97047	.97086	.97126	.97165	.97205
24.70	.97441	.97480	.97519	.97559	.97598
24.80	.97834	.97874	.97913	.97953	.97992
24.90	.98228	.98268	.98307	.98346	.98386
25.00	0.98622	0.98661	0.98701	0.98740	0.98779
25.10	.99016	.99055	.99094	.99134	.99173
25.20	.99409	.99449	.99488	.99527	.99567
25.30	.99803	.99842	.99882	.99921	.99960
25.40	....	....	....	....	....

The above tables converting millimetres to inches may be used to convert centimetres to inches by moving the decimal point 1 place to the right, and decimeters to inches by moving the decimal point 2 places to the right.

EXAMPLE: 1 millimetre = 0.03937 inches
1 centimetre = 0.3937   "
1 decimetre = 3.937   "
1 metre   = 39.37   "

LENGTH—METRES TO FEET

[Reduction factor: 1 metre = 3.280833333 feet]

Metres	Feet	Metres	Feet	Metres	Feet	Metres	Feet	Metres	Feet
0		50	164.04167	100	328.08333	150	492.12500	200	656.16667
1	3.28083	1	167.32250	1	331.36417	1	495.40583	1	659.44750
2	6.56167	2	170.60333	2	334.64500	2	498.68667	2	662.72833
3	9.84250	3	173.88417	3	337.92583	3	501.96750	3	666.00917
4	13.12333	4	177.16500	4	341.20667	4	505.24833	4	669.29000
5	16.40417	5	180.44583	5	344.48750	5	508.52917	5	672.57083
6	19.68500	6	183.72667	6	347.76833	6	511.81000	6	675.85167
7	22.96583	7	187.00750	7	351.04917	7	515.09083	7	679.13250
8	26.24667	8	190.28833	8	354.33000	8	518.37167	8	682.41333
9	29.52750	9	193.56917	9	357.61083	9	521.65250	9	685.69417
10	32.80833	60	196.85000	110	360.89167	160	524.93333	210	688.97500
1	36.08917	1	200.13083	1	364.17250	1	528.21417	1	692.25583
2	39.37000	2	203.41167	2	367.45333	2	531.49500	2	695.53667
3	42.65083	3	206.69250	3	370.73417	3	534.77583	3	698.81750
4	45.93167	4	209.97333	4	374.01500	4	538.05667	4	702.09833
5	49.21250	5	213.25417	5	377.29583	5	541.33750	5	705.37917
6	52.49333	6	216.53500	6	380.57667	6	544.61833	6	708.66000
7	55.77417	7	219.81583	7	383.85750	7	547.89917	7	711.94083
8	59.05500	8	223.09667	8	387.13833	8	551.18000	8	715.22167
9	62.33583	9	226.37750	9	390.41917	9	554.46085	9	718.50250
20	65.61667	70	229.65833	120	393.70000	170	557.74167	220	721.78333
1	68.89750	1	232.93917	1	396.98083	1	561.02250	1	725.06417
2	72.17833	2	236.22000	2	400.26167	2	564.30333	2	728.34500
3	75.45917	3	239.50083	3	403.54250	3	567.58417	3	731.62583
4	78.74000	4	242.78167	4	406.82333	4	570.86500	4	734.90667
5	82.02083	5	246.06250	5	410.10417	5	574.14583	5	738.18750
6	85.30167	6	249.34333	6	413.38500	6	577.42667	6	741.46833
7	88.58250	7	252.62417	7	416.66583	7	580.70750	7	744.74917
8	91.86333	8	255.90500	8	419.94667	8	583.98833	8	748.03000
9	95.14417	9	259.18583	9	423.22750	9	587.26917	9	751.31083
30	98.42500	80	262.46667	130	426.50833	180	590.55000	230	754.59167
1	101.70583	1	265.74750	1	429.78917	1	593.83083	1	757.87250
2	104.98667	2	269.02833	2	433.07000	2	597.11167	2	761.15333
3	108.26750	3	272.30917	3	436.35083	3	600.39250	3	764.43417
4	111.54833	4	275.59000	4	439.63167	4	603.67333	4	767.71500
5	114.82917	5	278.87083	5	442.91250	5	606.95417	5	770.99583
6	118.11000	6	282.15167	6	446.19333	6	610.23500	6	774.27667
7	121.39083	7	285.43250	7	449.47417	7	613.51583	7	777.55750
8	124.67167	8	288.71333	8	452.75500	8	616.79667	8	780.83833
9	127.95250	9	291.99417	9	456.03583	9	620.07750	9	784.11917
40	131.23333	90	295.27500	140	459.31667	190	623.35833	240	787.40000
1	134.51417	1	298.55583	1	462.59750	1	626.63917	1	790.68083
2	137.79500	2	301.83667	2	465.87833	2	629.92000	2	793.96167
3	141.07583	3	305.11750	3	469.15917	3	633.20083	3	797.24250
4	144.35667	4	308.39833	4	472.44000	4	636.48167	4	800.52333
5	147.63750	5	311.67917	5	475.72083	5	639.76250	5	803.80417
6	150.91833	6	314.96000	6	479.00167	6	643.04333	6	807.08500
7	154.19917	7	318.24083	7	482.28250	7	646.32417	7	810.36583
8	157.48000	8	321.52167	8	485.56333	8	649.60500	8	813.64667
9	160.76083	9	324.80250	9	488.84417	9	652.88583	9	816.92750

LENGTH—METRES TO FEET

[Reduction factor: 1 metre = 3.280833333 feet]

Metres	Feet	Metres	Feet	Metres	Feet	Metres	Feet	Metres	Feet
250	820.20833	**300**	984.25000	**350**	1,148.29167	**400**	1,312.33333	**450**	1,476.37500
1	823.48917	1	987.53083	1	1,151.57250	1	1,315.61417	1	1,479.65583
2	826.77000	2	990.81167	2	1,154.85333	2	1,318.89500	2	1,482.93667
3	830.05083	3	994.09250	3	1,158.13417	3	1,322.17583	3	1,486.21750
4	833.33167	4	997.37333	4	1,161.41500	4	1,325.45667	4	1,489.49833
5	836.61250	5	1,000.65417	5	1,164.69583	5	1,328.73750	5	1,492.77917
6	839.89333	6	1,003.93500	6	1,167.97667	6	1,332.01833	6	1,496.06000
7	843.17417	7	1,007.21583	7	1,171.25750	7	1,335.29917	7	1,499.34083
8	846.45500	8	1,010.49667	8	1,174.53833	8	1,338.58000	8	1,502.62167
9	849.73583	9	1,013.77750	9	1,177.81917	9	1,341.86083	9	1,505.90250
260	853.01667	**310**	1,017.05833	**360**	1,181.10000	**410**	1,345.14167	**460**	1,509.18333
1	856.29750	1	1,020.33917	1	1,184.38083	1	1,348.42250	1	1,512.46417
2	859.57833	2	1,023.62000	2	1,187.66167	2	1,351.70333	2	1,515.74500
3	862.85917	3	1,026.90083	3	1,190.94250	3	1,354.98417	3	1,519.02583
4	866.14000	4	1,030.18167	4	1,194.22333	4	1,358.26500	4	1,522.30667
5	869.42083	5	1,033.46250	5	1,197.50417	5	1,361.54583	5	1,525.58750
6	872.70167	6	1,036.74333	6	1,200.78500	6	1,364.82667	6	1,528.86833
7	875.98250	7	1,040.02417	7	1,204.06583	7	1,368.10750	7	1,532.14917
8	879.26333	8	1,043.30500	8	1,207.34667	8	1,371.38833	8	1,535.43000
9	882.54417	9	1,046.58583	9	1,210.62750	9	1,374.66917	9	1,538.71083
270	885.82500	**320**	1,049.86667	**370**	1,213.90833	**420**	1,377.95000	**470**	1,541.99167
1	889.10583	1	1,053.14750	1	1,217.18917	1	1,381.23083	1	1,545.27250
2	892.38667	2	1,056.42833	2	1,220.47000	2	1,384.51167	2	1,548.55333
3	895.66750	3	1,059.70917	3	1,223.75083	3	1,387.79250	3	1,551.83417
4	898.94833	4	1,062.99000	4	1,227.03167	4	1,391.07333	4	1,555.11500
5	902.22917	5	1,066.27083	5	1,230.31250	5	1,394.35417	5	1,558.39583
6	905.51000	6	1,069.55167	6	1,233.59333	6	1,397.63500	6	1,561.67667
7	908.79083	7	1,072.83250	7	1,236.87417	7	1,400.91583	7	1,564.95750
8	912.07167	8	1,076.11333	8	1,240.15500	8	1,404.19667	8	1,568.23833
9	915.35250	9	1,079.39417	9	1,243.43583	9	1,407.47750	9	1,571.51917
280	918.63333	**330**	1,082.67500	**380**	1,246.71667	**430**	1,410.75833	**480**	1,574.80000
1	921.91417	1	1,085.95583	1	1,249.99750	1	1,414.03917	1	1,578.08083
2	925.19500	2	1,089.23667	2	1,253.27833	2	1,417.32000	2	1,581.36167
3	928.47583	3	1,092.51750	3	1,256.55917	3	1,420.60083	3	1,584.64250
4	931.75667	4	1,095.79833	4	1,259.84000	4	1,423.88167	4	1,587.92333
5	935.03750	5	1,099.07917	5	1,263.12083	5	1,427.16250	5	1,591.20417
6	938.31833	6	1,102.36000	6	1,266.40167	6	1,430.44333	6	1,594.48500
7	941.59917	7	1,105.64083	7	1,269.68250	7	1,433.72417	7	1,597.76583
8	944.88000	8	1,108.92167	8	1,272.96333	8	1,437.00500	8	1,601.04667
9	948.16083	9	1,112.20250	9	1,276.24417	9	1,440.28583	9	1,604.32750
290	951.44167	**340**	1,115.48333	**390**	1,279.52500	**440**	1,443.56667	**490**	1,607.60833
1	954.72250	1	1,118.76417	1	1,282.80583	1	1,446.84750	1	1,610.88917
2	958.00333	2	1,122.04500	2	1,286.08667	2	1,450.12833	2	1,614.17000
3	961.28417	3	1,125.32583	3	1,289.36750	3	1,453.40917	3	1,617.45083
4	964.56500	4	1,128.60667	4	1,292.64833	4	1,456.69000	4	1,620.73167
5	967.84583	5	1,131.88750	5	1,295.92917	5	1,459.97083	5	1,624.01250
6	971.12667	6	1,135.16833	6	1,299.21000	6	1,463.25167	6	1,627.29333
7	974.40750	7	1,138.44917	7	1,302.49083	7	1,466.53250	7	1,630.57417
8	977.68833	8	1,141.73000	8	1,305.77167	8	1,469.81333	8	1,633.85500
9	980.96917	9	1,145.01083	9	1,309.05250	9	1,473.09417	9	1,637.13583

LENGTH—METRES TO FEET

[Reduction factor: 1 metre = 3.280833333 feet]

Metres	Feet	Metres	Feet	Metres	Feet	Metres	Feet	Metres	Feet
500	1,640.41667	550	1,804.45833	600	1,968.50000	650	2,132.54167	700	2,296.58333
1	1,643.69750	1	1,807.73917	1	1,971.78083	1	2,135.82250	1	2,299.86417
2	1,646.97833	2	1,811.02000	2	1,975.06167	2	2,139.10333	2	2,303.14500
3	1,650.25917	3	1,814.30083	3	1,978.34250	3	2,142.38417	3	2,306.42583
4	1,653.54000	4	1,817.58167	4	1,981.62333	4	2,145.66500	4	2,309.70667
5	1,656.82083	5	1,820.86250	5	1,984.90417	5	2,148.94583	5	2,312.98750
6	1,660.10167	6	1,824.14333	6	1,988.18500	6	2,152.22667	6	2,316.26833
7	1,663.38250	7	1,827.42417	7	1,991.46583	7	2,155.50750	7	2,319.54917
8	1,666.66333	8	1,830.70500	8	1,994.74667	8	2,158.78833	8	2,322.83000
9	1,669.94417	9	1,833.98583	9	1,998.02750	9	2,162.06917	9	2,326.11083
510	1,673.22500	560	1,837.26667	610	2,001.30833	660	2,165.35000	710	2,329.39167
1	1,676.50583	1	1,840.54750	1	2,004.58917	1	2,168.63083	1	2,332.67250
2	1,679.78667	2	1,843.82833	2	2,007.87000	2	2,171.91167	2	2,335.95333
3	1,683.06750	3	1,847.10917	3	2,011.15083	3	2,175.19250	3	2,339.23417
4	1,686.34833	4	1,850.39000	4	2,014.43167	4	2,178.47333	4	2,342.51500
5	1,689.62917	5	1,853.67083	5	2,017.71250	5	2,181.75417	5	2,345.79583
6	1,692.91000	6	1,856.95167	6	2,020.99333	6	2,185.03500	6	2,349.07667
7	1,696.19083	7	1,860.23250	7	2,024.27417	7	2,188.31583	7	2,352.35750
8	1,699.47167	8	1,863.51333	8	2,027.55500	8	2,191.59667	8	2,355.63833
9	1,702.75250	9	1,866.79417	9	2,030.83583	9	2,194.87750	9	2,358.91917
520	1,706.03333	570	1,870.07500	620	2,034.11667	670	2,198.15833	720	2,362.20000
1	1,709.31417	1	1,873.35583	1	2,037.39750	1	2,201.43917	1	2,365.48083
2	1,712.59500	2	1,876.63667	2	2,040.67833	2	2,204.72000	2	2,368.76167
3	1,715.87583	3	1,879.91750	3	2,043.95917	3	2,208.00083	3	2,372.04250
4	1,719.15667	4	1,883.19833	4	2,047.24000	4	2,211.28167	4	2,375.32333
5	1,722.43750	5	1,886.47917	5	2,050.52083	5	2,214.56250	5	2,378.60417
6	1,725.71833	6	1,889.76000	6	2,053.80167	6	2,217.84333	6	2,381.88500
7	1,728.99917	7	1,893.04083	7	2,057.08250	7	2,221.12417	7	2,385.16583
8	1,732.28000	8	1,896.32167	8	2,060.36333	8	2,224.40500	8	2,388.44667
9	1,735.56083	9	1,899.60250	9	2,063.64417	9	2,227.68583	9	2,391.72750
530	1,738.84167	580	1,902.88333	630	2,066.92500	680	2,230.96667	730	2,395.00833
1	1,742.12250	1	1,906.16417	1	2,070.20583	1	2,234.24750	1	2,398.28917
2	1,745.40333	2	1,909.44500	2	2,073.48667	2	2,237.52833	2	2,401.57000
3	1,748.68417	3	1,912.72583	3	2,076.76750	3	2,240.80917	3	2,404.85083
4	1,751.96500	4	1,916.00667	4	2,080.04833	4	2,244.09000	4	2,408.13167
5	1,755.24583	5	1,919.28750	5	2,083.32917	5	2,247.37083	5	2,411.41250
6	1,758.52667	6	1,922.56833	6	2,086.61000	6	2,250.65167	6	2,414.69333
7	1,761.80750	7	1,925.84917	7	2,089.89083	7	2,253.93250	7	2,417.97417
8	1,765.08833	8	1,929.13000	8	2,093.17167	8	2,257.21333	8	2,421.25500
9	1,768.36917	9	1,932.41083	9	2,096.45250	9	2,260.49417	9	2,424.53583
540	1,771.65000	590	1,935.69167	640	2,099.73333	690	2,263.77500	740	2,427.81667
1	1,774.93083	1	1,938.97250	1	2,103.01417	1	2,267.05583	1	2,431.09750
2	1,778.21167	2	1,942.25333	2	2,106.29500	2	2,270.33667	2	2,434.37833
3	1,781.49250	3	1,945.53417	3	2,109.57583	3	2,273.61750	3	2,437.65917
4	1,784.77333	4	1,948.81500	4	2,112.85667	4	2,276.89833	4	2,440.94000
5	1,788.05417	5	1,952.09583	5	2,116.13750	5	2,280.17917	5	2,444.22083
6	1,791.33500	6	1,955.37667	6	2,119.41833	6	2,283.46000	6	2,447.50167
7	1,794.61583	7	1,958.65750	7	2,122.69917	7	2,286.74083	7	2,450.78250
8	1,797.89667	8	1,961.93833	8	2,125.98000	8	2,290.02167	8	2,454.06333
9	1,801.17750	9	1,965.21917	9	2,129.26083	9	2,293.30250	9	2,457.34417

LENGTH—METRES TO FEET

[Reduction factor: 1 metre = 3.280833333 feet]

Metres	Feet	Metres	Feet	Metres	Feet	Metres	Feet	Metres	Feet
750	2,460.62500	800	2,624.66667	850	2,788.70833	900	2,952.75000	950	3,116.79167
1	2,463.90583	1	2,627.94750	1	2,791.98917	1	2,956.03083	1	3,120.07250
2	2,467.18667	2	2,631.22833	2	2,795.27000	2	2,959.31167	2	3,123.35333
3	2,470.46750	3	2,634.50917	3	2,798.55083	3	2,962.59250	3	3,126.63417
4	2,473.74833	4	2,637.79000	4	2,801.83167	4	2,965.87333	4	3,129.91500
5	2,477.02917	5	2,641.07083	5	2,805.11250	5	2,969.15417	5	3,133.19583
6	2,480.31000	6	2,644.35167	6	2,808.39333	6	2,972.43500	6	3,136.47667
7	2,483.59083	7	2,647.63250	7	2,811.67417	7	2,975.71583	7	3,139.75750
8	2,486.87167	8	2,650.91333	8	2,814.95500	8	2,978.99667	8	3,143.03833
9	2,490.15250	9	2,654.19417	9	2,818.23583	9	2,982.27750	9	3,146.31917
760	2,493.43333	810	2,657.47500	860	2,821.51667	910	2,985.55833	960	3,149.60000
1	2,496.71417	1	2,660.75583	1	2,824.79750	1	2,988.83917	1	3,152.88083
2	2,499.99500	2	2,664.03667	2	2,828.07833	2	2,992.12000	2	3,156.16167
3	2,503.27583	3	2,667.31750	3	2,831.35917	3	2,995.40083	3	3,159.44250
4	2,506.55667	4	2,670.59833	4	2,834.64000	4	2,998.68167	4	3,162.72333
5	2,509.83750	5	2,673.87917	5	2,837.92083	5	3,001.96250	5	3,166.00417
6	2,513.11833	6	2,677.16000	6	2,841.20167	6	3,005.24333	6	3,169.28500
7	2,516.39917	7	2,680.44083	7	2,844.48250	7	3,008.52417	7	3,172.56583
8	2,519.68000	8	2,683.72167	8	2,847.76333	8	3,011.80500	8	3,175.84667
9	2,522.96083	9	2,687.00250	9	2,851.04417	9	3,015.08583	9	3,179.12750
770	2,526.24167	820	2,690.28333	870	2,854.32500	920	3,018.36667	970	3,182.40833
1	2,529.52250	1	2,693.56417	1	2,857.60583	1	3,021.64750	1	3,185.68917
2	2,532.80333	2	2,696.84500	2	2,860.88667	2	3,024.92833	2	3,188.97000
3	2,536.08417	3	2,700.12583	3	2,864.16750	3	3,028.20917	3	3,192.25083
4	2,539.36500	4	2,703.40667	4	2,867.44833	4	3,031.49000	4	3,195.53167
5	2,542.64583	5	2,706.68750	5	2,870.72917	5	3,034.77083	5	3,198.81250
6	2,545.92667	6	2,709.96833	6	2,874.01000	6	3,038.05167	6	3,202.09333
7	2,549.20750	7	2,713.24917	7	2,877.29083	7	3,041.33250	7	3,205.37417
8	2,552.48833	8	2,716.53000	8	2,880.57167	8	3,044.61333	8	3,208.65500
9	2,555.76917	9	2,719.81083	9	2,883.85250	9	3,047.89417	9	3,211.93583
780	2,559.05000	830	2,723.09167	880	2,887.13333	930	3,051.17500	980	3,215.21667
1	2,562.33083	1	2,726.37250	1	2,890.41417	1	3,054.45583	1	3,218.49750
2	2,565.61167	2	2,729.65333	2	2,893.69500	2	3,057.73667	2	3,221.77833
3	2,568.89250	3	2,732.93417	3	2,896.97583	3	3,061.01750	3	3,225.05917
4	2,572.17333	4	2,736.21500	4	2,900.25667	4	3,064.29833	4	3,228.34000
5	2,575.45417	5	2,739.49583	5	2,903.53750	5	3,067.57917	5	3,231.62083
6	2,578.73500	6	2,742.77667	6	2,906.81833	6	3,070.86000	6	3,234.90167
7	2,582.01583	7	2,746.05750	7	2,910.09917	7	3,074.14083	7	3,238.18250
8	2,585.29667	8	2,749.33833	8	2,913.38000	8	3,077.42167	8	3,241.46333
9	2,588.57750	9	2,752.61917	9	2,916.66083	9	3,080.70250	9	3,244.74417
790	2,591.85833	840	2,755.90000	890	2,919.94167	940	3,083.98333	990	3,248.02500
1	2,595.13917	1	2,759.18083	1	2,923.22250	1	3,087.26417	1	3,251.30583
2	2,598.42000	2	2,762.46167	2	2,926.50333	2	3,090.54500	2	3,254.58667
3	2,601.70083	3	2,765.74250	3	2,929.78417	3	3,093.82583	3	3,257.86750
4	2,604.98167	4	2,769.02333	4	2,933.06500	4	3,097.10667	4	3,261.14833
5	2,608.26250	5	2,772.30417	5	2,936.34583	5	3,100.38750	5	3,264.42917
6	2,611.54333	6	2,775.58500	6	2,939.62667	6	3,103.66833	6	3,267.71000
7	2,614.82417	7	2,778.86583	7	2,942.90750	7	3,106.94917	7	3,270.99083
8	2,618.10500	8	2,782.14667	8	2,946.18833	8	3,110.23000	8	3,274.27167
9	2,621.38583	9	2,785.42750	9	2,949.46917	9	3,113.51083	9	3,277.55250

LENGTH—FEET TO METRES

[Reduction factor: 1 foot = 0.3048006096 metre]

Feet	Metres	Feet	Metres	Feet	Metres	Feet	Metres	Feet	Metres
0		50	15.24003	100	30.48006	150	45.72009	200	60.96012
1	0.30480	1	15.54483	1	30.78486	1	46.02489	1	61.26492
2	.60960	2	15.84963	2	31.08966	2	46.32969	2	61.56972
3	.91440	3	16.15443	3	31.39446	3	46.63449	3	61.87452
4	1.21920	4	16.45923	4	31.69926	4	46.93929	4	62.17932
5	1.52400	5	16.76403	5	32.00406	5	47.24409	5	62.48412
6	1.82880	6	17.06883	6	32.30886	6	47.54890	6	62.78893
7	2.13360	7	17.37363	7	32.61367	7	47.85370	7	63.09373
8	2.43840	8	17.67844	8	32.91847	8	48.15850	8	63.39853
9	2.74321	9	17.98324	9	33.22327	9	48.46330	9	63.70333
10	3.04801	60	18.28804	110	33.52807	160	48.76810	210	64.00813
1	3.35281	1	18.59284	1	33.83287	1	49.07290	1	64.31293
2	3.65761	2	18.89764	2	34.13767	2	49.37770	2	64.61773
3	3.96241	3	19.20244	3	34.44247	3	49.68250	3	64.92253
4	4.26721	4	19.50724	4	34.74727	4	49.98730	4	65.22733
5	4.57201	5	19.81204	5	35.05207	5	50.29210	5	65.53213
6	4.87681	6	20.11684	6	35.35687	6	50.59690	6	65.83693
7	5.18161	7	20.42164	7	35.66167	7	50.90170	7	66.14173
8	5.48641	8	20.72644	8	35.96647	8	51.20650	8	66.44653
9	5.79121	9	21.03124	9	36.27127	9	51.51130	9	66.75133
20	6.09601	70	21.33604	120	36.57607	170	51.81610	220	67.05613
1	6.40081	1	21.64084	1	36.88087	1	52.12090	1	67.36093
2	6.70561	2	21.94564	2	37.18567	2	52.42570	2	67.66574
3	7.01041	3	22.25044	3	37.49047	3	52.73051	3	67.97054
4	7.31521	4	22.55525	4	37.79528	4	53.03531	4	68.27534
5	7.62002	5	22.86005	5	38.10008	5	53.34011	5	68.58014
6	7.92482	6	23.16485	6	38.40488	6	53.64491	6	68.88494
7	8.22962	7	23.46965	7	38.70968	7	53.94971	7	69.18974
8	8.53442	8	23.77445	8	39.01448	8	54.25451	8	69.49454
9	8.83922	9	24.07925	9	39.31928	9	54.55931	9	69.79934
30	9.14402	80	24.38405	130	39.62408	180	54.86411	230	70.10414
1	9.44882	1	24.68885	1	39.92888	1	55.16891	1	70.40894
2	9.75362	2	24.99365	2	40.23368	2	55.47371	2	70.71374
3	10.05842	3	25.29845	3	40.53848	3	55.77851	3	71.01854
4	10.36322	4	25.60325	4	40.84328	4	56.08331	4	71.32334
5	10.66802	5	25.90805	5	41.14808	5	56.38811	5	71.62814
6	10.97282	6	26.21285	6	41.45288	6	56.69291	6	71.93294
7	11.27762	7	26.51765	7	41.75768	7	56.99771	7	72.23774
8	11.58242	8	26.82245	8	42.06248	8	57.30251	8	72.54255
9	11.88722	9	27.12725	9	42.36728	9	57.60732	9	72.84735
40	12.19202	90	27.43205	140	42.67209	190	57.91212	240	73.15215
1	12.49682	1	27.73686	1	42.97689	1	58.21692	1	73.45695
2	12.80163	2	28.04166	2	43.28169	2	58.52172	2	73.76175
3	13.10643	3	28.34646	3	43.58649	3	58.82652	3	74.06655
4	13.41123	4	28.65126	4	43.89129	4	59.13132	4	74.37135
5	13.71603	5	28.95606	5	44.19609	5	59.43612	5	74.67615
6	14.02083	6	29.26086	6	44.50089	6	59.74092	6	74.98095
7	14.32563	7	29.56566	7	44.80569	7	60.04572	7	75.28575
8	14.63043	8	29.87046	8	45.11049	8	60.35052	8	75.59055
9	14.93523	9	30.17526	9	45.41529	9	60.65532	9	75.89535

LENGTH—FEET TO METRES

[Reduction factor: 1 foot = 0.3048006096 metre]

Feet	Metres	Feet	Metres	Feet	Metres	Feet	Metres	Feet	Metres
250	76.20015	300	91.44018	350	106.68021	400	121.92024	450	137.16027
1	76.50495	1	91.74498	1	106.98501	1	122.22504	1	137.46507
2	76.80975	2	92.04978	2	107.28981	2	122.52985	2	137.76988
3	77.11455	3	92.35458	3	107.59462	3	122.83465	3	138.07468
4	77.41935	4	92.65939	4	107.89942	4	123.13945	4	138.37948
5	77.72416	5	92.96419	5	108.20422	5	123.44425	5	138.68428
6	78.02896	6	93.26899	6	108.50902	6	123.74905	6	138.98908
7	78.33376	7	93.57379	7	108.81382	7	124.05385	7	139.29388
8	78.63856	8	93.87859	8	109.11862	8	124.35865	8	139.59868
9	78.94336	9	94.18339	9	109.42342	9	124.66345	9	139.90348
260	79.24816	310	94.48819	360	109.72822	410	124.96825	460	140.20828
1	79.55296	1	94.79299	1	110.03302	1	125.27305	1	140.51308
2	79.85776	2	95.09779	2	110.33782	2	125.57785	2	140.81788
3	80.16256	3	95.40259	3	110.64262	3	125.88265	3	141.12268
4	80.46736	4	95.70739	4	110.94742	4	126.18745	4	141.42748
5	80.77216	5	96.01219	5	111.25222	5	126.49225	5	141.73228
6	81.07696	6	96.31699	6	111.55702	6	126.79705	6	142.03708
7	81.38176	7	96.62179	7	111.86182	7	127.10185	7	142.34188
8	81.68656	8	96.92659	8	112.16662	8	127.40665	8	142.64669
9	81.99136	9	97.23139	9	112.47142	9	127.71146	9	142.95149
270	82.29616	320	97.53620	370	112.77623	420	128.01626	470	143.25629
1	82.60097	1	97.84100	1	113.08103	1	128.32106	1	143.56109
2	82.90577	2	98.14580	2	113.38583	2	128.62586	2	143.86589
3	83.21057	3	98.45060	3	113.69063	3	128.93066	3	144.17069
4	83.51537	4	98.75540	4	113.99543	4	129.23546	4	144.47549
5	83.82017	5	99.06020	5	114.30023	5	129.54026	5	144.78029
6	84.12497	6	99.36500	6	114.60503	6	129.84506	6	145.08509
7	84.42977	7	99.66980	7	114.90983	7	130.14986	7	145.38989
8	84.73457	8	99.97460	8	115.21463	8	130.45466	8	145.69469
9	85.03937	9	100.27940	9	115.51943	9	130.75946	9	145.99949
280	85.34417	330	100.58420	380	115.82423	430	131.06426	480	146.30429
1	85.64897	1	100.88900	1	116.12903	1	131.36906	1	146.60909
2	85.95377	2	101.19380	2	116.43383	2	131.67386	2	146.91389
3	86.25857	3	101.49860	3	116.73863	3	131.97866	3	147.21869
4	86.56337	4	101.80340	4	117.04343	4	132.28346	4	147.52350
5	86.86817	5	102.10820	5	117.34823	5	132.58827	5	147.82830
6	87.17297	6	102.41300	6	117.65304	6	132.89307	6	148.13310
7	87.47777	7	102.71781	7	117.95784	7	133.19787	7	148.43790
8	87.78258	8	103.02261	8	118.26264	8	133.50267	8	148.74270
9	88.08738	9	103.32741	9	118.56744	9	133.80747	9	149.04750
290	88.39218	340	103.63221	390	118.87224	440	134.11227	490	149.35230
1	88.69698	1	103.93701	1	119.17704	1	134.41707	1	149.65710
2	89.00178	2	104.24181	2	119.48184	2	134.72187	2	149.96190
3	89.30658	3	104.54661	3	119.78664	3	135.02667	3	150.26670
4	89.61138	4	104.85141	4	120.09144	4	135.33147	4	150.57150
5	89.91618	5	105.15621	5	120.39624	5	135.63627	5	150.87630
6	90.22098	6	105.46101	6	120.70104	6	135.94107	6	151.18110
7	90.52578	7	105.76581	7	121.00584	7	136.24587	7	151.48590
8	90.83058	8	106.07061	8	121.31064	8	136.55067	8	151.79070
9	91.13538	9	106.37541	9	121.61544	9	136.85547	9	152.09550

THE METRIC ENCYCLOPEDIA

LENGTH—FEET TO METRES

[Reduction factor: 1 foot = 0.3048006096 metre]

Feet	Metres	Feet	Metres	Feet	Metres	Feet	Metres	Feet	Metres
500	152.40030	**550**	167.64034	**600**	182.88037	**650**	198.12040	**700**	213.36043
1	152.70511	1	167.94514	1	183.18517	1	198.42520	1	213.66523
2	153.00991	2	168.24994	2	183.48997	2	198.73000	2	213.97003
3	153.31471	3	168.55474	3	183.79477	3	199.03480	3	214.27483
4	153.61951	4	168.85954	4	184.09957	4	199.33960	4	214.57963
5	153.92431	5	169.16434	5	184.40437	5	199.64440	5	214.88443
6	154.22911	6	169.46914	6	184.70917	6	199.94920	6	215.18923
7	154.53391	7	169.77394	7	185.01397	7	200.25400	7	215.49403
8	154.83871	8	170.07874	8	185.31877	8	200.55880	8	215.79883
9	155.14351	9	170.38354	9	185.62357	9	200.86360	9	216.10363
510	155.44831	**560**	170.68834	**610**	185.92837	**660**	201.16840	**710**	216.40843
1	155.75311	1	170.99314	1	186.23317	1	201.47320	1	216.71323
2	156.05791	2	171.29794	2	186.53797	2	201.77800	2	217.01803
3	156.36271	3	171.60274	3	186.84277	3	202.08280	3	217.32283
4	156.66751	4	171.90754	4	187.14757	4	202.38760	4	217.62764
5	156.97231	5	172.21234	5	187.45237	5	202.69241	5	217.93244
6	157.27711	6	172.51715	6	187.75718	6	202.99721	6	218.23724
7	157.58192	7	172.82195	7	188.06198	7	203.30201	7	218.54204
8	157.88672	8	173.12675	8	188.36678	8	203.60681	8	218.84684
9	158.19152	9	173.43155	9	188.67158	9	203.91161	9	219.15164
520	158.49632	**570**	173.73635	**620**	188.97638	**670**	204.21641	**720**	219.45644
1	158.80112	1	174.04115	1	189.28118	1	204.52121	1	219.76124
2	159.10592	2	174.34595	2	189.58598	2	204.82601	2	220.06604
3	159.41072	3	174.65075	3	189.89078	3	205.13081	3	220.37084
4	159.71552	4	174.95555	4	190.19558	4	205.43561	4	220.67564
5	160.02032	5	175.26035	5	190.50038	5	205.74041	5	220.98044
6	160.32512	6	175.56515	6	190.80518	6	206.04521	6	221.28524
7	160.62992	7	175.86995	7	191.10998	7	206.35001	7	221.59004
8	160.93472	8	176.17475	8	191.41478	8	206.65481	8	221.89484
9	161.23952	9	176.47955	9	191.71958	9	206.95961	9	222.19964
530	161.54432	**580**	176.78435	**630**	192.02438	**680**	207.26441	**730**	222.50445
1	161.84912	1	177.08915	1	192.32918	1	207.56922	1	222.80925
2	162.15392	2	177.39395	2	192.63399	2	207.87402	2	223.11405
3	162.45872	3	177.69876	3	192.93879	3	208.17882	3	223.41885
4	162.76353	4	178.00356	4	193.24359	4	208.48362	4	223.72365
5	163.06833	5	178.30836	5	193.54839	5	208.78842	5	224.02845
6	163.37313	6	178.61316	6	193.85319	6	209.09322	6	224.33325
7	163.67793	7	178.91796	7	194.15799	7	209.39802	7	224.63805
8	163.98273	8	179.22276	8	194.46279	8	209.70282	8	224.94285
9	164.28753	9	179.52756	9	194.76759	9	210.00762	9	225.24765
540	164.59233	**590**	179.83236	**640**	195.07239	**690**	210.31242	**740**	225.55245
1	164.89713	1	180.13716	1	195.37719	1	210.61722	1	225.85725
2	165.20193	2	180.44196	2	195.68199	2	210.92202	2	226.16205
3	165.50673	3	180.74676	3	195.98679	3	211.22682	3	226.46685
4	165.81153	4	181.05156	4	196.29159	4	211.53162	4	226.77165
5	166.11633	5	181.35636	5	196.59639	5	211.83642	5	227.07645
6	166.42113	6	181.66116	6	196.90119	6	212.14122	6	227.38125
7	166.72593	7	181.96596	7	197.20599	7	212.44602	7	227.68606
8	167.03073	8	182.27076	8	197.51080	8	212.75083	8	227.99086
9	167.33553	9	182.57557	9	197.81560	9	213.05563	9	228.29566

LENGTH—FEET TO METRES

[Reduction factor: 1 foot = 0.3048006096 metre]

Feet	Metres	Feet	Metres	Feet	Metres	Feet	Metres	Feet	Metres
750	228.60046	800	243.84049	850	259.08052	900	274.32055	950	289.56058
1	228.90526	1	244.14529	1	259.38532	1	274.62535	1	289.86538
2	229.21006	2	244.45009	2	259.69012	2	274.93015	2	290.17018
3	229.51486	3	244.75489	3	259.99492	3	275.23495	3	290.47498
4	229.81966	4	245.05969	4	260.29972	4	275.53975	4	290.77978
5	230.12446	5	245.36449	5	260.60452	5	275.84455	5	291.08458
6	230.42926	6	245.66929	6	260.90932	6	276.14935	6	291.33938
7	230.73406	7	245.97409	7	261.21412	7	276.45415	7	291.69418
8	231.03886	8	246.27889	8	261.51892	8	276.75895	8	291.99898
9	231.34366	9	246.53369	9	261.82372	9	277.06375	9	292.30378
760	231.64846	810	246.88849	860	262.12852	910	277.36855	960	292.60859
1	231.95326	1	247.19329	1	262.43332	1	277.67336	1	292.91339
2	232.25806	2	247.49809	2	262.73813	2	277.97816	2	293.21819
3	232.56287	3	247.80290	3	263.04293	3	278.28296	3	293.52299
4	232.86767	4	248.10770	4	263.34773	4	278.58776	4	293.82779
5	233.17247	5	248.41250	5	263.65253	5	278.89256	5	234.13259
6	233.47727	6	248.71730	6	263.95733	6	279.19736	6	294.43739
7	233.78207	7	249.02210	7	264.26213	7	279.50216	7	294.74219
8	234.08687	8	249.32690	8	264.56693	8	279.80696	8	295.04699
9	234.39167	9	249.63170	9	264.87173	9	280.11176	9	295.35179
770	234.69647	820	249.93650	870	265.17653	920	280.41656	970	295.65659
1	235.00127	1	250.24130	1	265.48133	1	280.72136	1	295.96139
2	235.30607	2	250.54610	2	265.78613	2	281.02616	2	296.26619
3	235.61087	3	250.85090	3	266.09093	3	281.33096	3	296.57099
4	235.91567	4	251.15570	4	266.39573	4	281.63576	4	296.87579
5	236.22047	5	251.46050	5	266.70053	5	281.94056	5	297.18059
6	236.52527	6	251.76530	6	267.00533	6	282.24536	6	297.48539
7	236.83007	7	252.07010	7	267.31013	7	282.55017	7	297.79020
8	237.13487	8	252.37490	8	267.61494	8	282.85497	8	298.09500
9	237.43967	9	252.67971	9	267.91974	9	283.15977	9	298.39980
780	237.74448	830	252.98451	880	268.22454	930	283.46457	980	298.70460
1	238.04928	1	253.28931	1	268.52934	1	283.76937	1	299.00940
2	238.35408	2	253.59411	2	268.83414	2	284.07417	2	299.31420
3	238.65888	3	253.89891	3	269.13894	3	284.37897	3	299.61900
4	238.96368	4	254.20371	4	269.44374	4	284.68377	4	299.92380
5	239.26848	5	254.50851	5	269.74854	5	284.98857	5	300.22860
6	239.57328	6	254.81331	6	270.05334	6	285.29337	6	300.53340
7	239.87808	7	255.11811	7	270.35814	7	285.59817	7	300.83820
8	240.18288	8	255.42291	8	270.66294	8	285.90297	8	301.14300
9	240.48768	9	255.72771	9	270.96774	9	286.20777	9	301.44780
790	240.79248	840	256.03251	890	271.27254	940	286.51257	990	301.75260
1	241.09728	1	256.33731	1	271.57734	1	286.81737	1	302.05740
2	241.40208	2	256.64211	2	271.88214	2	287.12217	2	302.36220
3	241.70688	3	256.94691	3	272.18694	3	287.42697	3	302.66701
4	242.01168	4	257.25171	4	272.49174	4	287.73178	4	302.97181
5	242.31648	5	257.55652	5	272.79655	5	288.03658	5	303.27661
6	242.62129	6	257.86132	6	273.10135	6	288.34138	6	303.58141
7	242.92609	7	258.16612	7	273.40615	7	288.64618	7	303.88621
8	243.23089	8	258.47092	8	273.71095	8	288.95098	8	304.19101
9	243.53569	9	258.77572	9	274.01575	9	289.25578	9	304.49581

LENGTH—KILOMETRES TO MILES

[Reduction factor: 1 kilometre = 0.6213699495 mile]

Kilometres	Miles	Kilometres	Miles	Kilometres	Miles	Kilometres	Miles	Kilometres	Miles
0		50	31.06850	100	62.13699	150	93.20549	200	124.27399
1	0.62137	1	31.68987	1	62.75836	1	93.82686	1	124.89536
2	1.24274	2	32.31124	2	63.37973	2	94.44823	2	125.51673
3	1.86411	3	32.93261	3	64.00110	3	95.06960	3	126.13810
4	2.48548	4	33.55398	4	64.62247	4	95.69097	4	126.75947
5	3.10685	5	34.17535	5	65.24384	5	96.31234	5	127.38084
6	3.72822	6	34.79672	6	65.86521	6	96.93371	6	128.00221
7	4.34959	7	35.41809	7	66.48658	7	97.55508	7	128.62358
8	4.97096	8	36.03946	8	67.10795	8	98.17645	8	129.24495
9	5.59233	9	36.66083	9	67.72932	9	98.79782	9	129.86632
10	6.21370	60	37.28220	110	68.35069	160	99.41919	210	130.48769
1	6.83507	1	37.90357	1	68.97206	1	100.04056	1	131.10906
2	7.45644	2	38.52494	2	69.59343	2	100.66193	2	131.73043
3	8.07781	3	39.14631	3	70.21480	3	101.28330	3	132.35180
4	8.69918	4	39.76768	4	70.83617	4	101.90467	4	132.97317
5	9.32055	5	40.38905	5	71.45754	5	102.52604	5	133.59454
6	9.94192	6	41.01042	6	72.07891	6	103.14741	6	134.21591
7	10.56329	7	41.63179	7	72.70028	7	103.76878	7	134.83728
8	11.18466	8	42.25316	8	73.32165	8	104.39015	8	135.45865
9	11.80603	9	42.87453	9	73.94302	9	105.01152	9	136.08002
20	12.42740	70	43.49590	120	74.56439	170	105.63289	220	136.70139
1	13.04877	1	44.11727	1	75.18576	1	106.25426	1	137.32276
2	13.67014	2	44.73864	2	75.80713	2	106.87563	2	137.94413
3	14.29151	3	45.36001	3	76.42850	3	107.49700	3	138.56550
4	14.91288	4	45.98138	4	77.04987	4	108.11837	4	139.18687
5	15.53425	5	46.60275	5	77.67124	5	108.73974	5	139.80824
6	16.15562	6	47.22412	6	78.29261	6	109.36111	6	140.42961
7	16.77699	7	47.84549	7	78.91398	7	109.98248	7	141.05098
8	17.39836	8	48.46686	8	79.53535	8	110.60385	8	141.67235
9	18.01973	9	49.08823	9	80.15672	9	111.22522	9	142.29372
30	18.64110	80	49.70960	130	80.77809	180	111.84659	230	142.91509
1	19.26247	1	50.33097	1	81.39946	1	112.46796	1	143.53646
2	19.88384	2	50.95234	2	82.02083	2	113.08933	2	144.15783
3	20.50521	3	51.57371	3	82.64220	3	113.71070	3	144.77920
4	21.12658	4	52.19508	4	83.26357	4	114.33207	4	145.40057
5	21.74795	5	52.81645	5	83.88494	5	114.95344	5	146.02194
6	22.36932	6	53.43782	6	84.50631	6	115.57481	6	146.64331
7	22.99069	7	54.05919	7	85.12768	7	116.19618	7	147.26468
8	23.61206	8	54.68056	8	85.74905	8	116.81755	8	147.88605
9	24.23343	9	55.30193	9	86.37042	9	117.43892	9	148.50742
40	24.85480	90	55.92330	140	86.99179	190	118.06029	240	149.12879
1	25.47617	1	56.54467	1	87.61316	1	118.68166	1	149.75016
2	26.09754	2	57.16604	2	88.23453	2	119.30303	2	150.37153
3	26.71891	3	57.78741	3	88.85590	3	119.92440	3	150.99290
4	27.34028	4	58.40878	4	89.47727	4	120.54577	4	151.61427
5	27.96165	5	59.03015	5	90.09864	5	121.16714	5	152.23564
6	28.58302	6	59.65152	6	90.72001	6	121.78851	6	152.85701
7	29.20439	7	60.27289	7	91.34138	7	122.40988	7	153.47838
8	29.82576	8	60.89426	8	91.96275	8	123.03125	8	154.09975
9	30.44713	9	61.51562	9	92.58412	9	123.65262	9	154.72112

LENGTH—KILOMETRES TO MILES

[Reduction factor: 1 kilometre = 0.6213699495 mile]

Kilo-metres	Miles	Kilo-metres	Miles	Kilo-metres	Miles	Kilo-metres	Miles	Kilo-metres	Miles
250	155.34249	300	186.41098	350	217.47948	400	248.54798	450	279.61648
1	155.96386	1	187.03235	1	218.10085	1	249.16935	1	280.23785
2	156.58523	2	187.65372	2	218.72222	2	249.79072	2	280.85922
3	157.20660	3	188.27509	3	219.34359	3	250.41209	3	281.48059
4	157.82797	4	188.89646	4	219.96496	4	251.03346	4	282.10196
5	158.44934	5	189.51783	5	220.58633	5	251.65483	5	282.72333
6	159.07071	6	190.13920	6	221.20770	6	252.27620	6	283.34470
7	159.69208	7	190.76057	7	221.82907	7	252.89757	7	283.96607
8	160.31345	8	191.38194	8	222.45044	8	253.51894	8	284.58744
9	160.93482	9	192.00331	9	223.07181	9	254.14031	9	285.20881
260	161.55619	310	192.62468	360	223.69318	410	254.76168	460	285.83018
1	162.17756	1	193.24605	1	224.31455	1	255.38305	1	286.45155
2	162.79893	2	193.86742	2	224.93592	2	256.00442	2	287.07292
3	163.42030	3	194.48879	3	225.55729	3	256.62579	3	287.69429
4	164.04167	4	195.11016	4	226.17866	4	257.24716	4	288.31566
5	164.66304	5	195.73153	5	226.80003	5	257.86853	5	288.93703
6	165.28441	6	196.35290	6	227.42140	6	258.48990	6	289.55840
7	165.90578	7	196.97427	7	228.04277	7	259.11127	7	290.17977
8	166.52715	8	197.59564	8	228.66414	8	259.73264	8	290.80114
9	167.14852	9	198.21701	9	229.28551	9	260.35401	9	291.42251
270	167.76989	320	198.83838	370	229.90688	420	260.97538	470	292.04388
1	168.39126	1	199.45975	1	230.52825	1	261.59675	1	292.66525
2	169.01263	2	200.08112	2	231.14962	2	262.21812	2	293.28662
3	169.63400	3	200.70249	3	231.77099	3	262.83949	3	293.90799
4	170.25537	4	201.32386	4	232.39236	4	263.46086	4	294.52936
5	170.87674	5	201.94523	5	233.01373	5	264.08223	5	295.15073
6	171.49811	6	202.56660	6	233.63510	6	264.70360	6	295.77210
7	172.11948	7	203.18797	7	234.25647	7	265.32497	7	296.39347
8	172.74085	8	203.80934	8	234.87784	8	265.94634	8	297.01484
9	173.36222	9	204.43071	9	235.49921	9	266.56771	9	297.63621
280	173.98359	330	205.05208	380	236.12058	430	267.18908	480	298.25758
1	174.60496	1	205.67345	1	236.74195	1	267.81045	1	298.87895
2	175.22633	2	206.29482	2	237.36332	2	268.43182	2	299.50032
3	175.84770	3	206.91619	3	237.98469	3	269.05319	3	300.12169
4	176.46907	4	207.53756	4	238.60606	4	269.67456	4	300.74306
5	177.09044	5	208.15893	5	239.22743	5	270.29593	5	301.36443
6	177.71181	6	208.78030	6	239.84880	6	270.91730	6	301.98580
7	178.33318	7	209.40167	7	240.47017	7	271.53867	7	302.60717
8	178.95455	8	210.02304	8	241.09154	8	272.16004	8	303.22854
9	179.57592	9	210.64441	9	241.71291	9	272.78141	9	303.84991
290	180.19729	340	211.26578	390	242.33428	440	273.40278	490	304.47128
1	180.81866	1	211.88715	1	242.95565	1	274.02415	1	305.09265
2	181.44003	2	212.50852	2	243.57702	2	274.64552	2	305.71402
3	182.06140	3	213.12989	3	244.19839	3	275.26689	3	306.33539
4	182.68277	4	213.75126	4	244.81976	4	275.88826	4	306.95676
5	183.30414	5	214.37263	5	245.44113	5	276.50963	5	307.57812
6	183.92551	6	214.99400	6	246.06250	6	277.13100	6	308.19949
7	184.54687	7	215.61537	7	246.68387	7	277.75237	7	308.82086
8	185.16824	8	216.23674	8	247.30524	8	278.37374	8	309.44223
9	185.78961	9	216.85811	9	247.92661	9	278.99511	9	310.06360

LENGTH—KILOMETRES TO MILES

[Reduction factor: 1 kilometre = 0.6213699495 mile]

Kilo-metres	Miles	Kilo-metres	Miles	Kilo-metres	Miles	Kilo-metres	Miles	Kilo-metres	Miles
500	310.68497	550	341.75347	600	372.82197	650	403.89047	700	434.95896
1	311.30634	1	342.37484	1	373.44334	1	404.51184	1	435.58033
2	311.92771	2	342.99621	2	374.06471	2	405.13321	2	436.20170
3	312.54908	3	343.61758	3	374.68608	3	405.75458	3	436.82307
4	313.17045	4	344.23895	4	375.30745	4	406.37595	4	437.44444
5	313.79182	5	344.86032	5	375.92882	5	406.99732	5	438.06581
6	314.41319	6	345.48169	6	376.55019	6	407.61869	6	438.68718
7	315.03456	7	346.10306	7	377.17156	7	408.24006	7	439.30855
8	315.65593	8	346.72443	8	377.79293	8	408.86143	8	439.92992
9	316.27730	9	347.34580	9	378.41430	9	409.48280	9	440.55129
510	316.89867	560	347.96717	610	379.03567	660	410.10417	710	441.17266
1	317.52004	1	348.58854	1	379.65704	1	410.72554	1	441.79403
2	318.14141	2	349.20991	2	380.27841	2	411.34691	2	442.41540
3	318.76278	3	349.83128	3	380.89978	3	411.96828	3	443.03677
4	319.38415	4	350.45265	4	381.52115	4	412.58965	4	443.65814
5	320.00552	5	351.07402	5	382.14252	5	413.21102	5	444.27951
6	320.62689	6	351.69539	6	382.76389	6	413.83239	6	444.90088
7	321.24826	7	352.31676	7	383.38526	7	414.45376	7	445.52225
8	321.86963	8	352.93813	8	384.00663	8	415.07513	8	446.14362
9	322.49100	9	353.55950	9	384.62800	9	415.69650	9	446.76499
520	323.11237	570	354.18087	620	385.24937	670	416.31787	720	447.38636
1	323.73374	1	354.80224	1	385.87074	1	416.93924	1	448.00773
2	324.35511	2	355.42361	2	386.49211	2	417.56061	2	448.62910
3	324.97648	3	356.04498	3	387.11348	3	418.18198	3	449.25047
4	325.59785	4	356.66635	4	387.73485	4	418.80335	4	449.87184
5	326.21922	5	357.28772	5	388.35622	5	419.42472	5	450.49321
6	326.84059	6	357.90909	6	388.97759	6	420.04609	6	451.11458
7	327.46196	7	358.53046	7	389.59896	7	420.66746	7	451.73595
8	328.08333	8	359.15183	8	390.22033	8	421.28883	8	452.35732
9	328.70470	9	359.77320	9	390.84170	9	421.91020	9	452.97869
530	329.32607	580	360.39457	630	391.46307	680	422.53157	730	453.60006
1	329.94744	1	361.01594	1	392.08444	1	423.15294	1	454.22143
2	330.56881	2	361.63731	2	392.70581	2	423.77431	2	454.84280
3	331.19018	3	362.25868	3	393.32718	3	424.39568	3	455.46417
4	331.81155	4	362.88005	4	393.94855	4	425.01705	4	456.08554
5	332.43292	5	363.50142	5	394.56992	5	425.63842	5	456.70691
6	333.05429	6	364.12279	6	395.19129	6	426.25979	6	457.32828
7	333.67566	7	364.74416	7	395.81266	7	426.88116	7	457.94965
8	334.29703	8	365.36553	8	396.43403	8	427.50253	8	458.57102
9	334.91840	9	365.98690	9	397.05540	9	428.12390	9	459.19239
540	335.53977	590	366.60827	640	397.67677	690	428.74527	740	459.81376
1	336.16114	1	367.22964	1	398.29814	1	429.36664	1	460.43513
2	336.78251	2	367.85101	2	398.91951	2	429.98801	2	461.05650
3	337.40388	3	368.47238	3	399.54088	3	430.60937	3	461.67787
4	338.02525	4	369.09375	4	400.16225	4	431.23074	4	462.29924
5	338.64662	5	369.71512	5	400.78362	5	431.85211	5	462.52061
6	339.26799	6	370.33649	6	401.40499	6	432.47348	6	463.54198
7	339.88936	7	370.95786	7	402.02636	7	433.09485	7	464.16335
8	340.51073	8	371.57923	8	402.64773	8	433.71622	8	464.78472
9	341.13210	9	372.20060	9	403.26910	9	434.33759	9	465.40609

LENGTH—KILOMETRES TO MILES

[Reduction factor: 1 kilometre = 0.6213699495 mile]

Kilo-metres	Miles	Kilo-metres	Miles	Kilo-metres	Miles	Kilo-metres	Miles	Kilo-metres	Miles
750	466.02746	800	497.09596	850	528.16446	900	559.23295	950	590.30145
1	466.64883	1	497.71733	1	528.78583	1	559.85432	1	590.92282
2	467.27020	2	498.33870	2	529.40720	2	560.47569	2	591.54419
3	467.89157	3	498.96007	3	530.02857	3	561.09706	3	592.16556
4	468.51294	4	499.58144	4	530.64994	4	561.71843	4	592.78693
5	469.13431	5	500.20281	5	531.27131	5	562.33980	5	593.40830
6	469.75568	6	500.82418	6	531.89268	6	562.96117	6	594.02967
7	470.37705	7	501.44555	7	532.51405	7	563.58254	7	594.65104
8	470.99842	8	502.06692	8	533.13542	8	564.20391	8	595.27241
9	471.61979	9	502.68829	9	533.75679	9	564.82528	9	595.89378
760	472.24116	810	503.30966	860	534.37816	910	565.44665	960	596.51515
1	472.86253	1	503.93103	1	534.99953	1	566.06802	1	597.13652
2	473.48390	2	504.55240	2	535.62090	2	566.68939	2	597.75789
3	474.10527	3	505.17377	3	536.24227	3	567.31076	3	598.37926
4	474.72664	4	505.79514	4	536.86364	4	567.93213	4	599.00063
5	475.34801	5	506.41651	5	537.48501	5	568.55350	5	599.62200
6	475.96938	6	507.03788	6	538.10638	6	569.17487	6	600.24337
7	476.59075	7	507.65925	7	538.72775	7	569.79624	7	600.86474
8	477.21212	8	508.28062	8	539.34912	8	570.41761	8	601.48611
9	477.83349	9	508.90199	9	539.97049	9	571.03898	9	602.10748
770	478.45486	820	509.52336	870	540.59186	920	571.66035	970	602.72885
1	479.07623	1	510.14473	1	541.21323	1	572.28172	1	603.35022
2	479.69760	2	510.76610	2	541.83460	2	572.90309	2	603.97159
3	480.31897	3	511.38747	3	542.45597	3	573.52446	3	604.59296
4	480.94034	4	512.00884	4	543.07734	4	574.14583	4	605.21433
5	481.56171	5	512.63021	5	543.69871	5	574.76720	5	605.83570
6	482.18308	6	513.25158	6	544.32008	6	575.38857	6	606.45707
7	482.80445	7	513.87295	7	544.94145	7	576.00994	7	607.07844
8	483.42582	8	514.49432	8	545.56282	8	576.63131	8	607.69981
9	484.04719	9	515.11569	9	546.18419	9	577.25268	9	608.32118
780	484.66856	830	515.73706	880	546.80556	930	577.87405	980	608.94255
1	485.28993	1	516.35843	1	547.42693	1	578.49542	1	609.56392
2	485.91130	2	516.97980	2	548.04830	2	579.11679	2	610.18529
3	486.53267	3	517.60117	3	548.66967	3	579.73816	3	610.80666
4	487.15404	4	518.22254	4	549.29104	4	580.35953	4	611.42803
5	487.77541	5	518.84391	5	549.91241	5	580.98090	5	612.04940
6	488.39678	6	519.46528	6	550.53378	6	581.60227	6	612.67077
7	489.01815	7	520.08665	7	551.15515	7	582.22364	7	613.29214
8	489.63952	8	520.70802	8	551.77652	8	582.84501	8	613.91351
9	490.26089	9	521.32939	9	552.39789	9	583.46638	9	614.53488
790	490.88226	840	521.95076	890	553.01926	940	584.08775	990	615.15625
1	491.50363	1	522.57213	1	553.64062	1	584.70912	1	615.77762
2	492.12500	2	523.19350	2	554.26199	2	585.33049	2	616.39899
3	492.74637	3	523.81487	3	554.88336	3	585.95186	3	617.02036
4	493.36774	4	524.43624	4	555.50473	4	586.57323	4	617.64173
5	493.98911	5	525.05761	5	556.12610	5	587.19460	5	618.26310
6	494.61048	6	525.67898	6	556.74747	6	587.81597	6	618.88447
7	495.23185	7	526.30035	7	557.36884	7	588.43734	7	619.50584
8	495.85322	8	526.92172	8	557.99021	8	589.05871	8	620.12721
9	496.47459	9	527.54309	9	558.61158	9	589.68008	9	620.74858

LENGTH—MILES TO KILOMETRES

[Reduction factor: 1 mile = 1.609347219 kilometres]

Miles	Kilo-metres	Miles	Kilo-metres	Miles	Kilo-metres	Miles	Kilo-metres	Miles	Kilo-metres
0		50	80.4674	100	160.9347	150	241.4021	200	321.8694
1	1.6093	1	82.0767	1	162.5441	1	243.0114	1	323.4788
2	3.2187	2	83.6861	2	164.1534	2	244.6208	2	325.0881
3	4.8280	3	85.2954	3	165.7628	3	246.2301	3	326.6975
4	6.4374	4	86.9047	4	167.3721	4	247.8395	4	328.3068
5	8.0467	5	88.5141	5	168.9815	5	249.4488	5	329.9162
6	9.6561	6	90.1234	6	170.5908	6	251.0582	6	331.5255
7	11.2654	7	91.7328	7	172.2002	7	252.6675	7	333.1349
8	12.8748	8	93.3421	8	173.8095	8	254.2769	8	334.7442
9	14.4841	9	94.9515	9	175.4188	9	255.8862	9	336.3536
10	16.0935	60	96.5608	110	177.0282	160	257.4956	210	337.9629
1	17.7028	1	98.1702	1	178.6375	1	259.1049	1	339.5723
2	19.3122	2	99.7795	2	180.2469	2	260.7142	2	341.1816
3	20.9215	3	101.3889	3	181.8562	3	262.3236	3	342.7910
4	22.5309	4	102.9982	4	183.4656	4	263.9329	4	344.4003
5	24.1402	5	104.6076	5	185.0749	5	265.5423	5	346.0097
6	25.7496	6	106.2169	6	186.6843	6	267.1516	6	347.6190
7	27.3589	7	107.8263	7	188.2936	7	268.7610	7	349.2283
8	28.9682	8	109.4356	8	189.9030	8	270.3703	8	350.8377
9	30.5776	9	111.0450	9	191.5123	9	271.9797	9	352.4470
20	32.1869	70	112.6543	120	193.1217	170	273.5890	220	354.0564
1	33.7963	1	114.2637	1	194.7310	1	275.1984	1	355.6657
2	35.4056	2	115.8730	2	196.3404	2	276.8077	2	357.2751
3	37.0150	3	117.4823	3	197.9497	3	278.4171	3	358.8844
4	38.6243	4	119.0917	4	199.5591	4	280.0264	4	360.4938
5	40.2337	5	120.7010	5	201.1684	5	281.6358	5	362.1031
6	41.8430	6	122.3104	6	202.7777	6	283.2451	6	363.7125
7	43.4524	7	123.9197	7	204.3871	7	284.8545	7	365.3218
8	45.0617	8	125.5291	8	205.9954	8	286.4638	8	366.9312
9	46.6711	9	127.1384	9	207.6058	9	288.0732	9	368.5405
30	48.2804	80	128.7478	130	209.2151	180	289.6825	230	370.1499
1	49.8898	1	130.3571	1	210.8245	1	291.2918	1	371.7592
2	51.4991	2	131.9665	2	212.4338	2	292.9012	2	373.3686
3	53.1085	3	133.5758	3	214.0432	3	294.5105	3	374.9779
4	54.7178	4	135.1852	4	215.6525	4	296.1199	4	376.5872
5	56.3272	5	136.7945	5	217.2619	5	297.7292	5	378.1966
6	57.9365	6	138.4039	6	218.8712	6	299.3386	6	379.8059
7	59.5458	7	140.0132	7	220.4806	7	300.9479	7	381.4153
8	61.1552	8	141.6226	8	222.0899	8	302.5573	8	383.0246
9	62.7645	9	143.2319	9	223.6993	9	304.1666	9	384.6340
40	64.3739	90	144.8412	140	225.3086	190	305.7760	240	386.2433
1	65.9832	1	146.4506	1	226.9180	1	307.3853	1	387.8527
2	67.5926	2	148.0599	2	228.5273	2	308.9947	2	389.4620
3	69.2019	3	149.6693	3	230.1366	3	310.6040	3	391.0714
4	70.8113	4	151.2786	4	231.7460	4	312.2134	4	392.6807
5	72.4206	5	152.8880	5	233.3553	5	313.8227	5	394.2901
6	74.0300	6	154.4973	6	234.9647	6	315.4321	6	395.8994
7	75.6393	7	156.1067	7	236.5740	7	317.0414	7	397.5088
8	77.2487	8	157.7160	8	238.1834	8	318.6507	8	399.1181
9	78.8580	9	159.3254	9	239.7927	9	320.2601	9	400.7275

LENGTH—MILES TO KILOMETRES

[Reduction factor: 1 mile = 1.609347219 kilometres]

Miles	Kilo-metres	Miles	Kilo-metres	Miles	Kilo-metres	Miles	Kilo-metres	Miles	Kilo-metres
250	402.3368	300	482.8042	350	563.2715	400	643.7389	450	724.2062
1	403.9461	1	484.4135	1	564.8809	1	645.3482	1	725.8156
2	405.5555	2	486.0229	2	566.4902	2	646.9576	2	727.4249
3	407.1648	3	487.6322	3	568.0996	3	648.5669	3	729.0343
4	408.7742	4	489.2416	4	569.7089	4	650.1763	4	730.6436
5	410.3835	5	490.8509	5	571.3183	5	651.7856	5	732.2530
6	411.9929	6	492.4602	6	572.9276	6	653.3950	6	733.8623
7	413.6022	7	494.0696	7	574.5370	7	655.0043	7	735.4717
8	415.2116	8	495.6789	8	576.1463	8	656.6137	8	737.0810
9	416.8209	9	497.2883	9	577.7557	9	658.2230	9	738.6904
260	418.4303	310	498.8976	360	579.3650	410	659.8824	460	740.2997
1	420.0396	1	500.5070	1	580.9743	1	661.4417	1	741.9091
2	421.6490	2	502.1163	2	582.5837	2	663.0511	2	743.5184
3	423.2583	3	503.7257	3	584.1930	3	664.6604	3	745.1278
4	424.8677	4	505.3350	4	585.8024	4	666.2697	4	746.7371
5	426.4770	5	506.9444	5	587.4117	5	667.8791	5	748.3465
6	428.0864	6	508.5537	6	589.0211	6	669.4884	6	749.9558
7	429.6957	7	510.1631	7	590.6304	7	671.0978	7	751.5652
8	431.3051	8	511.7724	8	592.2398	8	672.7071	8	753.1745
9	432.9144	9	513.3818	9	593.8491	9	674.3165	9	754.7838
270	434.5237	320	514.9911	370	595.4585	420	675.9258	470	756.3932
1	436.1331	1	516.6005	1	597.0678	1	677.5352	1	758.0025
2	437.7424	2	518.2098	2	598.6772	2	679.1445	2	759.6119
3	439.3518	3	519.8192	3	600.2865	3	680.7539	3	761.2212
4	440.9611	4	521.4285	4	601.8959	4	682.3632	4	762.8306
5	442.5705	5	523.0378	5	603.5052	5	683.9726	5	764.4399
6	444.1798	6	524.6472	6	605.1145	6	685.5819	6	766.0493
7	445.7892	7	526.2565	7	606.7239	7	687.1913	7	767.6586
8	447.3985	8	527.8659	8	608.3332	8	688.8006	8	769.2680
9	449.0079	9	529.4752	9	609.9426	9	690.4100	9	770.8773
280	450.6172	330	531.0846	380	611.5519	430	692.0193	480	772.4867
1	452.2266	1	532.6939	1	613.1613	1	693.6287	1	774.0960
2	453.8359	2	534.3033	2	614.7706	2	695.2380	2	775.7054
3	455.4453	3	535.9126	3	616.3800	3	696.8473	3	777.3147
4	457.0546	4	537.5220	4	617.9893	4	698.4567	4	778.9241
5	458.6640	5	539.1313	5	619.5987	5	700.0660	5	780.5334
6	460.2733	6	540.7407	6	621.2080	6	701.6754	6	782.1427
7	461.8827	7	542.3500	7	622.8174	7	703.2847	7	783.7521
8	463.4920	8	543.9594	8	624.4267	8	704.8941	8	785.3614
9	465.1013	9	545.5687	9	626.0361	9	706.5034	9	786.9708
290	466.7107	340	547.1781	390	627.6454	440	708.1128	490	788.5801
1	468.3200	1	548.7874	1	629.2548	1	709.7221	1	790.1895
2	469.9294	2	550.3967	2	630.8641	2	711.3315	2	791.7988
3	471.5387	3	552.0061	3	632.4735	3	712.9408	3	793.4082
4	473.1481	4	553.6154	4	634.0828	4	714.5502	4	795.0175
5	474.7574	5	555.2248	5	635.6922	5	716.1595	5	796.6269
6	476.3668	6	556.8341	6	637.3015	6	717.7689	6	798.2362
7	477.9761	7	558.4435	7	638.9108	7	719.3782	7	799.8456
8	479.5855	8	560.0528	8	640.5202	8	720.9876	8	801.4549
9	481.1948	9	561.6622	9	642.1295	9	722.5969	9	803.0643

LENGTH—MILES TO KILOMETRES

[Reduction factor: 1 mile = 1.609347219 kilometres]

Miles	Kilo-metres	Miles	Kilo-metres	Miles	Kilo-metres	Miles	Kilo-metres	Miles	Kilo-metres
500	804.6736	550	885.1410	600	965.6083	650	1,046.0757	700	1,126.5431
1	806.2830	1	886.7503	1	967.2177	1	1,047.6850	1	1,128.1524
2	807.8923	2	888.3597	2	968.8270	2	1,049.2944	2	1,129.7617
3	809.5017	3	889.9690	3	970.4364	3	1,050.9037	3	1,131.3711
4	811.1110	4	891.5784	4	972.0457	4	1,052.5131	4	1,132.9804
5	812.7203	5	893.1877	5	973.6551	5	1,054.1224	5	1,134.5898
6	814.3297	6	894.7971	6	975.2644	6	1,055.7318	6	1,136.1991
7	815.9390	7	896.4064	7	976.8738	7	1,057.3411	7	1,137.8085
8	817.5484	8	898.0157	8	978.4831	8	1,058.9505	8	1,139.4178
9	819.1577	9	899.6251	9	980.0925	9	1,060.5598	9	1,141.0272
510	820.7671	560	901.2344	610	981.7018	660	1,062.1692	710	1,142.6365
1	822.3764	1	902.8438	1	983.3112	1	1,063.7785	1	1,144.2459
2	823.9858	2	904.4531	2	984.9205	2	1,065.3879	2	1,145.8552
3	825.5951	3	906.0625	3	986.5298	3	1,066.9972	3	1,147.4646
4	827.2045	4	907.6718	4	988.1392	4	1,068.6066	4	1,149.0739
5	828.8138	5	909.2812	5	989.7485	5	1,070.2159	5	1,150.6833
6	830.4232	6	910.8905	6	991.3579	6	1,071.8252	6	1,152.2926
7	832.0325	7	912.4999	7	992.9672	7	1,073.4346	7	1,153.9020
8	833.6419	8	914.1092	8	994.5766	8	1,075.0439	8	1,155.5113
9	835.2512	9	915.7186	9	996.1859	9	1,076.6533	9	1,157.1207
520	836.8606	570	917.3279	620	997.7953	670	1,078.2626	720	1,158.7300
1	838.4699	1	918.9373	1	999.4046	1	1,079.8720	1	1,160.3393
2	840.0792	2	920.5466	2	1,001.0140	2	1,081.4813	2	1,161.9487
3	841.6886	3	922.1560	3	1,002.6233	3	1,083.0907	3	1,163.5580
4	843.2979	4	923.7653	4	1,004.2327	4	1,084.7000	4	1,165.1674
5	844.9073	5	925.3747	5	1,005.8420	5	1,086.3094	5	1,166.7767
6	846.5166	6	926.9840	6	1,007.4514	6	1,087.9187	6	1,168.3861
7	848.1260	7	928.5933	7	1,009.0607	7	1,089.5281	7	1,169.9954
8	849.7353	8	930.2027	8	1,010.6701	8	1,091.1374	8	1,171.6048
9	851.3447	9	931.8120	9	1,012.2794	9	1,092.7468	9	1,173.2141
530	852.9540	580	933.4214	630	1,013.8887	680	1,094.3561	730	1,174.8235
1	854.5634	1	935.0307	1	1,015.4981	1	1,095.9655	1	1,176.4328
2	856.1727	2	936.6401	2	1,017.1074	2	1,097.5748	2	1,178.0422
3	857.7821	3	938.2494	3	1,018.7168	3	1,099.1842	3	1,179.6515
4	859.3914	4	939.8588	4	1,020.3261	4	1,100.7935	4	1,181.2609
5	861.0008	5	941.4681	5	1,021.9355	5	1,102.4028	5	1,182.8702
6	862.6101	6	943.0775	6	1,023.5448	6	1,104.0122	6	1,184.4796
7	864.2195	7	944.6868	7	1,025.1542	7	1,105.6215	7	1,186.0889
8	865.8288	8	946.2962	8	1,026.7635	8	1,107.2309	8	1,187.6982
9	867.4382	9	947.9055	9	1,028.3729	9	1,108.8402	9	1,189.3076
540	869.0475	590	949.5149	640	1,029.9822	690	1,110.4496	740	1,190.9169
1	870.6568	1	951.1242	1	1,031.5916	1	1,112.0589	1	1,192.5263
2	872.2662	2	952.7336	2	1,033.2009	2	1,113.6683	2	1,194.1356
3	873.8755	3	954.3429	3	1,034.8103	3	1,115.2776	3	1,195.7450
4	875.4849	4	955.9522	4	1,036.4196	4	1,116.8870	4	1,197.3543
5	877.0942	5	957.5616	5	1,038.0290	5	1,118.4963	5	1,198.9637
6	878.7036	6	959.1709	6	1,039.6383	6	1,120.1057	6	1,200.5730
7	880.3129	7	960.7803	7	1,041.2477	7	1,121.7150	7	1,202.1824
8	881.9223	8	962.3896	8	1,042.8570	8	1,123.3244	8	1,203.7917
9	883.5316	9	963.9990	9	1,044.4663	9	1,124.9337	9	1,205.4011

LENGTH—MILES TO KILOMETRES

[Reduction factor: 1 mile = 1.609347219 kilometres]

Miles	Kilo-metres	Miles	Kilo-metres	Miles	Kilo-metres	Miles	Kilo-metres	Miles	Kilo-metres
750	1,207.0104	800	1,287.4778	850	1,367.9451	900	1,448.4125	950	1,528.8799
1	1,208.6198	1	1,289.0871	1	1,369.5545	1	1,450.0218	1	1,530.4892
2	1,210.2291	2	1,290.6965	2	1,371.1638	2	1,451.6312	2	1,532.0986
3	1,211.8385	3	1,292.3058	3	1,372.7732	3	1,453.2405	3	1,533.7079
4	1,213.4478	4	1,293.9152	4	1,374.3825	4	1,454.8499	4	1,535.3172
5	1,215.0572	5	1,295.5245	5	1,375.9919	5	1,456.4592	5	1,536.9266
6	1,216.6665	6	1,297.1339	6	1,377.6012	6	1,458.0686	6	1,538.5359
7	1,218.2758	7	1,298.7432	7	1,379.2106	7	1,459.6779	7	1,540.1453
8	1,219.8852	8	1,300.3526	8	1,380.8199	8	1,461.2873	8	1,541.7546
9	1,221.4945	9	1,301.9619	9	1,382.4293	9	1,462.8966	9	1,543.3640
760	1,223.1039	810	1,303.5712	860	1,384.0386	910	1,464.5060	960	1,544.9733
1	1,224.7132	1	1,305.1806	1	1,385.6480	1	1,466.1153	1	1,546.5827
2	1,226.3226	2	1,306.7899	2	1,387.2573	2	1,467.7247	2	1,548.1920
3	1,227.9319	3	1,308.3993	3	1,388.8666	3	1,469.3340	3	1,549.8014
4	1,229.5413	4	1,310.0086	4	1,390.4760	4	1,470.9434	4	1,551.4107
5	1,231.1506	5	1,311.6180	5	1,392.0853	5	1,472.5527	5	1,553.0201
6	1,232.7600	6	1,313.2273	6	1,393.6947	6	1,474.1621	6	1,554.6294
7	1,234.3693	7	1,314.8367	7	1,395.3040	7	1,475.7714	7	1,556.2388
8	1,235.9787	8	1,316.4460	8	1,396.9134	8	1,477.3807	8	1,557.8481
9	1,237.5880	9	1,318.0554	9	1,398.5227	9	1,478.9901	9	1,559.4575
770	1,239.1974	820	1,319.6647	870	1,400.1321	920	1,480.5994	970	1,561.0668
1	1,240.8067	1	1,321.2741	1	1,401.7414	1	1,482.2088	1	1,562.6761
2	1,242.4161	2	1,322.8834	2	1,403.3508	2	1,483.8181	2	1,564.2855
3	1,244.0254	3	1,324.4928	3	1,404.9601	3	1,485.4275	3	1,565.8948
4	1,245.6347	4	1,326.1021	4	1,406.5695	4	1,487.0368	4	1,567.5042
5	1,247.2441	5	1,327.7115	5	1,408.1788	5	1,488.6462	5	1,569.1135
6	1,248.8534	6	1,329.3208	6	1,409.7882	6	1,490.2555	6	1,570.7229
7	1,250.4628	7	1,330.9301	7	1,411.3975	7	1,491.8649	7	1,572.3322
8	1,252.0721	8	1,332.5395	8	1,413.0069	8	1,493.4742	8	1,573.9416
9	1,253.6815	9	1,334.1488	9	1,414.6162	9	1,495.0836	9	1,575.5509
780	1,255.2908	830	1,335.7582	880	1,416.2256	930	1,496.6929	980	1,577.1603
1	1,256.9002	1	1,337.3675	1	1,417.8349	1	1,498.3023	1	1,578.7696
2	1,258.5095	2	1,338.9769	2	1,419.4442	2	1,499.9116	2	1,580.3790
3	1,260.1189	3	1,340.5862	3	1,421.0536	3	1,501.5210	3	1,581.9883
4	1,261.7282	4	1,342.1956	4	1,422.6629	4	1,503.1303	4	1,583.5977
5	1,263.3376	5	1,343.8049	5	1,424.2723	5	1,504.7396	5	1,585.2070
6	1,264.9469	6	1,345.4143	6	1,425.8816	6	1,506.3490	6	1,586.8164
7	1,266.5563	7	1,347.0236	7	1,427.4910	7	1,507.9583	7	1,588.4257
8	1,268.1656	8	1,348.6330	8	1,429.1003	8	1,509.5677	8	1,590.0351
9	1,269.7750	9	1,350.2423	9	1,430.7097	9	1,511.1770	9	1,591.6444
790	1,271.3843	840	1,351.8517	890	1,432.3190	940	1,512.7864	990	1,593.2537
1	1,272.9936	1	1,353.4610	1	1,433.9284	1	1,514.3957	1	1,594.8631
2	1,274.6030	2	1,355.0704	2	1,435.5377	2	1,516.0051	2	1,596.4724
3	1,276.2123	3	1,356.6797	3	1,437.1471	3	1,517.6144	3	1 598.0818
4	1,277.8217	4	1,358.2891	4	1,438.7564	4	1,519.2238	4	1,599.6911
5	1,279.4310	5	1,359.8984	5	1,440.3658	5	1,520.8331	5	1,601.3005
6	1,281.0404	6	1,361.5077	6	1,441.9751	6	1,522.4425	6	1,602.9098
7	1,282.6497	7	1,363.1171	7	1,443.5845	7	1,524.0518	7	1,604.5192
8	1,284.2591	8	1,364.7264	8	1,445.1938	8	1,525.6612	8	1,606.1285
9	1,285.8684	9	1,366.3358	9	1,446.8031	9	1,527.2705	9	1,607.7379

AREA—HECTARES TO ACRES

[Reduction factor: 1 hectare = 2.471043930 acres]

Hectares	Acres	Hectares	Acres	Hectares	Acres	Hectares	Acres	Hectares	Acres
0		50	123.55220	100	247.10439	150	370.65659	200	494.20879
1	2.47104	1	126.02324	1	249.57544	1	373.12763	1	496.67983
2	4.94209	2	128.49428	2	252.04648	2	375.59868	2	499.15087
3	7.41313	3	130.96533	3	254.51752	3	378.06972	3	501.62192
4	9.88418	4	133.43637	4	256.98857	4	380.54077	4	504.09296
5	12.35522	5	135.90742	5	259.45961	5	383.01181	5	506.56401
6	14.82626	6	138.37846	6	261.93066	6	385.48285	6	509.03505
7	17.29731	7	140.84950	7	264.40170	7	387.95390	7	511.50609
8	19.76835	8	143.32055	8	266.87274	8	390.42494	8	513.97714
9	22.23940	9	145.79159	9	269.34379	9	392.89598	9	516.44818
10	24.71044	60	148.26264	110	271.81483	160	395.36703	210	518.91923
1	27.18148	1	150.73368	1	274.28588	1	397.83807	1	521.39027
2	29.65253	2	153.20472	2	276.75692	2	400.30912	2	523.86131
3	32.12357	3	155.67577	3	279.22796	3	402.78016	3	526.33236
4	34.59462	4	158.14681	4	281.69901	4	405.25120	4	528.80340
5	37.06566	5	160.61786	5	284.17005	5	407.72225	5	531.27444
6	39.53670	6	163.08890	6	286.64110	6	410.19329	6	533.74549
7	42.00775	7	165.55994	7	289.11214	7	412.66434	7	536.21653
8	44.47879	8	168.03099	8	291.58318	8	415.13538	8	538.68758
9	46.94983	9	170.50203	9	294.05423	9	417.60642	9	541.15862
20	49.42088	70	172.97308	120	296.52527	170	420.07747	220	543.62966
1	51.89192	1	175.44412	1	298.99632	1	422.54851	1	546.10071
2	54.36297	2	177.91516	2	301.46736	2	425.01956	2	548.57175
3	56.83401	3	180.38621	3	303.93840	3	427.49060	3	551.04280
4	59.30505	4	182.85725	4	306.40945	4	429.96164	4	553.51384
5	61.77610	5	185.32829	5	308.88049	5	432.43269	5	555.98488
6	64.24714	6	187.79934	6	311.35154	6	434.90373	6	558.45593
7	66.71819	7	190.27038	7	313.82258	7	437.37478	7	560.92697
8	69.18923	8	192.74143	8	316.29362	8	439.84582	8	563.39802
9	71.66027	9	195.21247	9	318.76467	9	442.31686	9	565.86906
30	74.13132	80	197.68351	130	321.23571	180	444.78791	230	568.34010
1	76.60236	1	200.15456	1	323.70675	1	447.25895	1	570.81115
2	79.07341	2	202.62560	2	326.17780	2	449.73000	2	573.28219
3	81.54445	3	205.09665	3	328.64884	3	452.20104	3	575.75324
4	84.01549	4	207.56769	4	331.11989	4	454.67208	4	578.22428
5	86.48654	5	210.03873	5	333.59093	5	457.14313	5	580.69532
6	88.95758	6	212.50978	6	336.06197	6	459.61417	6	583.16637
7	91.42863	7	214.98082	7	338.53302	7	462.08521	7	585.63741
8	93.89967	8	217.45187	8	341.00406	8	464.55626	8	588.10846
9	96.37071	9	219.92291	9	343.47511	9	467.02730	9	590.57950
40	98.84176	90	222.39395	140	345.94615	190	469.49835	240	593.05054
1	101.31280	1	224.86500	1	348.41719	1	471.96939	1	595.52159
2	103.78385	2	227.33604	2	350.88824	2	474.44043	2	597.99263
3	106.25489	3	229.80709	3	353.35928	3	476.91148	3	600.46367
4	108.72593	4	232.27813	4	355.83033	4	479.38252	4	602.93472
5	111.19698	5	234.74917	5	358.30137	5	481.85357	5	605.40576
6	113.66802	6	237.22022	6	360.77241	6	484.32461	6	607.87681
7	116.13906	7	239.69126	7	363.24346	7	486.79565	7	610.34785
8	118.61011	8	242.16231	8	365.71450	8	489.26670	8	612.81889
9	121.08115	9	244.63335	9	368.18555	9	491.73774	9	615.28994

AREA—HECTARES TO ACRES

[Reduction factor: 1 hectare = 2.471043930 acres]

Hectares	Acres	Hectares	Acres	Hectares	Acres	Hectares	Acres	Hectares	Acres
250	617.76098	300	741.31318	350	864.86538	400	988.41757	450	1,111.96977
1	620.23203	1	743.78422	1	867.33642	1	990.88862	1	1,114.44081
2	622.70307	2	746.25527	2	869.80746	2	993.35966	2	1,116.91186
3	625.17411	3	748.72631	3	872.27851	3	995.83070	3	1,119.38290
4	627.64516	4	751.19735	4	874.74955	4	998.30175	4	1,121.85394
5	630.11620	5	753.66840	5	877.22060	5	1,000.77279	5	1,124.32499
6	632.58725	6	756.13944	6	879.69164	6	1,003.24384	6	1,126.79603
7	635.05829	7	758.61049	7	882.16268	7	1,005.71488	7	1,129.26708
8	637.52933	8	761.08153	8	884.63373	8	1,008.18592	8	1,131.73812
9	640.00038	9	763.55257	9	887.10477	9	1,010.65697	9	1,134.20916
260	642.47142	310	766.02362	360	889.57581	410	1,013.12801	460	1,136.68021
1	644.94247	1	768.49466	1	892.04686	1	1,015.59906	1	1,139.15125
2	647.41351	2	770.96571	2	894.51790	2	1,018.07010	2	1,141.62230
3	649.88455	3	773.43675	3	896.98895	3	1,020.54114	3	1,144.09334
4	652.35560	4	775.90779	4	899.45999	4	1,023.01219	4	1,146.56438
5	654.82664	5	778.37884	5	901.93103	5	1,025.48323	5	1,149.03543
6	657.29769	6	780.84988	6	904.40208	6	1,027.95427	6	1,151.50647
7	659.76873	7	783.32093	7	906.87312	7	1,030.42532	7	1,153.97752
8	662.23977	8	785.79197	8	909.34417	8	1,032.89636	8	1,156.44856
9	664.71082	9	788.26301	9	911.81521	9	1,035.36741	9	1,158.91960
270	667.18186	320	790.73406	370	914.28625	420	1,037.83845	470	1,161.39065
1	669.65291	1	793.20510	1	916.75730	1	1,040.30949	1	1,163.86169
2	672.12395	2	795.67615	2	919.22834	2	1,042.78054	2	1,166.33273
3	674.59499	3	798.14719	3	921.69939	3	1,045.25158	3	1,168.80378
4	677.06604	4	800.61823	4	924.17043	4	1,047.72263	4	1,171.27482
5	679.53708	5	803.08928	5	926.64147	5	1,050.19367	5	1,173.74587
6	682.00812	6	805.56032	6	929.11252	6	1,052.66471	6	1,176.21691
7	684.47917	7	808.03137	7	931.58356	7	1,055.13576	7	1,178.68795
8	686.95021	8	810.50241	8	934.05461	8	1,057.60680	8	1,181.15900
9	689.42126	9	812.97345	9	936.52565	9	1,060.07785	9	1,183.63004
280	691.89230	330	815.44450	380	938.99669	430	1,062.54889	480	1,186.10109
1	694.36334	1	817.91554	1	941.46774	1	1,065.01993	1	1,188.57213
2	696.83439	2	820.38658	2	943.93878	2	1,067.49098	2	1,191.04317
3	699.30543	3	822.85763	3	946.40983	3	1,069.96202	3	1,193.51422
4	701.77648	4	825.32867	4	948.88087	4	1,072.43307	4	1,195.98526
5	704.24752	5	827.79972	5	951.35191	5	1,074.90411	5	1,198.45631
6	706.71856	6	830.27076	6	953.82296	6	1,077.37515	6	1,200.92735
7	709.18961	7	832.74180	7	956.29400	7	1,079.84620	7	1,203.39839
8	711.66065	8	835.21285	8	958.76504	8	1,082.31724	8	1,205.86944
9	714.13170	9	837.68389	9	961.23609	9	1,084.78829	9	1,208.34048
290	716.60274	340	840.15494	390	963.70713	440	1,087.25933	490	1,210.81153
1	719.07378	1	842.62598	1	966.17818	1	1,089.73037	1	1,213.28257
2	721.54483	2	845.09702	2	968.64922	2	1,092.20142	2	1,215.75361
3	724.01587	3	847.56807	3	971.12026	3	1,094.67246	3	1,218.22466
4	726.48692	4	850.03911	4	973.59131	4	1,097.14350	4	1,220.69570
5	728.95796	5	852.51016	5	976.06235	5	1,099.61455	5	1,223.16675
6	731.42900	6	854.98120	6	978.53340	6	1,102.08559	6	1,225.63779
7	733.90005	7	857.45224	7	981.00444	7	1,104.55664	7	1,228.10883
8	736.37109	8	859.92329	8	983.47548	8	1,107.02768	8	1,230.57988
9	738.84214	9	862.39433	9	985.94653	9	1,109.49872	9	1,233.05092

THE METRIC ENCYCLOPEDIA

AREA—HECTARES TO ACRES

[Reduction factor: 1 hectare = 2.471043930 acres]

Hectares	Acres	Hectares	Acres	Hectares	Acres	Hectares	Acres	Hectares	Acres
500	1,235.52197	550	1,359.07416	600	1,482.62636	650	1,606.17855	700	1,729.73075
1	1,237.99301	1	1,361.54521	1	1,485.09740	1	1,608.64960	1	1,732.20180
2	1,240.46405	2	1,364.01625	2	1,487.56845	2	1,611.12064	2	1,734.67284
3	1,242.93510	3	1,366.48729	3	1,490.03949	3	1,613.59169	3	1,737.14388
4	1,245.40614	4	1,368.95834	4	1,492.51053	4	1,616.06273	4	1,739.61493
5	1,247.87718	5	1,371.42938	5	1,494.98158	5	1,618.53377	5	1,742.08597
6	1,250.34823	6	1,373.90043	6	1,497.45262	6	1,621.00482	6	1,744.55701
7	1,252.81927	7	1,376.37147	7	1,499.92367	7	1,623.47586	7	1,747.02806
8	1,255.29032	8	1,378.84251	8	1,502.39471	8	1,625.94691	8	1,749.49910
9	1,257.76136	9	1,381.31356	9	1,504.86575	9	1,628.41795	9	1,751.97015
510	1,260.23240	560	1,383.78460	610	1,507.33680	660	1,630.88899	710	1,754.44119
1	1,262.70345	1	1,386.25564	1	1,509.80784	1	1,633.36004	1	1,756.91223
2	1,265.17449	2	1,388.72669	2	1,512.27889	2	1,635.83108	2	1,759.38328
3	1,267.64554	3	1,391.19773	3	1,514.74993	3	1,638.30213	3	1,761.85432
4	1,270.11658	4	1,393.66878	4	1,517.22097	4	1,640.77317	4	1,764.32537
5	1,272.58762	5	1,396.13982	5	1,519.69202	5	1,643.24421	5	1,766.79641
6	1,275.05867	6	1,398.61086	6	1,522.16306	6	1,645.71526	6	1,769.26745
7	1,277.52971	7	1,401.08191	7	1,524.63411	7	1,648.18630	7	1,771.73850
8	1,280.00076	8	1,403.55295	8	1,527.10515	8	1,650.65735	8	1,774.20954
9	1,282.47180	9	1,406.02400	9	1,529.57619	9	1,653.12839	9	1,776.68059
520	1,284.94284	570	1,408.49504	620	1,532.04724	670	1,655.59943	720	1,779.15163
1	1,287.41389	1	1,410.96608	1	1,534.51828	1	1,658.07048	1	1,781.62267
2	1,289.88493	2	1,413.43713	2	1,536.98932	2	1,660.54152	2	1,784.09372
3	1,292.35598	3	1,415.90817	3	1,539.46037	3	1,663.01257	3	1,786.56476
4	1,294.82702	4	1,418.37922	4	1,541.93141	4	1,665.48361	4	1,789.03581
5	1,297.29806	5	1,420.85026	5	1,544.40246	5	1,667.95465	5	1,791.50685
6	1,299.76911	6	1,423.32130	6	1,546.87350	6	1,670.42570	6	1,793.97789
7	1,302.24015	7	1,425.79235	7	1,549.34454	7	1,672.89674	7	1,796.44894
8	1,304.71120	8	1,428.26339	8	1,551.81559	8	1,675.36778	8	1,798.91998
9	1,307.18224	9	1,430.73444	9	1,554.28663	9	1,677.83883	9	1,801.39103
530	1,309.65328	580	1,433.20548	630	1,556.75768	680	1,680.30987	730	1,803.86207
1	1,312.12433	1	1,435.67652	1	1,559.22872	1	1,682.78092	1	1,806.33311
2	1,314.59537	2	1,438.14757	2	1,561.69976	2	1,685.25196	2	1,808.80416
3	1,317.06641	3	1,440.61861	3	1,564.17081	3	1,687.72300	3	1,811.27520
4	1,319.53746	4	1,443.08966	4	1,566.64185	4	1,690.19405	4	1,813.74624
5	1,322.00850	5	1,445.56070	5	1,569.11290	5	1,692.66509	5	1,816.21729
6	1,324.47955	6	1,448.03174	6	1,571.58394	6	1,695.13614	6	1,818.68833
7	1,326.95059	7	1,450.50279	7	1,574.05498	7	1,697.60718	7	1,821.15938
8	1,329.42163	8	1,452.97383	8	1,576.52603	8	1,700.07822	8	1,823.63042
9	1,331.89268	9	1,455.44487	9	1,578.99707	9	1,702.54927	9	1,826.10146
540	1,334.36372	590	1,457.91592	640	1,581.46812	690	1,705.02031	740	1,828.57251
1	1,336.83477	1	1,460.38696	1	1,583.93916	1	1,707.49136	1	1,831.04355
2	1,339.30581	2	1,462.85801	2	1,586.41020	2	1,709.96240	2	1,833.51460
3	1,341.77685	3	1,465.32905	3	1,588.88125	3	1,712.43344	3	1,835.98564
4	1,344.24790	4	1,467.80009	4	1,591.35229	4	1,714.90449	4	1,838.45668
5	1,346.71894	5	1,470.27114	5	1,593.82334	5	1,717.37553	5	1,840.92773
6	1,349.18999	6	1,472.74218	6	1,596.29438	6	1,719.84658	6	1,843.39877
7	1,351.66103	7	1,475.21323	7	1,598.76542	7	1,722.31762	7	1,845.86982
8	1,354.13207	8	1,477.68427	8	1,601.23647	8	1,724.78866	8	1,848.34086
9	1,356.60312	9	1,480.15531	9	1,603.70751	9	1,727.25971	9	1,850.81190

AREA—HECTARES TO ACRES

[Reduction factor: 1 hectare = 2.471043930 acres]

Hectares	Acres	Hectares	Acres	Hectares	Acres	Hectares	Acres	Hectares	Acres
750	1,853.28295	800	1,976.83514	850	2,100.38734	900	2,223.93954	950	2,347.49173
1	1,855.75399	1	1,979.30619	1	2,102.85838	1	2,226.41058	1	2,349.96278
2	1,858.22504	2	1,981.77723	2	2,105.32943	2	2,228.88163	2	2,352.43382
3	1,860.69608	3	1,984.24828	3	2,107.80047	3	2,231.35267	3	2,354.90487
4	1,863.16712	4	1,986.71932	4	2,110.27152	4	2,233.82371	4	2,357.37591
5	1,865.63817	5	1,989.19036	5	2,112.74256	5	2,236.29476	5	2,359.84695
6	1,868.10921	6	1,991.66141	6	2,115.21360	6	2,238.76580	6	2,362.31800
7	1,870.58026	7	1,994.13245	7	2,117.68465	7	2,241.23684	7	2,364.78904
8	1,873.05130	8	1,996.60350	8	2,120.15569	8	2,243.70789	8	2,367.26009
9	1,875.52234	9	1,999.07454	9	2,122.62674	9	2,246.17893	9	2,369.73113
760	1,877.99339	810	2,001.54558	860	2,125.09778	910	2,248.64998	960	2,372.20217
1	1,880.46443	1	2,004.01663	1	2,127.56882	1	2,251.12102	1	7,374.67322
2	1,882.93547	2	2,006.48767	2	2,130.03987	2	2,253.59206	2	2,377.14426
3	1,885.40652	3	2,008.95872	3	2,132.51091	3	2,256.06311	3	2,379.61530
4	1,887.87756	4	2,011.42976	4	2,134.98196	4	2,258.53415	4	2,382.08635
5	1,890.34861	5	2,013.90080	5	2,137.45300	5	2,261.00520	5	2,384.55739
6	1,892.81965	6	2,016.37185	6	2,139.92404	6	2,263.47624	6	2,387.02844
7	1,895.29069	7	2,018.84289	7	2,142.39509	7	2,265.94728	7	2,389.49948
8	1,897.76174	8	2,021.31394	8	2,144.86613	8	2,268.41833	8	2,391.97052
9	1,900.23278	9	2,023.78498	9	2,147.33718	9	2,270.88937	9	2,394.44157
770	1,902.70383	820	2,026.25602	870	2,149.80822	920	2,273.36042	970	2,396.91261
1	1,905.17487	1	2,028.72707	1	2,152.27926	1	2,275.83146	1	2,399.38366
2	1,907.64591	2	2,031.19811	2	2,154.75031	2	2,278.30250	2	2,401.85470
3	1,910.11696	3	2,033.66915	3	2,157.22135	3	2,280.77355	3	2,404.32574
4	1,912.58800	4	2,036.14020	4	2,159.69240	4	2,283.24459	4	2,406.796/9
5	1,915.05905	5	2,038.61124	5	2,162.16344	5	2,285.71564	5	2,409.26783
6	1,917.53009	6	2,041.08229	6	2,164.63448	6	2,288.18668	6	2,411.73888
7	1,920.00113	7	2,043.55333	7	2,167.10553	7	2,290.65772	7	2,414.20992
8	1,922.47218	8	2,046.02437	8	2,169.57657	8	2,293.12877	8	2,416.68096
9	1,924.94322	9	2,048.49542	9	2,172.04761	9	2,295.59981	9	2,419.15201
780	1,927.41427	830	2,050.96646	880	2,174.51866	930	2,298.07086	980	2,421.62305
1	1,929.88531	1	2,053.43751	1	2,176.98970	1	2,300.54190	1	2,424.09410
2	1,932.35635	2	2,055.90855	2	2,179.46075	2	2,303.01294	2	2,426.56514
3	1,934.82740	3	2,058.37959	3	2,181.93179	3	2,305.48399	3	2,429.03618
4	1,937.29844	4	2,060.85064	4	2,184.40283	4	2,307.95503	4	2,431.50723
5	1,939.76949	5	2,063.32168	5	2,186.87388	5	2,310.42607	5	2,433.97827
6	1,942.24053	6	2,065.79273	6	2,189.34492	6	2,312.89712	6	2,436.44932
7	1,944.71157	7	2,068.26377	7	2,191.81597	7	2,315.36816	7	2,438.92036
8	1,947.18262	8	2,070.73481	8	2,194.28701	8	2,317.83921	8	2,441.39140
9	1,949.65366	9	2,073.20586	9	2,196.75805	9	2,320.31025	9	2,443.86245
790	1,952.12471	840	2,075.67690	890	2,199.22910	940	2,322.78129	990	2,446.33349
1	1,954.59575	1	2,078.14795	1	2,201.70014	1	2,325.25234	1	2,448.80454
2	1,957.06679	2	2,080.61899	2	2,204.17119	2	2,327.72338	2	2,451.27558
3	1,959.53784	3	2,083.09003	3	2,206.64223	3	2,330.19443	3	2,453.74662
4	1,962.00888	4	2,085.56108	4	2,209.11327	4	2,332.66547	4	2,456.21767
5	1,964.47992	5	2,088.03212	5	2,211.58432	5	2,335.13651	5	2,458.68871
6	1,966.95097	6	2,090.50317	6	2,214.05536	6	2,337.60756	6	2,461.15975
7	1,969.42201	7	2,092.97421	7	2,216.52641	7	2,340.07860	7	2,463.63080
8	1,971.89305	8	2,095.44525	8	2,218.99745	8	2,342.54965	8	2,466.10184
9	1,974.36410	9	2,097.91630	9	2,221.46849	9	2,345.02069	9	2,468.57289

THE METRIC ENCYCLOPEDIA

AREA—ACRES TO HECTARES

[Reduction factor: 1 acre = 0.4046872610 hectare]

Acres	Hectares	Acres	Hectares	Acres	Hectares	Acres	Hectares	Acres	Hectares
0		50	20.23436	100	40.46873	150	60.70309	200	80.93745
1	0.40469	1	20.63905	1	40.87341	1	61.10778	1	81.34214
2	0.80937	2	21.04374	2	41.27810	2	61.51246	2	81.74683
3	1.21406	3	21.44842	3	41.68279	3	61.91715	3	82.15151
4	1.61875	4	21.85311	4	42.08748	4	62.32184	4	82.55620
5	2.02344	5	22.25780	5	42.49216	5	62.72653	5	82.96089
6	2.42812	6	22.66249	6	42.89685	6	63.13121	6	83.36558
7	2.83281	7	23.06717	7	43.30154	7	63.53590	7	83.77026
8	3.23750	8	23.47186	8	43.70622	8	63.94059	8	84.17495
9	3.64219	9	23.87655	9	44.11091	9	64.34527	9	84.57964
10	4.04687	60	24.28124	110	44.51560	160	64.74996	210	84.98432
1	4.45156	1	24.68592	1	44.92029	1	65.15465	1	85.38901
2	4.85625	2	25.09061	2	45.32497	2	65.55934	2	85.79370
3	5.26093	3	25.49530	3	45.72966	3	65.96402	3	86.19839
4	5.66562	4	25.89998	4	46.13435	4	66.36871	4	86.60307
5	6.07031	5	26.30467	5	46.53904	5	66.77340	5	87.00776
6	6.47500	6	26.70936	6	46.94372	6	67.17809	6	87.41245
7	6.87968	7	27.11405	7	47.34841	7	67.58277	7	87.81714
8	7.28437	8	27.51873	8	47.75310	8	67.98746	8	88.22182
9	7.68906	9	27.92342	9	48.15778	9	68.39215	9	88.62651
20	8.09375	70	28.32811	120	48.56247	170	68.79683	220	89.03120
1	8.49843	1	28.73280	1	48.96716	1	69.20152	1	89.43588
2	8.90312	2	29.13748	2	49.37185	2	69.60621	2	89.84057
3	9.30781	3	29.54217	3	49.77653	3	70.01090	3	90.24526
4	9.71249	4	29.94686	4	50.18122	4	70.41558	4	90.64995
5	10.11718	5	30.35154	5	50.58591	5	70.82027	5	91.05463
6	10.52187	6	30.75623	6	50.99059	6	71.22496	6	91.45932
7	10.92656	7	31.16092	7	51.39528	7	71.62965	7	91.86401
8	11.33124	8	31.56561	8	51.79997	8	72.03433	8	92.26870
9	11.73593	9	31.97029	9	52.20466	9	72.43902	9	92.67338
30	12.14062	80	32.37498	130	52.60934	180	72.84371	230	93.07807
1	12.54531	1	32.77967	1	53.01403	1	73.24839	1	93.48276
2	12.94999	2	33.18436	2	53.41872	2	73.65308	2	93.88744
3	13.35468	3	33.58904	3	53.82341	3	74.05777	3	94.29213
4	13.75937	4	33.99373	4	54.22809	4	74.46246	4	94.69682
5	14.16405	5	34.39842	5	54.63278	5	74.86714	5	95.10151
6	14.56874	6	34.80310	6	55.03747	6	75.27183	6	95.50619
7	14.97343	7	35.20779	7	55.44215	7	75.67652	7	95.91088
8	15.37812	8	35.61248	8	55.84684	8	76.08121	8	96.31557
9	15.78280	9	36.01717	9	56.25153	9	76.48589	9	96.72026
40	16.18749	90	36.42185	140	56.65622	190	76.89058	240	97.12494
1	16.59218	1	36.82654	1	57.06090	1	77.29527	1	97.52963
2	16.99686	2	37.23123	2	57.46559	2	77.69995	2	97.93432
3	17.40155	3	37.63592	3	57.87028	3	78.10464	3	98.33900
4	17.80624	4	38.04060	4	58.27497	4	78.50933	4	98.74369
5	18.21093	5	38.44529	5	58.67965	5	78.91402	5	99.14838
6	18.61561	6	38.84998	6	59.08434	6	79.31870	6	99.55307
7	19.02030	7	39.25466	7	59.48903	7	79.72339	7	99.95775
8	19.42499	8	39.65935	8	59.89371	8	80.12808	8	100.36244
9	19.82968	9	40.06404	9	60.29840	9	80.53276	9	100.76713

AREA—ACRES TO HECTARES

[Reduction factor: 1 acre = 0.4046872610 hectare]

Acres	Hectares	Acres	Hectares	Acres	Hectares	Acres	Hectares	Acres	Hectares
250	101.17182	300	121.40618	350	141.64054	400	161.87490	450	182.10927
1	101.57650	1	121.81087	1	142.04523	1	162.27959	1	182.51395
2	101.98119	2	122.21555	2	142.44992	2	162.68428	2	182.91864
3	102.38588	3	122.62024	3	142.85460	3	163.08897	3	183.32333
4	102.79056	4	123.02493	4	143.25929	4	163.49365	4	183.72802
5	103.19525	5	123.42961	5	143.66398	5	163.89834	5	184.13270
6	103.59994	6	123.83430	6	144.06866	6	164.30303	6	184.53739
7	104.00463	7	124.23899	7	144.47335	7	164.70772	7	184.94208
8	104.40931	8	124.64368	8	104.87804	8	165.11240	8	185.34677
9	104.81400	9	125.04836	9	145.28273	9	165.51709	9	185.75145
260	105.21869	310	125.45305	360	145.68741	410	165.92178	460	186.15614
1	105.62338	1	125.85774	1	146.09210	1	166.32646	1	186.56083
2	106.02806	2	126.26243	2	146.49679	2	166.73115	2	186.96551
3	106.43275	3	126.66711	3	146.90148	3	167.13584	3	187.37020
4	106.83744	4	127.07180	4	147.30616	4	167.54053	4	187.77489
5	107.24212	5	127.47649	5	147.71085	5	167.94521	5	188.17958
6	107.64681	6	127.88117	6	148.11554	6	168.34990	6	188.58426
7	108.05150	7	128.28586	7	148.52022	7	168.75459	7	188.98895
8	108.45619	8	128.69055	8	148.92491	8	169.15928	8	189.39364
9	108.86087	9	129.09524	9	149.32960	9	169.56396	9	189.79833
270	109.26556	320	129.49992	370	149.73429	420	169.96865	470	190.20301
1	109.67025	1	129.90461	1	150.13897	1	170.37334	1	190.60770
2	110.07493	2	130.30930	2	150.54366	2	170.77802	2	191.01239
3	110.47962	3	130.71399	3	150.94835	3	171.18271	3	191.41707
4	110.88431	4	131.11867	4	151.35304	4	171.58740	4	191.82176
5	111.28900	5	131.52336	5	151.75772	5	171.99209	5	192.22645
6	111.69368	6	131.92805	6	152.16241	6	172.39677	6	192.63114
7	112.09837	7	132.33273	7	152.56710	7	172.80146	7	193.03582
8	112.50306	8	132.73742	8	152.97178	8	173.20615	8	193.44051
9	112.90775	9	133.14211	9	153.37647	9	173.61083	9	193.84520
280	113.31243	330	133.54680	380	153.78116	430	174.01552	480	194.24989
1	113.71712	1	133.95148	1	154.18585	1	174.42021	1	194.65457
2	114.12181	2	134.35617	2	154.59053	2	174.82490	2	195.05926
3	114.52649	3	134.76086	3	154.99522	3	175.22958	3	195.46395
4	114.93118	4	135.16555	4	155.39991	4	175.63427	4	195.86863
5	115.33587	5	135.57023	5	155.80460	5	176.03896	5	196.27332
6	115.74056	6	135.97492	6	156.20928	6	176.44365	6	196.67801
7	116.14524	7	136.37961	7	156.61397	7	176.84833	7	197.08270
8	116.54993	8	136.78429	8	157.01866	8	177.25302	8	197.48738
9	116.95462	9	137.18898	9	157.42334	9	177.65771	9	197.89207
290	117.35931	340	137.59367	390	157.82803	440	178.06239	490	198.29676
1	117.76399	1	137.99836	1	158.23272	1	178.46708	1	198.70145
2	118.16868	2	138.40304	2	158.63741	2	178.87177	2	199.10613
3	118.57337	3	138.80773	3	159.04209	3	179.27646	3	199.51082
4	118.97805	4	139.21242	4	159.44678	4	179.68114	4	199.91551
5	119.38274	5	139.61711	5	159.85147	5	180.08583	5	200.32019
6	119.78743	6	140.02179	6	160.25616	6	180.49052	6	200.72488
7	120.19212	7	140.42648	7	160.66084	7	180.89521	7	201.12957
8	120.59680	8	140.83117	8	161.06553	8	181.29989	8	201.53426
9	121.00149	9	141.23585	9	161.47022	9	181.70458	9	201.93894

THE METRIC ENCYCLOPEDIA

AREA—ACRES TO HECTARES

[Reduction factor: 1 acre = 0.4046872610 hectare]

Acres	Hectares	Acres	Hectares	Acres	Hectares	Acres	Hectares	Acres	Hectares
500	202.34363	550	222.57799	600	242.81236	650	263.04672	700	283.28108
1	202.74832	1	222.98268	1	243.21704	1	263.45141	1	283.68577
2	203.15301	2	223.38737	2	243.62173	2	263.85609	2	284.09046
3	203.55769	3	223.79206	3	244.02642	3	264.26078	3	284.49514
4	203.96238	4	224.19674	4	244.43111	4	264.66547	4	284.89983
5	204.36707	5	224.60143	5	244.83579	5	265.07016	5	285.30452
6	204.77175	6	225.00612	6	245.24048	6	265.47484	6	285.70921
7	205.17644	7	225.41080	7	245.64517	7	265.87953	7	286.11389
8	205.58113	8	225.81549	8	246.04985	8	266.28422	8	286.51858
9	205.98582	9	226.22018	9	246.45454	9	266.68890	9	286.92327
510	206.39050	560	226.62487	610	246.85923	660	267.09359	710	287.32796
1	206.79519	1	227.02955	1	247.26392	1	267.49828	1	287.73264
2	207.19988	2	227.43424	2	247.66860	2	267.90297	2	288.13733
3	207.60456	3	227.83893	3	248.07329	3	268.30765	3	288.54202
4	208.00925	4	228.24362	4	248.47798	4	268.71234	4	288.94670
5	208.41394	5	228.64830	5	248.88267	5	269.11703	5	289.35139
6	208.81863	6	229.05299	6	249.28735	6	269.52172	6	289.75608
7	209.22331	7	229.45768	7	249.69204	7	269.92640	7	290.16077
8	209.62800	8	229.86236	8	250.09673	8	270.33109	8	290.56545
9	210.03269	9	230.26705	9	250.50141	9	270.73578	9	290.97014
520	210.43738	570	230.67174	620	250.90610	670	271.14046	720	291.37483
1	210.84206	1	231.07643	1	251.31079	1	271.54515	1	291.77952
2	211.24675	2	231.48111	2	251.71548	2	271.94984	2	292.18420
3	211.65144	3	231.88580	3	252.12016	3	272.35453	3	292.58889
4	212.05612	4	232.29049	4	252.52485	4	272.75921	4	292.99358
5	212.46081	5	232.69518	5	252.92954	5	273.16390	5	293.39826
6	212.86550	6	233.09986	6	253.33423	6	273.56859	6	293.80295
7	213.27019	7	233.50455	7	253.73891	7	273.97328	7	294.20764
8	213.67487	8	233.90924	8	254.14360	8	274.37796	8	294.61233
9	214.07956	9	234.31392	9	254.54829	9	274.78265	9	295.01701
530	214.48425	580	234.71861	630	254.95297	680	275.18734	730	295.42170
1	214.88894	1	235.12330	1	255.35766	1	275.59202	1	295.82639
2	215.29362	2	235.52799	2	255.76235	2	275.99671	2	296.23108
3	215.69831	3	235.93267	3	256.16704	3	276.40140	3	296.63576
4	216.10300	4	236.33736	4	256.57172	4	276.80609	4	297.04045
5	216.50768	5	236.74205	5	256.97641	5	277.21077	5	297.44514
6	216.91237	6	237.14673	6	257.38110	6	277.61546	6	297.84982
7	217.31706	7	237.55142	7	257.78579	7	278.02015	7	298.25451
8	217.72175	8	237.95611	8	258.19047	8	278.42484	8	298.65920
9	218.12643	9	238.36080	9	258.59516	9	278.82952	9	299.06389
540	218.53112	590	238.76548	640	258.99985	690	279.23421	740	299.46857
1	218.93581	1	239.17017	1	259.40453	1	279.63890	1	299.87326
2	219.34050	2	239.57486	2	259.80922	2	280.04358	2	300.27795
3	219.74518	3	239.97955	3	260.21391	3	280.44827	3	300.68263
4	220.14987	4	240.38423	4	260.61860	4	280.85296	4	301.08732
5	220.55456	5	240.78892	5	261.02328	5	281.25765	5	301.49201
6	220.95924	6	241.19361	6	261.42797	6	281.66233	6	301.89670
7	221.36393	7	241.59829	7	261.83266	7	282.06702	7	302.30138
8	221.76862	8	242.00298	8	262.23735	8	282.47171	8	302.70607
9	222.17331	9	242.40767	9	262.64203	9	282.87640	9	303.11076

AREA—ACRES TO HECTARES

[Reduction factor: 1 acre = 0.4046872610 hectare]

Acres	Hectares	Acres	Hectares	Acres	Hectares	Acres	Hectares	Acres	Hectares
750	303.51545	800	323.74981	850	343.98417	900	364.21853	950	384.45290
1	303.92013	1	324.15450	1	344.38886	1	364.62322	1	384.85759
2	304.32482	2	324.55918	2	344.79355	2	365.02791	2	385.26227
3	304.72951	3	324.96387	3	345.19823	3	365.43260	3	385.66696
4	305.13419	4	325.36856	4	345.60292	4	365.83728	4	386.07165
5	305.53888	5	325.77325	5	346.00761	5	366.24197	5	386.47633
6	305.94357	6	326.17793	6	346.41230	6	366.64666	6	386.88102
7	306.34826	7	326.58262	7	346.81698	7	367.05135	7	387.28571
8	306.75294	8	326.98731	8	347.22167	8	367.45603	8	387.69040
9	307.15763	9	327.39199	9	347.62636	9	367.86072	9	388.09508
760	307.56232	810	327.79668	860	348.03104	910	368.26541	960	388.49977
1	307.96701	1	328.20137	1	348.43573	1	368.67009	1	388.90446
2	308.37169	2	328.60606	2	348.84042	2	369.07478	2	389.30915
3	308.77638	3	329.01074	3	349.24511	3	369.47947	3	389.71383
4	309.18107	4	329.41543	4	349.64979	4	369.88416	4	390.11852
5	309.58575	5	329.82012	5	350.05448	5	370.28884	5	390.52321
6	309.99044	6	330.22480	6	350.45917	6	370.69353	6	390.92789
7	310.39513	7	330.62949	7	350.86386	7	371.09822	7	391.33258
8	310.79982	8	331.03418	8	351.26854	8	371.50291	8	391.73727
9	311.20450	9	331.43887	9	351.67323	9	371.90759	9	392.14196
770	311.60919	820	331.84355	870	352.07792	920	372.31228	970	392.54664
1	312.01388	1	332.24824	1	352.48260	1	372.71697	1	392.95133
2	312.41857	2	332.65293	2	352.88729	2	373.12165	2	393.35602
3	312.82325	3	333.05762	3	353.29198	3	373.52634	3	393.76070
4	313.22794	4	333.46230	4	353.69667	4	373.93103	4	394.16539
5	313.63263	5	333.86699	5	354.10135	5	374.33572	5	394.57008
6	314.03731	6	334.27168	6	354.50604	6	374.74040	6	394.97477
7	314.44200	7	334.67636	7	354.91073	7	375.14509	7	395.37945
8	314.84669	8	335.08105	8	355.31542	8	375.54978	8	395.78414
9	315.25138	9	335.48574	9	355.72010	9	375.95447	9	396.18883
780	315.65606	830	335.89043	880	356.12479	930	376.35915	980	396.59352
1	316.06075	1	336.29511	1	356.52948	1	376.76384	1	396.99820
2	316.46544	2	336.69980	2	356.93416	2	377.16853	2	397.40289
3	316.87013	3	337.10449	3	357.33885	3	377.57321	3	397.80758
4	317.27481	4	337.50918	4	357.74354	4	377.97790	4	398.21226
5	317.67950	5	337.91386	5	358.14823	5	378.38259	5	398.61695
6	318.08419	6	338.31855	6	358.55291	6	378.78728	6	399.02164
7	318.48887	7	338.72324	7	358.95760	7	379.19196	7	399.42633
8	318.89356	8	339.12792	8	359.36229	8	379.59665	8	399.83101
9	319.29825	9	339.53261	9	359.76698	9	380.00134	9	400.23570
790	319.70294	840	339.93730	890	360.17166	940	380.40603	990	400.64039
1	320.10762	1	340.34199	1	360.57635	1	380.81071	1	401.04508
2	320.51231	2	340.74667	2	360.98104	2	381.21540	2	401.44976
3	320.91700	3	341.15136	3	361.38572	3	381.62009	3	401.85445
4	321.32169	4	341.55605	4	361.79041	4	382.02477	4	402.25914
5	321.72637	5	341.96074	5	362.19510	5	382.42946	5	402.66382
6	322.13106	6	342.36542	6	362.59979	6	382.83415	6	403.06851
7	322.53575	7	342.77011	7	363.00447	7	383.23884	7	403.47320
8	322.94043	8	343.17480	8	363.40916	8	383.64352	8	403.87789
9	323.34512	9	343.57948	9	363.81385	9	384.04821	9	404.28257

VOLUME—CUBIC METRES TO CUBIC YARDS

[Reduction factor: 1 cubic metre = 1.307942772 cubic yards]

Cubic metres	Cubic yards	Cubic metres	Cubic yards	Cubic metres	Cubic yards	Cubic metres	Cubic yards	Cubic metres	Cubic yards
0		50	65.39714	100	130.79428	150	196.19142	200	261.58855
1	1.30794	1	66.70508	1	132.10222	1	197.49936	1	262.89650
2	2.61589	2	68.01302	2	133.41016	2	198.80730	2	264.20444
3	3.92383	3	69.32097	3	134.71811	3	200.11524	3	265.51238
4	5.23177	4	70.62891	4	136.02605	4	201.42319	4	266.82033
5	6.53971	5	71.93685	5	137.33399	5	202.73113	5	268.12827
6	7.84766	6	73.24480	6	138.64193	6	204.03907	6	269.43621
7	9.15560	7	74.55274	7	139.94988	7	205.34702	7	270.74415
8	10.46354	8	75.86068	8	141.25782	8	206.65496	8	272.05210
9	11.77148	9	77.16862	9	142.56576	9	207.96290	9	273.36004
10	13.07943	60	78.47657	110	143.87370	160	209.27084	210	274.66798
1	14.38737	1	79.78451	1	145.18165	1	210.57879	1	275.97592
2	15.69531	2	81.09245	2	146.48959	2	211.88673	2	277.28387
3	17.00326	3	82.40039	3	147.79753	3	213.19467	3	278.59181
4	18.31120	4	83.70834	4	149.10548	4	214.50261	4	279.89975
5	19.61914	5	85.01628	5	150.41342	5	215.81056	5	281.20770
6	20.92708	6	86.32422	6	151.72136	6	217.11850	6	282.51564
7	22.23503	7	87.63217	7	153.02930	7	218.42644	7	283.82358
8	23.54297	8	88.94011	8	154.33725	8	219.73439	8	285.13152
9	24.85091	9	90.24805	9	155.64519	9	221.04233	9	286.43947
20	26.15886	70	91.55599	120	156.95313	170	222.35027	220	287.74741
1	27.46680	1	92.86394	1	158.26108	1	223.65821	1	289.05535
2	28.77474	2	94.17188	2	159.56902	2	224.96616	2	290.36330
3	30.08268	3	95.47982	3	160.87696	3	226.27410	3	291.67124
4	31.39063	4	96.78777	4	162.18490	4	227.58204	4	292.97918
5	32.69857	5	98.09571	5	163.49285	5	228.88999	5	294.28712
6	34.00651	6	99.40365	6	164.80079	6	230.19793	6	295.59507
7	35.31445	7	100.71159	7	166.10873	7	231.50587	7	296.90301
8	36.62240	8	102.01954	8	167.41667	8	232.81381	8	298.21095
9	37.93034	9	103.32748	9	168.72462	9	234.12176	9	299.51889
30	39.23828	80	104.63542	130	170.03256	180	235.42970	230	300.82684
1	40.54623	1	105.94336	1	171.34050	1	236.73764	1	302.13478
2	41.85417	2	107.25131	2	172.64845	2	238.04558	2	303.44272
3	43.16211	3	108.55925	3	173.95639	3	239.35353	3	304.75067
4	44.47005	4	109.86719	4	175.26433	4	240.66147	4	306.05861
5	45.77800	5	111.17514	5	176.57227	5	241.96941	5	307.36655
6	47.08594	6	112.48308	6	177.88022	6	243.27736	6	308.67449
7	48.39388	7	113.79102	7	179.18816	7	244.58530	7	309.98244
8	49.70183	8	115.09896	8	180.49610	8	245.89324	8	311.29038
9	51.00977	9	116.40691	9	181.80405	9	247.20118	9	312.59832
40	52.31771	90	117.71485	140	183.11199	190	248.50913	240	313.90627
1	53.62565	1	119.02279	1	184.41993	1	249.81707	1	315.21421
2	54.93360	2	120.33074	2	185.72787	2	251.12501	2	316.52215
3	56.24154	3	121.63868	3	187.03582	3	252.43295	3	317.83009
4	57.54948	4	122.94662	4	188.34376	4	253.74090	4	319.13804
5	58.85742	5	124.25456	5	189.65170	5	255.04884	5	320.44598
6	60.16537	6	125.56251	6	190.95964	6	256.35678	6	321.75302
7	61.47331	7	126.87045	7	192.26759	7	257.66473	7	323.06186
8	62.78125	8	128.17839	8	193.57553	8	258.97267	8	324.36981
9	64.08920	9	129.48633	9	194.88347	9	260.28061	9	325.67775

VOLUME—CUBIC METRES TO CUBIC YARDS

[Reduction factor: 1 cubic metre = 1.307942772 cubic yards]

Cubic metres	Cubic yards	Cubic metres	Cubic yards	Cubic metres	Cubic yards	Cubic metres	Cubic yards	Cubic metres	Cubic yards
250	326.98569	300	392.38283	350	457.77997	400	523.17711	450	588.57425
1	328.29364	1	393.69077	1	459.08791	1	524.48505	1	589.88219
2	329.60158	2	394.99872	2	460.39586	2	525.79299	2	591.19013
3	330.90952	3	396.30666	3	461.70380	3	527.10094	3	592.49808
4	332.21746	4	397.61460	4	463.01174	4	528.40888	4	593.80602
5	333.52541	5	398.92255	5	464.31968	5	529.71682	5	595.11396
6	334.83335	6	400.23049	6	465.62763	6	531.02477	6	596.42190
7	336.14129	7	401.53843	7	466.93557	7	532.33271	7	597.72985
8	337.44924	8	402.84637	8	468.24351	8	533.64065	8	599.03779
9	338.75718	9	404.15432	9	469.55146	9	534.94859	9	600.34573
260	340.06512	310	405.46226	360	470.85940	410	536.25654	460	601.65368
1	341.37306	1	406.77020	1	472.16734	1	537.56448	1	602.96162
2	342.68101	2	408.07814	2	473.47528	2	538.87242	2	604.26956
3	343.98895	3	409.38609	3	474.78323	3	540.18036	3	605.57750
4	345.29689	4	410.69403	4	476.09117	4	541.48831	4	606.88545
5	346.60483	5	412.00197	5	477.39911	5	542.79625	5	608.19339
6	347.91278	6	413.30992	6	478.70705	6	544.10419	6	609.50133
7	349.22072	7	414.61786	7	480.01500	7	545.41214	7	610.80927
8	350.52866	8	415.92580	8	481.32294	8	546.72008	8	612.11722
9	351.83661	9	417.23374	9	482.63088	9	548.02802	9	613.42516
270	353.14455	320	418.54169	370	483.93883	420	549.33596	470	614.73310
1	354.45249	1	419.84963	1	485.24677	1	550.64391	1	616.04105
2	355.76043	2	421.15757	2	486.55471	2	551.95185	2	617.34899
3	357.06838	3	422.46552	3	487.86265	3	553.25979	3	618.65693
4	358.37632	4	423.77346	4	489.17060	4	554.56774	4	619.96487
5	359.68426	5	425.08140	5	490.47854	5	555.87568	5	621.27282
6	360.99221	6	426.38934	6	491.78648	6	557.18362	6	622.58076
7	362.30015	7	427.69729	7	493.09443	7	558.49156	7	623.88870
8	363.60809	8	429.00523	8	494.40237	8	559.79951	8	625.19665
9	364.91603	9	430.31317	9	495.71031	9	561.10745	9	626.50459
280	366.22398	330	431.62111	380	497.01825	430	562.41539	480	627.81253
1	367.53192	1	432.92906	1	498.32620	1	563.72333	1	629.12047
2	368.83986	2	434.23700	2	499.63414	2	565.03128	2	630.42842
3	370.14780	3	435.54494	3	500.94208	3	566.33922	3	631.73636
4	371.45575	4	436.85289	4	502.25002	4	567.64716	4	633.04430
5	372.76369	5	438.16083	5	503.55797	5	568.95511	5	634.35224
6	374.07163	6	439.46877	6	504.86591	6	570.26305	6	635.66019
7	375.37958	7	440.77671	7	506.17385	7	571.57099	7	636.96813
8	376.68752	8	442.08466	8	507.48180	8	572.87893	8	638.27607
9	377.99546	9	443.39260	9	508.78974	9	574.18688	9	639.58402
290	379.30340	340	444.70054	390	510.09768	440	575.49482	490	640.89196
1	380.61135	1	446.00849	1	511.40562	1	576.80276	1	642.19990
2	381.91929	2	447.31643	2	512.71357	2	578.11071	2	643.50784
3	383.22723	3	448.62437	3	514.02151	3	579.41865	3	644.81579
4	384.53517	4	449.93231	4	515.32945	4	580.72659	4	646.12373
5	385.84312	5	451.24026	5	516.63739	5	582.03453	5	647.43167
6	387.15106	6	452.54820	6	517.94534	6	583.34248	6	648.73961
7	388.45900	7	453.85614	7	519.25328	7	584.65042	7	650.04756
8	389.76695	8	455.16408	8	520.56122	8	585.95836	8	651.35550
9	391.07489	9	456.47203	9	521.86917	9	587.26630	9	652.66344

VOLUME—CUBIC METRES TO CUBIC YARDS

[Reduction factor: 1 cubic metre = 1.307942772 cubic yards]

Cubic metres	Cubic yards	Cubic metres	Cubic yards	Cubic metres	Cubic yards	Cubic metres	Cubic yards	Cubic metres	Cubic yards
500	653.97139	550	719.36852	600	784.76566	650	850.16280	700	915.55994
1	655.27933	1	720.67647	1	786.07361	1	851.47074	1	916.86788
2	656.58727	2	721.98441	2	787.38155	2	852.77869	2	918.17583
3	657.89521	3	723.29235	3	788.68949	3	854.08663	3	919.48377
4	659.20316	4	724.60030	4	789.99743	4	855.39457	4	920.79171
5	660.51110	5	725.90824	5	791.30538	5	856.70252	5	922.09965
6	661.81904	6	727.21618	6	792.61332	6	858.01046	6	923.40760
7	663.12699	7	728.52412	7	793.92126	7	859.31840	7	924.71554
8	664.43493	8	729.83207	8	795.22921	8	860.62634	8	926.02348
9	665.74287	9	731.14001	9	796.53715	9	861.93429	9	927.33143
510	667.05081	560	732.44795	610	797.84509	660	863.24223	710	928.63937
1	668.35876	1	733.75590	1	799.15303	1	864.55017	1	929.94731
2	669.66670	2	735.06384	2	800.46098	2	865.85812	2	931.25525
3	670.97464	3	736.37178	3	801.76892	3	867.16606	3	932.56320
4	672.28258	4	737.67972	4	803.07686	4	868.47400	4	933.87114
5	673.59053	5	738.98767	5	804.38480	5	869.78194	5	935.17908
6	674.89847	6	740.29561	6	805.69275	6	871.08989	6	936.48702
7	676.20641	7	741.60355	7	807.00069	7	872.39783	7	937.79497
8	677.51436	8	742.91149	8	808.30863	8	873.70577	8	939.10291
9	678.82230	9	744.21944	9	809.61658	9	875.01371	9	940.41085
520	680.13024	570	745.52738	620	810.92452	670	876.32166	720	941.71880
1	681.43818	1	746.83532	1	812.23246	1	877.62960	1	943.02674
2	682.74613	2	748.14327	2	813.54040	2	878.93754	2	944.33468
3	684.05407	3	749.45121	3	814.84835	3	880.24549	3	945.64262
4	685.36201	4	750.75915	4	816.15629	4	881.55343	4	946.95057
5	686.66996	5	752.06709	5	817.46423	5	882.86137	5	948.25851
6	687.97790	6	753.37504	6	818.77218	6	884.16931	6	949.56645
7	689.28584	7	754.68298	7	820.08012	7	885.47726	7	950.87440
8	690.59378	8	755.99092	8	821.38806	8	886.78520	8	952.18234
9	691.90173	9	757.29886	9	822.69600	9	888.09314	9	953.49028
530	693.20967	580	758.60681	630	824.00395	680	889.40108	730	954.79822
1	694.51761	1	759.91475	1	825.31189	1	890.70903	1	956.10617
2	695.82555	2	761.22269	2	826.61983	2	892.01697	2	957.41411
3	697.13350	3	762.53064	3	827.92777	3	893.32491	3	958.72205
4	698.44144	4	763.83858	4	829.23572	4	894.63286	4	960.02999
5	699.74938	5	765.14652	5	830.54366	5	895.94080	5	961.33794
6	701.05733	6	766.45446	6	831.85160	6	897.24874	6	962.64588
7	702.36527	7	767.76241	7	833.15955	7	898.55668	7	963.95382
8	703.67321	8	769.07035	8	834.46749	8	899.86463	8	965.26177
9	704.98115	9	770.37829	9	835.77543	9	901.17257	9	966.56971
540	706.28910	590	771.68624	640	837.08337	690	902.48051	740	967.87765
1	707.59704	1	772.99418	1	838.39132	1	903.78846	1	969.18559
2	708.90498	2	774.30212	2	839.69926	2	905.09640	2	970.49354
3	710.21293	3	775.61006	3	841.00720	3	906.40434	3	971.80148
4	711.52087	4	776.91801	4	842.31515	4	907.71228	4	973.10942
5	712.82881	5	778.22595	5	843.62309	5	909.02023	5	974.41737
6	714.13675	6	779.53389	6	844.93103	6	910.32531	6	975.72531
7	715.44470	7	780.84183	7	846.23897	7	911.63611	7	977.03325
8	716.75264	8	782.14978	8	847.54692	8	912.94405	8	978.34119
9	718.06058	9	783.45772	9	848.85486	9	914.25200	9	979.64914

VOLUME—CUBIC METRES TO CUBIC YARDS

[Reduction factor: 1 cubic metre = 1.307942772 cubic yards]

Cubic metres	Cubic yards	Cubic metres	Cubic yards	Cubic metres	Cubic yards	Cubic metres	Cubic yards	Cubic metres	Cubic yards
750	980.95708	800	1,046.35422	850	1,111.75136	900	1,177.14849	950	1,242.54569
1	982.26502	1	1,047.66216	1	1,113.05930	1	1,178.45644	1	1,243.85358
2	983.57296	2	1,048.97010	2	1,114.36724	2	1,179.76438	2	1,245.16152
3	984.88091	3	1,050.27805	3	1,115.67518	3	1,181.07232	3	1,246.46946
4	986.18885	4	1,051.58599	4	1,116.98313	4	1,182.38027	4	1,247.77740
5	987.49679	5	1,052.89393	5	1,118.29107	5	1,183.68821	5	1,249.08535
6	988.80474	6	1,054.20187	6	1,119.59901	6	1,184.99615	6	1,250.39329
7	990.11268	7	1,055.50982	7	1,120.90696	7	1,186.30409	7	1,251.70123
8	991.42062	8	1,056.81776	8	1,122.21490	8	1,187.61204	8	1,253.00918
9	992.72856	9	1,058.12570	9	1,123.52284	9	1,188.91998	9	1,254.31712
760	994.03651	810	1,059.43365	860	1,124.83078	910	1,190.22792	960	1,255.62506
1	995.34445	1	1,060.74159	1	1,126.13873	1	1,191.53587	1	1,256.93300
2	996.65239	2	1,062.04953	2	1,127.44667	2	1,192.84381	2	1,258.24095
3	997.96034	3	1,063.35747	3	1,128.75461	3	1,194.15175	3	1,259.54889
4	999.26828	4	1,064.66542	4	1,130.06256	4	1,195.45969	4	1,260.85683
5	1,000.57622	5	1,065.97336	5	1,131.37050	5	1,196.76764	5	1,262.16477
6	1,001.88416	6	1,067.28130	6	1,132.67844	6	1,198.07558	6	1,263.47272
7	1,003.19211	7	1,068.58924	7	1,133.98638	7	1,199.38352	7	1,264.78066
8	1,004.50005	8	1,069.89719	8	1,135.29433	8	1,200.69146	8	1,266.08860
9	1,005.80799	9	1,071.20513	9	1,136.60227	9	1,201.99941	9	1,267.39655
770	1,007.11593	820	1,072.51307	870	1,137.91021	920	1,203.30735	970	1,268.70449
1	1,008.42388	1	1,073.82102	1	1,139.21815	1	1,204.61529	1	1,270.01243
2	1,009.73182	2	1,075.12896	2	1,140.52610	2	1,205.92324	2	1,271.32037
3	1,011.03976	3	1,076.43690	3	1,141.83404	3	1,207.23118	3	1,272.62832
4	1,012.34771	4	1,077.74484	4	1,143.14198	4	1,208.53912	4	1,273.93626
5	1,013.65565	5	1,079.05279	5	1,144.44993	5	1,209.84706	5	1,275.24420
6	1,014.96359	6	1,080.36073	6	1,145.75787	6	1,211.15501	6	1,276.55215
7	1,016.27153	7	1,081.66867	7	1,147.06581	7	1,212.46295	7	1,277.86009
8	1,017.57948	8	1,082.97662	8	1,148.37375	8	1,213.77089	8	1,279.16803
9	1,018.88742	9	1,084.28456	9	1,149.68170	9	1,215.07884	9	1,280.47597
780	1,020.19536	830	1,085.59250	880	1,150.98964	930	1,216.38678	980	1,281.78392
1	1,021.50330	1	1,086.90044	1	1,152.29758	1	1,217.69472	1	1,283.09186
2	1,022.81125	2	1,088.20839	2	1,153.60552	2	1,219.00266	2	1,284.39980
3	1,024.11919	3	1,089.51633	3	1,154.91347	3	1,220.31061	3	1,285.70774
4	1,025.42713	4	1,090.82427	4	1,156.22141	4	1,221.61855	4	1,287.01569
5	1,026.73508	5	1,092.13221	5	1,157.52935	5	1,222.92649	5	1,288.32363
6	1,028.04302	6	1,093.44016	6	1,158.83730	6	1,224.23443	6	1,289.63157
7	1,029.35096	7	1,094.74810	7	1,160.14524	7	1,225.54238	7	1,290.93952
8	1,030.65890	8	1,096.05604	8	1,161.45318	8	1,226.85032	8	1,292.24746
9	1,031.96685	9	1,097.36399	9	1,162.76112	9	1,228.15826	9	1,293.55540
790	1,033.27479	840	1,098.67193	890	1,164.06907	940	1,229.46621	990	1,294.86334
1	1,034.58273	1	1,099.97987	1	1,165.37701	1	1,230.77415	1	1,296.17129
2	1,035.89068	2	1,101.28781	2	1,166.68495	2	1,232.08209	2	1,297.47923
3	1,037.19862	3	1,102.59576	3	1,167.99290	3	1,233.39003	3	1,298.78717
4	1,038.50656	4	1,103.90370	4	1,169.30084	4	1,234.69798	4	1,300.09512
5	1,039.81450	5	1,105.21164	5	1,170.60878	5	1,236.00592	5	1,301.40306
6	1,041.12245	6	1,106.51959	6	1,171.91672	6	1,237.31386	6	1,302.71100
7	1,042.43039	7	1,107.82753	7	1,173.22467	7	1,238.62181	7	1,304.01894
8	1,043.73833	8	1,109.13547	8	1,174.53261	8	1,239.92975	8	1,305.32689
9	1,045.04627	9	1,110.44341	9	1,175.84055	9	1,241.23769	9	1,306.63483

VOLUME—CUBIC YARDS TO CUBIC METRES

[Reduction factor: 1 cubic yard = 0.7645594453 cubic metre]

Cubic yards	Cubic metres	Cubic yards	Cubic metres	Cubic yards	Cubic metres	Cubic yards	Cubic metres	Cubic yards	Cubic metres
0		50	38.22797	100	76.45594	150	114.68392	200	152.91189
1	0.76456	1	38.99253	1	77.22050	1	115.44848	1	153.67645
2	1.52912	2	39.75709	2	77.98506	2	116.21304	2	154.44101
3	2.29368	3	40.52165	3	78.74962	3	116.97760	3	155.20557
4	3.05824	4	41.28621	4	79.51418	4	117.74215	4	155.97013
5	3.82280	5	42.05077	5	80.27874	5	118.50671	5	156.73469
6	4.58736	6	42.81533	6	81.04330	6	119.27127	6	157.49925
7	5.35192	7	43.57989	7	81.80786	7	120.03583	7	158.26381
8	6.11648	8	44.34445	8	82.57242	8	120.80039	8	159.02836
9	6.88104	9	45.10901	9	83.33698	9	121.56495	9	159.79292
10	7.64559	60	45.87357	110	84.10154	160	122.32951	210	160.55748
1	8.41015	1	46.63813	1	84.86610	1	123.09407	1	161.32204
2	9.17471	2	47.40269	2	85.63066	2	123.85863	2	162.08660
3	9.93927	3	48.16725	3	86.39522	3	124.62319	3	162.85116
4	10.70383	4	48.93180	4	87.15978	4	125.38775	4	163.61572
5	11.46839	5	49.69636	5	87.92434	5	126.15231	5	164.38028
6	12.23295	6	50.46092	6	88.68890	6	126.91687	6	165.14484
7	12.99751	7	51.22548	7	89.45346	7	127.68143	7	165.90940
8	13.76207	8	51.99004	8	90.21801	8	128.44599	8	166.67396
9	14.52663	9	52.75460	9	90.98257	9	129.21055	9	167.43852
20	15.29119	70	53.51916	120	91.74713	170	129.97511	220	168.20308
1	16.05575	1	54.28372	1	92.51169	1	130.73967	1	168.96764
2	16.82031	2	55.04828	2	93.27625	2	131.50422	2	169.73220
3	17.58487	3	55.81284	3	94.04081	3	132.26878	3	170.49676
4	18.34943	4	56.57740	4	94.80537	4	133.03334	4	171.26132
5	19.11399	5	57.34196	5	95.56993	5	133.79790	5	172.02588
6	19.87855	6	58.10652	6	96.33449	6	134.56246	6	172.79043
7	20.64311	7	58.87108	7	97.09905	7	135.32702	7	173.55499
8	21.40766	8	59.63564	8	97.86361	8	136.09158	8	174.31955
9	22.17222	9	60.40020	9	98.62817	9	136.85614	9	175.08411
30	22.93678	80	61.16476	130	99.39273	180	137.62070	230	175.84867
1	23.70134	1	61.92932	1	100.15729	1	138.38526	1	176.61323
2	24.46590	2	62.69387	2	100.92185	2	139.14982	2	177.37779
3	25.23046	3	63.45843	3	101.68641	3	139.91438	3	178.14235
4	25.99502	4	64.22299	4	102.45097	4	140.67894	4	178.90691
5	26.75958	5	64.98755	5	103.21553	5	141.44350	5	179.67147
6	27.52414	6	65.75211	6	103.98008	6	142.20806	6	180.43603
7	28.28870	7	66.51667	7	104.74464	7	142.97262	7	181.20059
8	29.05326	8	67.28123	8	105.50920	8	143.73718	8	181.96515
9	29.81782	9	68.04579	9	106.27376	9	144.50174	9	182.72971
40	30.58238	90	68.81035	140	107.03832	190	145.26629	240	183.49427
1	31.34694	1	69.57491	1	107.80288	1	146.03085	1	184.25883
2	32.11150	2	70.33947	2	108.56744	2	146.79541	2	185.02339
3	32.87606	3	71.10403	3	109.33200	3	147.55997	3	185.78795
4	33.64062	4	71.86859	4	110.09656	4	148.32453	4	186.55250
5	34.40518	5	72.63315	5	110.86112	5	149.08909	5	187.31706
6	35.16973	6	73.39771	6	111.62568	6	149.85365	6	188.08162
7	35.93429	7	74.16227	7	112.39024	7	150.61821	7	188.84618
8	36.69885	8	74.92683	8	113.15480	8	151.38277	8	189.61074
9	37.46341	9	75.69139	9	113.91936	9	152.14733	9	190.37530

VOLUME—CUBIC YARDS TO CUBIC METRES

[Reduction factor: 1 cubic yard = 0.7645594453 cubic metre]

Cubic yards	Cubic metres	Cubic yards	Cubic metres	Cubic yards	Cubic metres	Cubic yards	Cubic metres	Cubic yards	Cubic metres
250	191.13986	300	229.36783	350	267.59581	400	305.82378	450	344.05175
1	191.90442	1	230.13239	1	268.36037	1	306.58834	1	344.81631
2	192.66898	2	230.89695	2	269.12492	2	307.35290	2	345.58087
3	193.43354	3	231.66151	3	269.88948	3	308.11746	3	346.34543
4	194.19810	4	232.42607	4	270.65404	4	308.88202	4	347.10999
5	194.96266	5	233.19063	5	271.41860	5	309.64658	5	347.87455
6	195.72722	6	233.95519	6	272.18316	6	310.41113	6	348.63911
7	196.49178	7	234.71975	7	272.94772	7	311.17569	7	349.40367
8	197.25634	8	235.48431	8	273.71228	8	311.94025	8	350.16823
9	198.02090	9	236.24887	9	274.47684	9	312.70481	9	350.93279
260	198.78546	310	237.01343	360	275.24140	410	313.46937	460	351.69734
1	199.55002	1	237.77799	1	276.00596	1	314.23393	1	352.46190
2	200.31457	2	238.54255	2	276.77052	2	314.99849	2	353.22646
3	201.07913	3	239.30711	3	277.53508	3	315.76305	3	353.99102
4	201.84369	4	240.07167	4	278.29964	4	316.52761	4	354.75558
5	202.60825	5	240.83623	5	279.06420	5	317.29217	5	355.52014
6	203.37281	6	241.60078	6	279.82876	6	318.05673	6	356.28470
7	204.13737	7	242.36534	7	280.59332	7	318.82129	7	357.04926
8	204.90193	8	243.12990	8	281.35788	8	319.58585	8	357.81382
9	205.66649	9	243.89446	9	282.12244	9	320.35041	9	358.57838
270	206.43105	320	244.65902	370	282.88699	420	321.11497	470	359.34294
1	207.19561	1	245.42358	1	283.65155	1	321.87953	1	360.10750
2	207.96017	2	246.18814	2	284.41611	2	322.64409	2	360.87206
3	208.72473	3	246.95270	3	285.18067	3	323.40865	3	361.63662
4	209.48929	4	247.71726	4	285.94523	4	324.17320	4	362.40118
5	210.25385	5	248.48182	5	286.70979	5	324.93776	5	363.16574
6	211.01841	6	249.24638	6	287.47435	6	325.70232	6	363.93030
7	211.78297	7	250.01094	7	288.23891	7	326.46688	7	364.69486
8	212.54753	8	250.77550	8	289.00347	8	327.23144	8	365.45941
9	213.31209	9	251.54006	9	289.76803	9	327.99600	9	366.22397
280	214.07664	330	252.30462	380	290.53259	430	328.76056	480	366.98853
1	214.84120	1	253.06918	1	291.29715	1	329.52512	1	367.75309
2	215.60576	2	253.83374	2	292.06171	2	330.28968	2	368.51765
3	216.37032	3	254.59830	3	292.82627	3	331.05424	3	369.28221
4	217.13488	4	255.36285	4	293.59083	4	331.81880	4	370.04677
5	217.89944	5	256.12741	5	594.35539	5	332.58336	5	370.81133
6	218.66400	6	256.89197	6	295.11995	6	333.34792	6	371.57589
7	219.42856	7	257.65653	7	295.88451	7	334.11248	7	372.34045
8	220.19312	8	258.42109	8	296.64906	8	334.87704	8	373.10501
9	220.95768	9	259.18565	9	297.41362	9	335.64160	9	373.86957
290	221.72224	340	259.95021	390	298.17818	440	336.40616	490	374.63413
1	222.48680	1	260.71477	1	298.94274	1	337.17072	1	375.39869
2	223.25136	2	261.47933	2	299.70730	2	337.93527	2	376.16325
3	224.01592	3	262.24389	3	300.47186	3	338.69983	3	376.92781
4	224.78048	4	263.00845	4	301.23642	4	339.46439	4	377.69237
5	225.54504	5	263.77301	5	302.00098	5	340.22895	5	378.45693
6	226.30960	6	264.53757	6	302.76554	6	340.99351	6	379.22148
7	227.07416	7	265.30213	7	303.53010	7	341.75807	7	379.98604
8	227.83871	8	266.06669	8	304.29466	8	342.52263	8	380.75060
9	228.60327	9	266.83125	9	305.05922	9	343.28719	9	381.51516

VOLUME—CUBIC YARDS TO CUBIC METRES

[Reduction factor: 1 cubic yard = 0.7645594453 cubic metre]

Cubic yards	Cubic metres	Cubic yards	Cubic metres	Cubic yards	Cubic metres	Cubic yards	Cubic metres	Cubic yards	Cubic metres
500	382.27972	550	420.50769	600	458.73567	650	496.96364	700	535.19161
1	383.04428	1	421.27225	1	459.50023	1	497.72820	1	535.95617
2	383.80884	2	422.03681	2	460.26479	2	498.49276	2	536.72073
3	384.57340	3	422.80137	3	461.02935	3	499.25732	3	537.48529
4	385.33796	4	423.56593	4	461.79390	4	500.02188	4	538.24985
5	386.10252	5	424.33049	5	462.55846	5	500.78644	5	539.01441
6	386.86708	6	425.09505	6	463.32302	6	501.55100	6	539.77877
7	387.63164	7	425.85961	7	464.08758	7	502.31556	7	540.54353
8	388.39620	8	426.62417	8	464.85214	8	503.08012	8	541.30809
9	389.16076	9	427.38873	9	465.61670	9	503.84467	9	542.07265
510	389.92532	560	428.15329	610	466.38126	660	504.60923	710	542.83721
1	390.68988	1	428.91785	1	467.14582	1	505.37379	1	543.60177
2	391.45444	2	429.68241	2	467.91038	2	506.13835	2	544.36633
3	392.21900	3	430.44697	3	468.67494	3	506.90291	3	545.13088
4	392.98355	4	431.21153	4	469.43950	4	507.66747	4	545.89544
5	393.74811	5	431.97609	5	470.20406	5	508.43203	5	546.66000
6	394.51267	6	432.74065	6	470.96862	6	509.19659	6	547.42456
7	395.27723	7	433.50521	7	471.73318	7	509.96115	7	548.18912
8	396.04179	8	434.26976	8	472.49774	8	510.72571	8	548.95368
9	396.80635	9	435.03432	9	473.26230	9	511.49027	9	549.71824
520	397.57091	570	435.79888	620	474.02686	670	512.25483	720	550.48280
1	398.33547	1	436.56344	1	474.79142	1	513.01939	1	551.24736
2	399.10003	2	437.32800	2	475.55597	2	513.78395	2	552.01192
3	399.86459	3	438.09256	3	476.32053	3	514.54851	3	552.77648
4	400.62915	4	438.85712	4	477.08509	4	515.31307	4	553.54104
5	401.39371	5	439.62168	5	477.84965	5	516.07763	5	554.30560
6	402.15827	6	440.38624	6	478.61421	6	516.84219	6	555.07016
7	402.92283	7	441.15080	7	479.37877	7	517.60674	7	555.83472
8	403.68739	8	441.91536	8	480.14333	8	518.37130	8	556.59928
9	404.45195	9	442.67992	9	480.90789	9	519.13586	9	557.36384
530	405.21651	580	443.44448	630	481.67245	680	519.90042	730	558.12840
1	405.98107	1	444.20904	1	482.43701	1	520.66498	1	558.89295
2	406.74562	2	444.97360	2	483.20157	2	521.42954	2	559.65751
3	407.51018	3	445.73816	3	483.96613	3	522.19410	3	560.42207
4	408.27474	4	446.50272	4	484.73069	4	522.95866	4	561.18663
5	409.03930	5	447.26728	5	485.49525	5	523.72322	5	561.95119
6	409.80386	6	448.03183	6	486.25981	6	524.48778	6	562.71575
7	410.56842	7	448.79639	7	487.02437	7	525.25234	7	563.48031
8	411.33298	8	449.56095	8	487.78893	8	526.01690	8	564.24487
9	412.09754	9	450.32551	9	488.55349	9	526.78146	9	565.00943
540	412.86210	590	451.09007	640	489.31804	690	527.54602	740	565.77399
1	413.62666	1	451.85463	1	490.08260	1	528.31058	1	566.53855
2	414.39122	2	452.61919	2	490.84716	2	529.07514	2	567.30311
3	415.15578	3	453.38375	3	491.61172	3	529.83970	3	568.06767
4	415.92034	4	454.14831	4	492.37628	4	530.60426	4	568.83223
5	416.68490	5	454.91287	5	493.14084	5	531.36881	5	569.59679
6	417.44946	6	455.67743	6	493.90540	6	532.13337	6	570.36135
7	418.21402	7	456.44199	7	494.66996	7	532.89793	7	571.12591
8	418.97858	8	457.20655	8	495.43452	8	533.66249	8	571.89047
9	419.74314	9	457.97111	9	496.19908	9	534.42705	9	572.65502

VOLUME—CUBIC YARDS TO CUBIC METRES

[Reduction factor: 1 cubic yard = 0.7645594453 cubic metre]

Cubic yards	Cubic metres	Cubic yards	Cubic metres	Cubic yards	Cubic metres	Cubic yards	Cubic metres	Cubic yards	Cubic metres
750	573.41958	800	611.64756	850	649.87553	900	688.10350	950	726.33147
1	574.18414	1	612.41212	1	650.64009	1	688.86806	1	727.09603
2	574.94870	2	613.17668	2	651.40465	2	689.63262	2	727.86059
3	575.71326	3	613.94123	3	652.16921	3	690.39718	3	728.62515
4	576.47782	4	614.70579	4	652.93377	4	691.16174	4	729.38971
5	577.24238	5	615.47035	5	653.69833	5	691.92630	5	730.15427
6	578.00694	6	616.23491	6	654.46289	6	692.69086	6	730.91883
7	578.77150	7	616.99947	7	655.22744	7	693.45542	7	731.68339
8	579.53606	8	617.76403	8	655.99200	8	694.21998	8	732.44795
9	580.30062	9	618.52859	9	656.75656	9	694.98454	9	733.21251
760	581.06518	810	619.29315	860	657.52112	910	695.74910	960	733.97707
1	581.82974	1	620.05771	1	658.28568	1	696.51365	1	734.74163
2	582.59430	2	620.82227	2	659.05024	2	697.27821	2	735.50619
3	583.35886	3	621.58683	3	659.81480	3	698.04277	3	736.27075
4	584.12342	4	622.35139	4	660.57936	4	698.80733	4	737.03531
5	584.88798	5	623.11595	5	661.34392	5	699.57189	5	737.79986
6	585.65254	6	623.88051	6	662.10848	6	700.33645	6	738.56442
7	586.41709	7	624.64507	7	662.87304	7	701.10101	7	739.32898
8	587.18165	8	625.40963	8	663.63760	8	701.86557	8	740.09354
9	587.94621	9	626.17419	9	664.40216	9	702.63013	9	740.85810
770	588.71077	820	626.93875	870	665.16672	920	703.39469	970	741.62266
1	589.47533	1	627.70330	1	665.93128	1	704.15925	1	742.38722
2	590.23989	2	628.46786	2	666.69584	2	704.92381	2	743.15178
3	591.00445	3	629.23242	3	667.46040	3	705.68837	3	743.91634
4	591.76901	4	629.99698	4	668.22496	4	706.45293	4	744.68090
5	592.53357	5	630.76154	5	668.98951	5	707.21749	5	745.44546
6	593.29813	6	631.52610	6	669.75407	6	707.98205	6	746.21002
7	594.06269	7	632.29066	7	670.51863	7	708.74661	7	746.97458
8	594.82725	8	633.05522	8	671.28319	8	709.51117	8	747.73914
9	595.59181	9	633.81978	9	672.04775	9	710.27572	9	748.50370
780	596.35637	830	634.58434	880	672.81231	930	711.04028	980	749.26826
1	597.12093	1	635.34890	1	673.57687	1	711.80484	1	750.03282
2	597.88549	2	636.11346	2	674.34143	2	712.56940	2	750.79738
3	598.65005	3	636.87802	3	675.10599	3	713.33396	3	751.56193
4	599.41461	4	637.64258	4	675.87055	4	714.09852	4	752.32649
5	600.17916	5	638.40714	5	676.63511	5	714.86308	5	753.09105
6	600.94372	6	639.17170	6	677.39967	6	715.62764	6	753.85561
7	601.70828	7	639.93626	7	678.16423	7	716.39220	7	754.62017
8	602.47284	8	640.70082	8	678.92879	8	717.15676	8	755.38473
9	603.23740	9	641.46537	9	679.69335	9	717.92132	9	756.14929
790	604.00196	840	642.22993	890	680.45791	940	718.68588	990	756.91385
1	604.76652	1	642.99449	1	681.22247	1	719.45044	1	757.67841
2	605.53108	2	643.75905	2	681.98703	2	720.21500	2	758.44297
3	606.29564	3	644.52361	3	682.75158	3	720.97956	3	759.20753
4	607.06020	4	645.28817	4	683.51614	4	721.74412	4	759.97209
5	607.82476	5	646.05273	5	684.28070	5	722.50868	5	760.73665
6	608.58932	6	646.81729	6	685.04526	6	723.27324	6	761.50121
7	609.35388	7	647.58185	7	685.80982	7	724.03779	7	762.26577
8	610.11844	8	648.34641	8	686.57438	8	724.80235	8	763.03033
9	610.88300	9	649.11097	9	687.33894	9	725.56691	9	763.79489

CAPACITY—LITRES TO LIQUID QUARTS

[Reduction factor: 1 litre = 1.0567104 quarts]

Litres	Liquid quarts	Litres	Liquid quarts	Litres	Liquid quarts	Litres	Liquid quarts	Litres	Liquid quarts
0		50	52.8355	100	105.671	150	158.507	200	211.342
1	1.0567	1	53.8922	1	106.728	1	159.563	1	212.399
2	2.1134	2	54.9489	2	107.784	2	160.620	2	213.456
3	3.1701	3	56.0057	3	108.841	3	161.677	3	214.512
4	4.2268	4	57.062+	4	109.898	4	162.733	4	215.569
5	5.2836	5	58.1191	5	110.955	5	163.790	5	216.626
6	6.3403	6	59.1758	6	112.011	6	164.847	6	217.682
7	7.3970	7	60.2325	7	113.068	7	165.904	7	218.739
8	8.4537	8	61.2892	8	114.125	8	166.960	8	219.796
9	9.5104	9	62.3459	9	115.181	9	168.017	9	220.852
10	10.5671	60	63.4026	110	116.238	160	169.074	210	221.909
1	11.6238	1	64.4593	1	117.295	1	170.130	1	222.966
2	12.6805	2	65.5160	2	118.352	2	171.187	2	224.023
3	13.7372	3	66.5728	3	119.408	3	172.244	3	225.079
4	14.7939	4	67.6295	4	120.465	4	173.301	4	226.136
5	15.8507	5	68.6862	5	121.522	5	174.357	5	227.193
6	16.9074	6	69.7429	6	122.578	6	175.414	6	228.249
7	17.9641	7	70.7996	7	123.635	7	176.471	7	229.306
8	19.0208	8	71.8563	8	124.692	8	177.527	8	230.363
9	20.0775	9	72.9130	9	125.749	9	178.584	9	231.420
20	21.1342	70	73.9697	120	126.805	170	179.641	220	232.476
1	22.1909	1	75.0264	1	127.862	1	180.697	1	233.533
2	23.2476	2	76.0831	2	128.919	2	181.754	2	234.590
3	24.3043	3	77.1399	3	129.975	3	182.811	3	235.646
4	25.3610	4	78.1966	4	131.032	4	183.868	4	236.703
5	26.4178	5	79.2533	5	132.089	5	184.924	5	237.760
6	27.4745	6	80.3100	6	133.146	6	185.981	6	238.817
7	28.5312	7	81.3667	7	134.202	7	187.038	7	239.873
8	29.5879	8	82.4234	8	135.259	8	188.094	8	240.930
9	30.6446	9	83.4801	9	136.316	9	189.151	9	241.987
30	31.7013	80	84.5368	130	137.372	180	190.208	230	243.043
1	32.7580	1	85.5935	1	138.429	1	191.265	1	244.100
2	33.8147	2	86.6503	2	139.486	2	192.321	2	245.157
3	34.8714	3	87.7070	3	140.542	3	193.378	3	246.214
4	35.9282	4	88.7637	4	141.599	4	194.435	4	247.270
5	36.9849	5	89.8204	5	142.656	5	195.491	5	248.327
6	38.0416	6	90.8771	6	143.713	6	196.548	6	249.384
7	39.0983	7	91.9338	7	144.769	7	197.605	7	250.440
8	40.1550	8	92.9905	8	145.826	8	198.662	8	251.497
9	41.2117	9	94.0472	9	146.883	9	199.718	9	252.554
40	42.2684	90	95.1039	140	147.939	190	200.775	240	253.610
1	43.3251	1	96.1606	1	148.996	1	201.832	1	254.667
2	44.3818	2	97.2174	2	150.053	2	202.888	2	255.724
3	45.4385	3	98.2741	3	151.110	3	203.945	3	256.781
4	46.4953	4	99.3308	4	152.166	4	205.002	4	257.837
5	47.5520	5	100.3875	5	153.223	5	206.059	5	258.894
6	48.6087	6	101.4442	6	154.280	6	207.115	6	259.951
7	49.6654	7	102.5009	7	155.336	7	208.172	7	261.007
8	50.7221	8	103.5576	8	156.393	8	209.229	8	262.064
9	51.7788	9	104.6143	9	157.450	9	210.285	9	263.121

CAPACITY—LITRES TO LIQUID QUARTS

[Reduction factor: 1 litre = 1.0567104 quarts]

Litres	Liquid quarts	Litres	Liquid quarts	Litres	Liquid quarts	Litres	Liquid quarts	Litres	Liquid quarts
250	264.178	300	317.013	350	369.849	400	422.684	450	475.520
1	265.234	1	318.070	1	370.905	1	423.741	1	476.576
2	266.291	2	319.127	2	371.962	2	424.798	2	477.633
3	267.348	3	320.183	3	373.019	3	425.854	3	478.690
4	268.404	4	321.240	4	374.075	4	426.911	4	479.747
5	269.461	5	322.297	5	375.132	5	427.968	5	480.803
6	270.518	6	323.353	6	376.189	6	429.024	6	481.860
7	271.575	7	324.410	7	377.246	7	430.081	7	482.917
8	272.631	8	325.467	8	378.302	8	431.138	8	483.973
9	273.688	9	326.524	9	379.359	9	432.195	9	485.030
260	274.745	310	327.580	360	380.416	410	433.251	460	486.087
1	275.801	1	328.637	1	381.472	1	434.308	1	487.143
2	276.858	2	329.694	2	382.529	2	435.365	2	488.200
3	277.915	3	330.750	3	383.586	3	436.421	3	489.257
4	278.972	4	331.807	4	384.643	4	437.478	4	490.314
5	280.028	5	332.864	5	385.699	5	438.535	5	491.370
6	281.085	6	333.920	6	386.756	6	439.592	6	492.427
7	282.142	7	334.977	7	387.813	7	440.648	7	493.484
8	283.198	8	336.034	8	388.869	8	441.705	8	494.540
9	284.255	9	337.091	9	389.926	9	442.762	9	495.597
270	285.312	320	338.147	370	390.983	420	443.818	470	496.654
1	286.369	1	339.204	1	392.040	1	444.875	1	497.711
2	287.425	2	340.261	2	393.096	2	445.932	2	498.767
3	288.482	3	341.317	3	394.153	3	446.988	3	499.824
4	289.539	4	342.374	4	395.210	4	448.045	4	500.881
5	290.595	5	343.431	5	396.266	5	449.102	5	501.937
6	291.652	6	344.488	6	397.323	6	450.159	6	502.994
7	292.709	7	345.544	7	398.380	7	451.215	7	504.051
8	293.765	8	346.601	8	399.437	8	452.272	8	505.108
9	294.822	9	347.658	9	400.493	9	453.329	9	506.164
280	295.879	330	348.714	380	401.550	430	454.385	480	507.221
1	296.936	1	349.771	1	402.607	1	455.442	1	508.278
2	297.992	2	350.828	2	403.663	2	456.499	2	509.334
3	299.049	3	351.885	3	404.720	3	457.556	3	510.391
4	300.106	4	352.941	4	405.777	4	458.612	4	511.448
5	301.162	5	353.998	5	406.834	5	459.669	5	512.505
6	302.219	6	355.055	6	407.890	6	460.726	6	513.561
7	303.276	7	356.111	7	408.947	7	461.782	7	514.618
8	304.333	8	357.168	8	410.004	8	462.839	8	515.675
9	305.389	9	358.225	9	411.060	9	463.896	9	516.731
290	306.446	340	359.282	390	412.117	440	464.953	490	517.788
1	307.503	1	360.338	1	413.174	1	466.009	1	518.845
2	308.559	2	361.395	2	414.230	2	467.066	2	519.902
3	309.616	3	362.452	3	415.287	3	468.123	3	520.958
4	310.673	4	363.508	4	416.344	4	469.179	4	522.015
5	311.730	5	364.565	5	417.401	5	470.236	5	523.072
6	312.786	6	365.622	6	418.457	6	471.293	6	524.128
7	313.843	7	366.679	7	419.514	7	472.350	7	525.185
8	314.900	8	367.735	8	420.571	8	473.406	8	526.242
9	315.956	9	368.792	9	421.627	9	474.463	9	527.298

CAPACITY—LITRES TO LIQUID QUARTS

[Reduction factor: 1 litre = 1.0567104 quarts]

Litres	Liquid quarts	Litres	Liquid quarts	Litres	Liquid quarts	Litres	Liquid quarts	Litres	Liquid quarts
500	528. 355	550	581. 191	600	634. 026	650	686. 862	700	739. 697
1	529. 412	1	582. 247	1	·635. 083	1	687. 918	1	740 754
2	530. 469	2	583. 304	2	636. 140	2	688. 975	2	741. 811
3	531. 525	3	584. 361	3	637. 196	3	690. 032	3	742. 867
4	532. 582	4	585. 418	4	638. 253	4	691. 089	4	743. 924
5	533. 639	5	586. 474	5	639. 310	5	692. 145	5	744. 981
6	534. 695	6	587. 531	6	640. 367	6	693. 202	6	746. 038
7	535. 752	7	588. 588	7	641. 423	7	694. 259	7	747. 094
8	536. 809	8	589. 644	8	642. 480	8	695. 315	8	748. 151
9	537. 866	9	590. 701	9	643. 537	9	696. 372	9	749. 208
510	538. 922	560	591. 758	610	644. 593	660	697. 429	710	750. 264
1	539. 979	1	592. 815	1	645. 650	1	698. 486	1	751. 321
2	541. 036	2	593. 871	2	646. 707	2	699. 542	2	752. 378
3	542. 092	3	594. 928	3	647. 763	3	700. 599	3	753. 435
4	543. 149	4	595. 985	4	648. 820	4	701. 656	4	754. 491
5	544. 206	5	597. 041	5	649. 877	5	702. 712	5	755. 548
6	545. 263	6	598. 098	6	650. 934	6	703. 769	6	756. 605
7	546. 319	7	599. 155	7	651. 990	7	704. 826	7	757. 661
8	547. 376	8	600. 212	8	653. 047	8	705. 883	8	758. 718
9	548. 433	9	601. 268	9	654. 104	9	706. 939	9	759. 775
520	549. 489	570	602. 325	620	655. 160	670	707. 996	720	760. 831
1	550. 546	1	603. 382	1	656. 217	1	709. 053	1	761. 888
2	551. 603	2	604. 438	2	657. 274	2	710. 109	2	762. 945
3	552. 660	3	605. 495	3	658. 331	3	711. 166	3	764. 002
4	553. 716	4	606. 552	4	659. 387	4	712. 223	4	765. 058
5	554. 773	5	607. 608	5	660. 444	5	713. 280	5	766. 115
6	555. 830	6	608. 665	6	661. 501	6	714. 336	6	767. 172
7	556. 886	7	609. 722	7	662. 557	7	715. 393	7	768. 228
8	557. 943	8	610. 779	8	663. 614	8	716. 450	8	769. 285
9	559. 000	9	611. 835	9	664. 671	9	717. 506	9	770. 342
530	560. 057	580	612 892	630	665. 728	680	718. 563	730	771. 399
1	561. 113	1	613. 949	1	666. 784	1	719. 620	1	772. 455
2	562. 170	2	615. 005	2	667. 841	2	720. 676	2	773. 512
3	563. 227	3	616. 062	3	668. 898	3	721. 733	3	774. 569
4	564. 283	4	617. 119	4	669. 954	4	722. 790	4	775. 625
5	565. 340	5	618. 176	5	671. 011	5	723. 847	5	776. 682
6	566. 397	6	619. 232	6	672. 068	6	724. 903	6	777. 739
7	567. 453	7	620. 289	7	673. 125	7	725. 960	7	778. 796
8	568. 510	8	621. 346	8	674. 181	8	727. 017	8	779. 852
9	569. 567	9	622. 402	9	675. 238	9	728. 073	9	780. 909
540	570. 624	590	623. 459	640	676. 295	690	729. 130	740	781. 966
1	571. 680	1	624. 516	1	677. 351	1	730. 187	1	783. 022
2	572. 737	2	625. 573	2	678. 408	2	731. 244	2	784. 079
3	573. 794	3	626. 629	3	679. 465	3	732. 300	3	785. 136
4	574. 850	4	627. 686	4	680. 521	4	733. 357	4	786. 193
5	575. 907	5	628. 743	5	681. 578	5	734. 414	5	787. 249
6	5'6. 964	6	629. 799	6	682. 635	6	735. 470	6	788. 306
7	578. 021	7	630. 856	7	683. 692	7	736. 527	7	789. 363
8	579. 077	8	631. 913	8	684. 748	8	737. 584	8	790. 419
9	580. 134	9	632. 970	9	685. 805	9	738. 641	9	791. 476

CAPACITY—LITRES TO LIQUID QUARTS

[Reduction factor: 1 litre = 1.0567104 quarts]

Litres	Liquid quarts	Litres	Liquid quarts	Litres	Liquid quarts	Litres	Liquid quarts	Litres	Liquid quarts
750	792.533	800	845.368	850	898.204	900	951.039	950	1,003.875
1	793.590	1	846.425	1	899.261	1	952.096	1	1,004.932
2	794.646	2	847.482	2	900.317	2	953.153	2	1,005.988
3	795.703	3	848.538	3	901.374	3	954.209	3	1,007.045
4	796.760	4	849.595	4	902.431	4	955.266	4	1,008.102
5	797.816	5	850.652	5	903.487	5	956.323	5	1,009.158
6	798.873	6	851.709	6	904.544	6	957.380	6	1,010.215
7	799.930	7	852.765	7	905.601	7	958.436	7	1,011.272
8	800.986	8	853.822	8	906.658	8	959.493	8	1,012.329
9	802.043	9	854.879	9	907.714	9	960.550	9	1,013.385
760	803.100	810	855.935	860	908.771	910	961.606	960	1,014.442
1	804.157	1	856.992	1	909.828	1	962.663	1	1,015.499
2	805.213	2	858.049	2	910.884	2	963.720	2	1,016.555
3	806.270	3	859.106	3	911.941	3	964.777	3	1,017.612
4	807.327	4	860.162	4	912.998	4	965.833	4	1,018.669
5	808.383	5	861.219	5	914.054	5	966.890	5	1,019.726
6	809.440	6	862.276	6	915.111	6	967.947	6	1,020.782
7	810.497	7	863.332	7	916.168	7	969.003	7	1,021.839
8	811.554	8	864.389	8	917.225	8	970.060	8	1,022.896
9	812.610	9	865.446	9	918.281	9	971.117	9	1,023.952
770	813.667	820	866.503	870	919.338	920	972.174	970	1,025.009
1	814.724	1	867.559	1	920.395	1	973.230	1	1,026.066
2	815.780	2	868.616	2	921.451	2	974.287	2	1,027.123
3	816.837	3	869.673	3	922.508	3	975.344	3	1,028.179
4	817.894	4	870.729	4	923.565	4	976.400	4	1,029.236
5	818.951	5	871.786	5	924.622	5	977.457	5	1,030.293
6	820.007	6	872.843	6	925.678	6	978.514	6	1,031.349
7	821.064	7	873.900	7	926.735	7	979.571	7	1,032.406
8	822.121	8	874.956	8	927.792	8	980.627	8	1,033.463
9	823.177	9	876.013	9	928.848	9	981.684	9	1,034.519
780	824.234	830	877.070	880	929.905	930	982.741	980	1,035.576
1	825.291	1	878.126	1	930.962	1	983.797	1	1,036.633
2	826.348	2	879.183	2	932.019	2	984.854	2	1,037.690
3	827.404	3	880.240	3	933.075	3	985.911	3	1,038.746
4	828.461	4	881.296	4	934.132	4	986.968	4	1,039.803
5	829.518	5	882.353	5	935.189	5	988.024	5	1,040.860
6	830.574	6	883.410	6	936.245	6	989.081	6	1,041.916
7	831.631	7	884.467	7	937.302	7	990.138	7	1,042.973
8	832.688	8	885.523	8	938.359	8	991.194	8	1,044.030
9	833.745	9	886.580	9	939.416	9	992.251	9	1,045.087
790	834.801	840	887.637	890	940.472	940	993.308	990	1,046.143
1	835.858	1	888.693	1	941.529	1	994.364	1	1,047.200
2	836.915	2	889.750	2	942.586	2	995.421	2	1,048.257
3	837.971	3	890.807	3	943.642	3	996.478	3	1,049.313
4	839.028	4	891.864	4	944.699	4	997.535	4	1,050.370
5	840.085	5	892.920	5	945.756	5	998.591	5	1,051.427
6	841.141	6	893.977	6	946.813	6	999.648	6	1,052.484
7	842.198	7	895.034	7	947.869	7	1,000.705	7	1,053.540
8	843.255	8	896.090	8	948.926	8	1,001.761	8	1,054.597
9	844.312	9	897.147	9	949.983	9	1,002.818	9	1,055.654

CAPACITY—LIQUID QUARTS TO LITRES

[Reduction factor: 1 liquid quart = 0.94633307 litre]

Liquid quarts	Litres	Liquid quarts	Litres	Liquid quarts	Litres	Liquid quarts	Litres	Liquid quarts	Litres
0		50	47.3167	100	94.633	150	141.950	200	189.267
1	0.9463	1	48.2630	1	95.580	1	142.896	1	190.213
2	1.8927	2	49.2093	2	96.526	2	143.843	2	191.159
3	2.8390	3	50.1557	3	97.472	3	144.789	3	192.106
4	3.7853	4	51.1020	4	98.419	4	145.735	4	193.052
5	4.7317	5	52.0483	5	99.365	5	146.682	5	193.998
6	5.6780	6	52.9947	6	100.311	6	147.628	6	194.945
7	6.6243	7	53.9410	7	101.258	7	148.574	7	195.891
8	7.5707	8	54.8873	8	102.204	8	149.521	8	196.837
9	8.5170	9	55.8337	9	103.150	9	150.467	9	197.784
10	9.4633	60	56.7800	110	104.097	160	151.413	210	198.730
1	10.4097	1	57.7263	1	105.043	1	152.360	1	199.676
2	11.3560	2	58.6727	2	105.989	2	153.306	2	200.623
3	12.3023	3	59.6190	3	106.936	3	154.252	3	201.569
4	13.2487	4	60.5653	4	107.882	4	155.199	4	202.515
5	14.1950	5	61.5116	5	108.828	5	156.145	5	203.462
6	15.1413	6	62.4580	6	109.775	6	157.091	6	204.408
7	16.0877	7	63.4043	7	110.721	7	158.038	7	205.354
8	17.0340	8	64.3506	8	111.667	8	158.984	8	206.301
9	17.9803	9	65.2970	9	112.614	9	159.930	9	207.247
20	18.9267	70	66.2433	120	113.560	170	160.877	220	208.193
1	19.8730	1	67.1896	1	114.506	1	161.823	1	209.140
2	20.8193	2	68.1360	2	115.453	2	162.769	2	210.086
3	21.7657	3	69.0823	3	116.399	3	163.716	3	211.032
4	22.7120	4	70.0286	4	117.345	4	164.662	4	211.979
5	23.6583	5	70.9750	5	118.292	5	165.608	5	212.925
6	24.6047	6	71.9213	6	119.238	6	166.555	6	213.871
7	25.5510	7	72.8676	7	120.184	7	167.501	7	214.818
8	26.4973	8	73.8140	8	121.131	8	168.447	8	215.764
9	27.4437	9	74.7603	9	122.077	9	169.394	9	216.710
30	28.3900	80	75.7066	130	123.023	180	170.340	230	217.657
1	29.3363	1	76.6530	1	123.970	1	171.286	1	218.603
2	30.2827	2	77.5993	2	124.916	2	172.233	2	219.549
3	31.2290	3	78.5456	3	125.862	3	173.179	3	220.496
4	32.1753	4	79.4920	4	126.809	4	174.125	4	221.442
5	33.1217	5	80.4383	5	127.755	5	175.072	5	222.388
6	34.0680	6	81.3846	6	128.701	6	176.018	6	223.335
7	35.0143	7	82.3310	7	129.648	7	176.964	7	224.281
8	35.9607	8	83.2773	8	130.594	8	177.911	8	225.227
9	36.9070	9	84.2236	9	131.540	9	178.857	9	226.174
40	37.8533	90	85.1700	140	132.487	190	179.803	240	227.120
1	38.7997	1	86.1163	1	133.433	1	180.750	1	228.066
2	39.7460	2	87.0626	2	134.379	2	181.696	2	229.013
3	40.6923	3	88.0090	3	135.326	3	182.642	3	229.959
4	41.6387	4	88.9553	4	136.272	4	183.589	4	230.905
5	42.5850	5	89.9016	5	137.218	5	184.535	5	231.852
6	43.5313	6	90.8480	6	138.165	6	185.481	6	232.798
7	44.4777	7	91.7943	7	139.111	7	186.428	7	233.744
8	45.4240	8	92.7406	8	140.057	8	187.374	8	234.691
9	46.3703	9	93.6870	9	141.004	9	188.320	9	235.637

CAPACITY—LIQUID QUARTS TO LITRES

[Reduction factor: 1 liquid quart = 0.94633307 litre]

Liquid quarts	Litres	Liquid quarts	Litres	Liquid quarts	Litres	Liquid quarts	Litres	Liquid quarts	Litres
250	236.583	300	283.900	350	331.217	400	378.533	450	425.850
1	237.530	1	284.846	1	332.163	1	379.480	1	426.796
2	238.476	2	285.793	2	333.109	2	380.426	2	427.743
3	239.422	3	286.739	3	334.056	3	381.372	3	428.689
4	240.369	4	287.685	4	335.002	4	382.319	4	429.635
5	241.315	5	288.632	5	335.948	5	383.265	5	430.582
6	242.261	6	289.578	6	336.895	6	384.211	6	431.528
7	243.208	7	290.524	7	337.841	7	385.158	7	432.474
8	244.154	8	291.471	8	338.787	8	386.104	8	433.421
9	245.100	9	292.417	9	339.734	9	387.050	9	434.367
260	246.047	310	293.363	360	340.680	410	387.997	460	435.313
1	246.993	1	294.310	1	341.626	1	388.943	1	436.260
2	247.939	2	295.256	2	342.573	2	389.889	2	437.206
3	248.886	3	296.202	3	343.519	3	390.836	3	438.152
4	249.832	4	297.149	4	344.465	4	391.782	4	439.099
5	250.778	5	298.095	5	345.412	5	392.728	5	440.045
6	251.725	6	299.041	6	346.358	6	393.675	6	440.991
7	252.671	7	299.988	7	347.304	7	394.621	7	441.938
8	253.617	8	300.934	8	348.251	8	395.567	8	442.884
9	254.564	9	301.880	9	349.197	9	396.514	9	443.830
270	255.510	320	302.827	370	350.143	420	397.460	470	444.777
1	256.456	1	303.773	1	351.090	1	398.406	1	445.723
2	257.403	2	304.719	2	352.036	2	399.353	2	446.669
3	258.349	3	305.666	3	352.982	3	400.299	3	447.616
4	259.295	4	306.612	4	353.929	4	401.245	4	448.562
5	260.242	5	307.558	5	354.875	5	402.192	5	449.508
6	261.188	6	308.505	6	355.821	6	403.138	6	450.455
7	262.134	7	309.451	7	356.768	7	404.084	7	451.401
8	263.081	8	310.397	8	357.714	8	405.031	8	452.347
9	264.027	9	311.344	9	358.660	9	405.977	9	453.294
280	264.973	330	312.290	380	359.607	430	406.923	480	454.240
1	265.920	1	313.236	1	360.553	1	407.870	1	455.186
2	266.866	2	314.183	2	361.499	2	408.816	2	456.133
3	267.812	3	315.129	3	362.446	3	409.762	3	457.079
4	268.759	4	316.075	4	363.392	4	410.709	4	458.025
5	269.705	5	317.022	5	364.338	5	411.655	5	458.972
6	270.651	6	317.968	6	365.285	6	412.601	6	459.918
7	271.598	7	318.914	7	366.231	7	413.548	7	460.864
8	272.544	8	319.861	8	367.177	8	414.494	8	461.811
9	273.490	9	320.807	9	368.124	9	415.440	9	462.757
290	274.437	340	321.753	390	369.070	440	416.387	490	463.703
1	275.383	1	322.700	1	370.016	1	417.333	1	464.650
2	276.329	2	323.646	2	370.963	2	418.279	2	465.596
3	277.276	3	324.592	3	371.909	3	419.226	3	466.542
4	278.222	4	325.539	4	372.855	4	420.172	4	467.489
5	279.168	5	326.485	5	373.802	5	421.118	5	468.435
6	280.115	6	327.431	6	374.748	6	422.065	6	469.381
7	281.061	7	328.378	7	375.694	7	423.011	7	470.328
8	282.007	8	329.324	8	376.641	8	423.957	8	471.274
9	282.954	9	330.270	9	377.587	9	424.904	9	472.220

CAPACITY—LIQUID QUARTS TO LITRES

[Reduction factor: 1 liquid quart = 0.94633307 litre]

Liquid quarts	Litres	Liquid quarts	Litres	Liquid quarts	Litres	Liquid quarts	Litres	Liquid quarts	Litres
500	473.167	550	520.483	600	567.800	650	615.116	700	662.433
1	474.113	1	521.430	1	568.746	1	616.063	1	663.379
2	475.059	2	522.376	2	569.693	2	617.009	2	664.326
3	476.006	3	523.322	3	570.639	3	617.955	3	665.272
4	476.952	4	524.269	4	571.585	4	618.902	4	666.218
5	477.898	5	525.215	5	572.532	5	619.848	5	667.165
6	478.845	6	526.161	6	573.478	6	620.794	6	668.111
7	479.791	7	527.108	7	574.424	7	621.741	7	669.057
8	480.737	8	528.054	8	575.371	8	622.687	8	670.004
9	481.684	9	529.000	9	576.317	9	623.633	9	670.950
510	482.630	560	529.947	610	577.263	660	624.580	710	671.896
1	483.576	1	530.893	1	578.210	1	625.526	1	672.843
2	484.523	2	531.839	2	579.156	2	626.472	2	673.789
3	485.469	3	532.786	3	580.102	3	627.419	3	674.735
4	486.415	4	533.732	4	581.049	4	628.365	4	675.682
5	487.362	5	534.678	5	581.995	5	629.311	5	676.628
6	488.308	6	535.625	6	582.941	6	630.258	6	677.574
7	489.254	7	536.571	7	583.888	7	631.204	7	678.521
8	490.201	8	537.517	8	584.834	8	632.150	8	679.467
9	491.147	9	538.464	9	585.780	9	633.097	9	680.413
520	492.093	570	539.410	620	586.727	670	634.043	720	681.360
1	493.040	1	540.356	1	587.673	1	634.989	1	682.306
2	493.986	2	541.303	2	588.619	2	635.936	2	683.252
3	494.932	3	542.249	3	589.566	3	636.882	3	684.199
4	495.879	4	543.195	4	590.512	4	637.828	4	685.145
5	496.825	5	544.142	5	591.458	5	638.775	5	686.091
6	497.771	6	545.088	6	592.405	6	639.721	6	687.038
7	498.718	7	546.034	7	593.351	7	640.667	7	687.984
8	499.664	8	546.981	8	594.297	8	641.614	8	688.930
9	500.610	9	547.927	9	595.244	9	642.560	9	689.877
530	501.557	580	548.873	630	596.190	680	643.506	730	690.823
1	502.503	1	549.820	1	597.136	1	644.453	1	691.769
2	503.449	2	550.766	2	598.083	2	645.399	2	692.716
3	504.396	3	551.712	3	599.029	3	646.345	3	693.662
4	505.342	4	552.659	4	599.975	4	647.292	4	694.608
5	506.288	5	553.605	5	600.922	5	648.238	5	695.555
6	507.235	6	554.551	6	601.868	6	649.184	6	696.501
7	508.181	7	555.498	7	602.814	7	650.131	7	697.447
8	509.127	8	556.444	8	603.761	8	651.077	8	698.394
9	510.074	9	557.390	9	604.707	9	652.023	9	699.340
540	511.020	590	558.337	640	605.653	690	652.970	740	700.286
1	511.966	1	559.283	1	606.599	1	653.916	1	701.233
2	512.913	2	560.229	2	607.546	2	654.862	2	702.179
3	513.859	3	561.176	3	608.492	3	655.809	3	703.125
4	514.805	4	562.122	4	609.438	4	656.755	4	704.072
5	515.752	5	563.068	5	610.385	5	657.701	5	705.018
6	516.698	6	564.015	6	611.331	6	658.648	6	705.964
7	517.644	7	564.961	7	612.277	7	659.594	7	706.911
8	518.591	8	565.907	8	613.224	8	660.540	8	707.857
9	519.537	9	566.854	9	614.170	9	661.487	9	708.803

CAPACITY—LIQUID QUARTS TO LITRES

[Reduction factor: 1 liquid quart = 0.94633307 litre]

Liquid quarts	Litres	Liquid quarts	Litres	Liquid quarts	Litres	Liquid quarts	Litres	Liquid quarts	Litres
750	709. 750	**800**	757. 066	**850**	804. 383	**900**	851. 700	**950**	899. 016
1	710. 696	1	758. 013	1	805. 329	1	852. 646	1	899. 963
2	711. 642	2	758. 959	2	806. 276	2	853. 592	2	900. 909
3	712. 589	3	759. 905	3	807. 222	3	854. 539	3	901. 855
4	713. 535	4	760. 852	4	808. 168	4	855. 485	4	902. 802
5	714. 481	5	761. 798	5	809. 115	5	856. 431	5	903. 748
6	715. 428	6	762. 744	6	810. 061	6	857. 378	6	904. 694
7	716. 374	7	763. 691	7	811. 007	7	858. 324	7	905. 641
8	717. 320	8	764. 637	8	811. 954	8	859. 270	8	906. 587
9	718. 267	9	765. 583	9	812. 900	9	860. 217	9	907. 533
760	719. 213	**810**	766. 530	**860**	813. 846	**910**	861. 163	**960**	908. 480
1	720. 159	1	767. 476	1	814. 793	1	862. 109	1	909. 426
2	721. 106	2	768. 422	2	815. 739	2	863. 056	2	910. 372
3	722. 052	3	769. 369	3	816. 685	3	864. 002	3	911. 319
4	722. 998	4	770. 315	4	817. 632	4	864. 948	4	912. 265
5	723. 945	5	771. 261	5	818. 578	5	865. 895	5	913. 211
6	724. 891	6	772. 208	6	819. 524	6	866. 841	6	914. 158
7	725. 837	7	773. 154	7	820. 471	7	867. 787	7	915. 104
8	726. 784	8	774. 100	8	821. 417	8	868. 734	8	916. 050
9	727. 730	9	775. 047	9	822. 363	9	869. 680	9	916. 997
770	728. 676	**820**	775. 993	**870**	823. 310	**920**	870. 626	**970**	917. 943
1	729. 623	1	776. 939	1	824. 256	1	871. 573	1	918. 889
2	730. 569	2	777. 886	2	825. 202	2	872. 519	2	919. 836
3	731. 515	3	778. 832	3	826. 149	3	873. 465	3	920. 782
4	732. 462	4	779. 778	4	827. 095	4	874. 412	4	921. 728
5	733. 408	5	780. 725	5	828. 041	5	875. 358	5	922. 675
6	734. 354	6	781. 671	6	828. 988	6	876. 304	6	923. 621
7	735. 301	7	782. 617	7	829. 934	7	877. 251	7	924. 567
8	736. 247	8	783. 564	8	830. 880	8	878. 197	8	925. 514
9	737. 193	9	784. 510	9	831. 827	9	879. 143	9	926. 460
780	738. 140	**830**	785. 456	**880**	832. 773	**930**	880. 090	**980**	927. 406
1	739. 086	1	786. 403	1	833. 719	1	881. 036	1	928. 353
2	740. 032	2	787. 349	2	834. 666	2	881. 982	2	929. 299
3	740. 979	3	788. 295	3	835. 612	3	882. 929	3	930. 245
4	741. 925	4	789. 242	4	836. 558	4	883. 875	4	931. 192
5	742. 871	5	790. 188	5	837. 505	5	884. 821	5	932. 138
6	743. 818	6	791. 134	6	838. 451	6	885. 768	6	933. 084
7	744. 764	7	792. 081	7	839. 397	7	886. 714	7	934. 031
8	745. 710	8	793. 027	8	840. 344	8	887. 660	8	934. 977
9	746. 657	9	793. 973	9	841. 290	9	888. 607	9	935. 923
790	747. 603	**840**	794. 920	**890**	842. 236	**940**	889. 553	**990**	936. 870
1	748. 549	1	795. 866	1	843. 183	1	890. 499	1	937. 816
2	749. 496	2	796. 812	2	844. 129	2	891. 446	2	938. 762
3	750. 442	3	797. 759	3	845. 075	3	892. 392	3	939. 709
4	751. 388	4	798. 705	4	846. 022	4	893. 338	4	940. 655
5	752. 335	5	799. 651	5	846. 968	5	894. 285	5	941. 601
6	753. 281	6	800. 598	6	847. 914	6	895. 231	6	942. 548
7	754. 227	7	801. 544	7	848. 861	7	896. 177	7	943. 494
8	755. 174	8	802. 490	8	849. 807	8	897. 124	8	944. 440
9	756. 120	9	803. 437	9	850. 753	9	898. 070	9	945. 387

CAPACITY—LITRES TO GALLONS

[Reduction factor: 1 litre = 0.26417760 gallon]

Litres	Gallons	Litres	Gallons	Litres	Gallons	Litres	Gallons	Litres	Gallons
0		50	13.20888	100	26.4178	150	39.6266	200	52.8355
1	0.26418	1	13.47306	1	26.6819	1	39.8908	1	53.0997
2	0.52836	2	13.73724	2	26.9461	2	40.1550	2	53.3639
3	0.79253	3	14.00141	3	27.2103	3	40.4192	3	53.6281
4	1.05671	4	14.26559	4	27.4745	4	40.6834	4	53.8922
5	1.32089	5	14.52977	5	27.7386	5	40.9475	5	54.1564
6	1.58507	6	14.79395	6	28.0028	6	41.2117	6	54.4206
7	1.84924	7	15.05812	7	28.2670	7	41.4759	7	54.6848
8	2.11342	8	15.32230	8	28.5312	8	41.7401	8	54.9489
9	2.37760	9	15.58648	9	28.7954	9	42.0042	9	55.2131
10	2.64178	60	15.85066	110	29.0595	160	42.2684	210	55.4773
1	2.90595	1	16.11483	1	29.3237	1	42.5326	1	55.7415
2	3.17013	2	16.37901	2	29.5879	2	42.7968	2	56.0057
3	3.43431	3	16.64319	3	29.8521	3	43.0609	3	56.2698
4	3.69849	4	16.90737	4	30.1162	4	43.3251	4	56.5340
5	3.96266	5	17.17154	5	30.3804	5	43.5893	5	56.7982
6	4.22684	6	17.43572	6	30.6446	6	43.8535	6	57.0624
7	4.49102	7	17.69990	7	30.9088	7	44.1177	7	57.3265
8	4.75520	8	17.96408	8	31.1730	8	44.3818	8	57.5907
9	5.01937	9	18.22825	9	31.4371	9	44.6460	9	57.8549
20	5.28355	70	18.49243	120	31.7013	170	44.9102	220	58.1191
1	5.54773	1	18.75661	1	31.9655	1	45.1744	1	58.3832
2	5.81191	2	19.02079	2	32.2297	2	45.4385	2	58.6474
3	6.07608	3	19.28496	3	32.4938	3	45.7027	3	58.9116
4	6.34026	4	19.54914	4	32.7580	4	45.9669	4	59.1758
5	6.60444	5	19.81332	5	33.0222	5	46.2311	5	59.4400
6	6.86862	6	20.07750	6	33.2864	6	46.4953	6	59.7041
7	7.13280	7	20.34168	7	33.5506	7	46.7594	7	59.9683
8	7.39697	8	20.60585	8	33.8147	8	47.0236	8	60.2325
9	7.66115	9	20.87003	9	34.0789	9	47.2878	9	60.4967
30	7.92533	80	21.13421	130	34.3431	180	47.5520	230	60.7608
1	8.18951	1	21.39839	1	34.6073	1	47.8161	1	61.0250
2	8.45368	2	21.66256	2	34.8714	2	48.0803	2	61.2892
3	8.71786	3	21.92674	3	35.1356	3	48.3445	3	61.5534
4	8.98204	4	22.19092	4	35.3998	4	48.6087	4	61.8176
5	9.24622	5	22.45510	5	35.6640	5	48.8729	5	62.0817
6	9.51039	6	22.71927	6	35.9282	6	49.1370	6	62.3459
7	9.77457	7	22.98345	7	36.1923	7	49.4012	7	62.6101
8	10.03875	8	23.24763	8	36.4565	8	49.6654	8	62.8743
9	10.30293	9	23.51181	9	36.7207	9	49.9296	9	63.1384
40	10.56710	90	23.77598	140	36.9849	190	50.1937	240	63.4026
1	10.83128	1	24.04016	1	37.2490	1	50.4579	1	63.6668
2	11.09546	2	24.30434	2	37.5132	2	50.7221	2	63.9310
3	11.35964	3	24.56852	3	37.7774	3	50.9863	3	64.1952
4	11.62381	4	24.83269	4	38.0416	4	51.2505	4	64.4593
5	11.88799	5	25.09687	5	38.3058	5	51.5146	5	64.7235
6	12.15217	6	25.36105	6	38.5699	6	51.7788	6	64.9877
7	12.41635	7	25.62523	7	38.8341	7	52.0430	7	65.2519
8	12.68052	8	25.88940	8	39.0983	8	52.3072	8	65.5160
9	12.94470	9	26.15358	9	39.3625	9	52.5713	9	65.7802

CAPACITY—LITRES TO GALLONS

[Reduction factor: 1 litre = 0.26417760 gallon]

Litres	Gallons	Litres	Gallons	Litres	Gallons	Litres	Gallons	Litres	Gallons
250	66.0444	300	79.2533	350	92.4622	400	105.6710	450	118.8799
1	66.3086	1	79.5175	1	92.7263	1	105.9352	1	119.1441
2	66.5728	2	79.7816	2	92.9905	2	106.1994	2	119.4083
3	66.8369	3	80.0458	3	93.2547	3	106.4636	3	119.6725
4	67.1011	4	80.3100	4	93.5189	4	106.7278	4	119.9366
5	67.3653	5	80.5742	5	93.7830	5	106.9919	5	120.2008
6	67.6295	6	80.8383	6	94.0472	6	107.2561	6	120.4650
7	67.8936	7	81.1025	7	94.3114	7	107.5203	7	120.7292
8	68.1578	8	81.3667	8	94.5756	8	107.7845	8	120.9933
9	68.4220	9	81.6309	9	94.8398	9	108.0486	9	121.2575
260	68.6862	310	81.8951	360	95.1039	410	108.3128	460	121.5217
1	68.9504	1	82.1592	1	95.3681	1	108.5770	1	121.7859
2	69.2145	2	82.4234	2	95.6323	2	108.8412	2	122.0501
3	69.4787	3	82.6876	3	95.8965	3	109.1053	3	122.3142
4	69.7429	4	82.9518	4	96.1606	4	109.3695	4	122.5784
5	70.0071	5	83.2159	5	96.4248	5	109.6337	5	122.8426
6	70.2712	6	83.4801	6	96.6890	6	109.8979	6	123.1068
7	70.5354	7	83.7443	7	96.9532	7	110.1621	7	123.3709
8	70.7996	8	84.0085	8	97.2174	8	110.4262	8	123.6351
9	71.0638	9	84.2727	9	97.4815	9	110.6904	9	123.8993
270	71.3280	320	84.5368	370	97.7457	420	110.9546	470	124.1635
1	71.5921	1	84.8010	1	98.0099	1	111.2188	1	124.4276
2	71.8563	2	85.0652	2	98.2741	2	111.4829	2	124.6918
3	72.1205	3	85.3294	3	98.5382	3	111.7471	3	124.9560
4	72.3847	4	85.5935	4	98.8024	4	112.0113	4	125.2202
5	72.6488	5	85.8577	5	99.0666	5	112.2755	5	125.4844
6	72.9130	6	86.1219	6	99.3308	6	112.5397	6	125.7485
7	73.1772	7	86.3861	7	99.5950	7	112.8038	7	126.0127
8	73.4414	8	86.6503	8	99.8591	8	113.0680	8	126.2769
9	73.7056	9	86.9144	9	100.1233	9	113.3322	9	126.5411
280	73.9697	330	87.1786	380	100.3875	430	113.5964	480	126.8052
1	74.2339	1	87.4428	1	100.6517	1	113.8605	1	127.0694
2	74.4981	2	87.7070	2	100.9158	2	114.1247	2	127.3336
3	74.7623	3	87.9711	3	101.1800	3	114.3889	3	127.5978
4	75.0264	4	88.2353	4	101.4442	4	114.6531	4	127.8620
5	75.2906	5	88.4995	5	101.7084	5	114.9173	5	128.1261
6	75.5548	6	88.7637	6	101.9726	6	115.1814	6	128.3903
7	75.8190	7	89.0279	7	102.2367	7	115.4456	7	128.6545
8	76.0831	8	89.2920	8	102.5009	8	115.7098	8	128.9187
9	76.3473	9	89.5562	9	102.7651	9	115.9740	9	129.1828
290	76.6115	340	89.8204	390	103.0293	440	116.2381	490	129.4470
1	76.8757	1	90.0846	1	103.2934	1	116.5023	1	129.7112
2	77.1399	2	90.3487	2	103.5576	2	116.7665	2	129.9754
3	77.4040	3	90.6129	3	103.8218	3	117.0307	3	130.2396
4	77.6682	4	90.8771	4	104.0860	4	117.2949	4	130.5037
5	77.9324	5	91.1413	5	104.3502	5	117.5590	5	130.7679
6	78.1966	6	91.4054	6	104.6143	6	117.8232	6	131.0321
7	78.4607	7	91.6696	7	104.8785	7	118.0874	7	131.2963
8	78.7249	8	91.9338	8	105.1427	8	118.3516	8	131.5604
9	78.9891	9	92.1980	9	105.4069	9	118.6157	9	131.8246

CAPACITY—LITRES TO GALLONS

[Reduction factor: 1 litre = 0.26417760 gallon]

Litres	Gallons	Litres	Gallons	Litres	Gallons	Litres	Gallons	Litres	Gallons
500	132.0888	550	145.2977	600	158.5066	650	171.7154	700	184.9243
1	132.3530	1	145.5619	1	158.7707	1	171.9796	1	185.1885
2	132.6172	2	145.8260	2	159.0349	2	172.2438	2	185.4527
3	132.8813	3	146.0902	3	159.2991	3	172.5080	3	185.7169
4	133.1455	4	146.3544	4	159.5633	4	172.7722	4	185.9810
5	133.4097	5	146.6186	5	159.8274	5	173.0363	5	186.2452
6	133.6739	6	146.8827	6	160.0916	6	173.3005	6	186.5094
7	133.9380	7	147.1469	7	160.3558	7	173.5647	7	186.7736
8	134.2022	8	147.4111	8	160.6200	8	173.8289	8	187.0377
9	134.4664	9	147.6753	9	160.8842	9	174.0930	9	187.3019
510	134.7306	560	147.9395	610	161.1483	660	174.3572	710	187.5661
1	134.9948	1	148.2036	1	161.4125	1	174.6214	1	187.8303
2	135.2589	2	148.4678	2	161.6767	2	174.8856	2	188.0945
3	135.5231	3	148.7320	3	161.9409	3	175.1497	3	188.3586
4	135.7873	4	148.9962	4	162.2050	4	175.4139	4	188.6228
5	136.0515	5	149.2603	5	162.4692	5	175.6781	5	188.8870
6	136.3156	6	149.5245	6	162.7334	6	175.9423	6	189.1512
7	136.5798	7	149.7887	7	162.9976	7	176.2065	7	189.4153
8	136.8440	8	150.0529	8	163.2618	8	176.4706	8	189.6795
9	137.1082	9	150.3171	9	163.5259	9	176.7348	9	189.9437
520	137.3724	570	150.5812	620	163.7901	670	176.9990	720	190.2079
1	137.6365	1	150.8454	1	164.0543	1	177.2632	1	190.4720
2	137.9007	2	151.1096	2	164.3185	2	177.5273	2	190.7362
3	138.1649	3	151.3738	3	164.5826	3	177.7915	3	191.0004
4	138.4291	4	151.6379	4	164.8468	4	178.0557	4	191.2646
5	138.6932	5	151.9021	5	165.1110	5	178.3199	5	191.5288
6	138.9574	6	152.1663	6	165.3752	6	178.5841	6	191.7929
7	139.2216	7	152.4305	7	165.6394	7	178.8482	7	192.0571
8	139.4858	8	152.6947	8	165.9035	8	179.1124	8	192.3213
9	139.7500	9	152.9588	9	166.1677	9	179.3766	9	192.5855
530	140.0141	580	153.2230	630	166.4319	680	179.6408	730	192.8496
1	140.2783	1	153.4872	1	166.6961	1	179.9049	1	193.1138
2	140.5425	2	153.7514	2	166.9602	2	180.1691	2	193.3780
3	140.8067	3	154.0155	3	167.2244	3	180.4333	3	193.6422
4	141.0708	4	154.2797	4	167.4886	4	180.6975	4	193.9064
5	141.3350	5	154.5439	5	167.7528	5	180.9617	5	194.1705
6	141.5992	6	154.8081	6	168.0170	6	181.2258	6	194.4347
7	141.8634	7	155.0723	7	168.2811	7	181.4900	7	194.6989
8	142.1275	8	155.3364	8	168.5453	8	181.7542	8	194.9631
9	142.3917	9	155.6006	9	168.8095	9	182.0184	9	195.2272
540	142.6559	590	155.8648	640	169.0737	690	182.2825	740	195.4914
1	142.9201	1	156.1290	1	169.3378	1	182.5467	1	195.7556
2	143.1843	2	156.3931	2	169.6020	2	182.8109	2	196.0198
3	143.4484	3	156.6573	3	169.8662	3	183.0751	3	196.2840
4	143.7126	4	156.9215	4	170.1304	4	183.3393	4	196.5481
5	143.9768	5	157.1857	5	170.3946	5	183.6034	5	196.8123
6	144.2410	6	157.4498	6	170.6587	6	183.8676	6	197.0765
7	144.5051	7	157.7140	7	170.9229	7	184.1318	7	197.3407
8	144.7693	8	157.9782	8	171.1871	8	184.3960	8	197.6048
9	145.0335	9	158.2424	9	171.4513	9	184.6601	9	197.8690

CAPACITY—LITRES TO GALLONS

[Reduction factor: 1 litre = 0.26417760 gallon]

Litres	Gallons	Litres	Gallons	Litres	Gallons	Litres	Gallons	Litres	Gallons
750	198.1332	800	211.3421	850	224.5510	900	237.7598	950	250.9687
1	198.3974	1	211.6063	1	224.8151	1	238.0240	1	251.2329
2	198.6616	2	211.8704	2	225.0793	2	238.2882	2	251.4971
3	198.9257	3	212.1346	3	225.3435	3	238.5524	3	251.7613
4	199.1899	4	212.3988	4	225.6077	4	238.8166	4	252.0254
5	199.4541	5	212.6630	5	225.8718	5	239.0807	5	252.2896
6	199.7183	6	212.9271	6	226.1360	6	239.3449	6	252.5538
7	199.9824	7	213.1913	7	226.4002	7	239.6091	7	252.8180
8	200.2466	8	213.4555	8	226.6644	8	239.8733	8	253.0821
9	200.5108	9	213.7197	9	226.9286	9	240.1374	9	253.3463
760	200.7750	810	213.9839	860	227.1927	910	240.4016	960	253.6105
1	201.0392	1	214.2480	1	227.4569	1	240.6658	1	253.8747
2	201.3033	2	214.5122	2	227.7211	2	240.9300	2	254.1389
3	201.5675	3	214.7764	3	227.9853	3	241.1941	3	254.4030
4	201.8317	4	215.0406	4	228.2494	4	241.4583	4	254.6672
5	202.0959	5	215.3047	5	228.5136	5	241.7225	5	254.9314
6	202.3600	6	215.5689	6	228.7778	6	241.9867	6	255.1956
7	202.6242	7	215.8331	7	229.0420	7	242.2509	7	255.4597
8	202.8884	8	216.0973	8	229.3062	8	242.5150	8	255.7239
9	203.1526	9	216.3615	9	229.5703	9	242.7792	9	255.9881
770	203.4168	820	216.6256	870	229.8345	920	243.0434	970	256.2523
1	203.6809	1	216.8898	1	230.0987	1	243.3076	1	256.5164
2	203.9451	2	217.1540	2	230.3629	2	243.5717	2	256.7806
3	204.2093	3	217.4182	3	230.6270	3	243.8359	3	257.0448
4	204.4735	4	217.6823	4	230.8912	4	244.1001	4	257.3090
5	204.7376	5	217.9465	5	231.1554	5	244.3643	5	257.5732
6	205.0018	6	218.2107	6	231.4196	6	244.6285	6	257.8373
7	205.2660	7	218.4749	7	231.6838	7	244.8926	7	258.1015
8	205.5302	8	218.7391	8	231.9479	8	245.1568	8	258.3657
9	205.7944	9	219.0032	9	232.2121	9	245.4210	9	258.6299
780	206.0585	830	219.2674	880	232.4763	930	245.6852	980	258.8940
1	206.3227	1	219.5316	1	232.7405	1	245.9493	1	259.1582
2	206.5869	2	219.7958	2	233.0046	2	246.2135	2	259.4224
3	206.8511	3	220.0599	3	233.2688	3	246.4777	3	259.6866
4	207.1152	4	220.3241	4	233.5330	4	246.7419	4	259.9508
5	207.3794	5	220.5883	5	233.7972	5	247.0061	5	260.2149
6	207.6436	6	220.8525	6	234.0614	6	247.2702	6	260.4791
7	207.9078	7	221.1167	7	234.3255	7	247.5344	7	260.7433
8	208.1719	8	221.3808	8	234.5897	8	247.7986	8	261.0075
9	208.4361	9	221.6450	9	234.8539	9	248.0628	9	261.2716
790	208.7003	840	221.9092	890	235.1181	940	248.3269	990	261.5358
1	208.9645	1	222.1734	1	235.3822	1	248.5911	1	261.8000
2	209.2287	2	222.4375	2	235.6464	2	248.8553	2	262.0642
3	209.4928	3	222.7017	3	235.9106	3	249.1195	3	262.3284
4	209.7570	4	222.9659	4	236.1748	4	249.3837	4	262.5925
5	210.0212	5	223.2301	5	236.4390	5	249.6478	5	262.8567
6	210.2854	6	223.4942	6	236.7031	6	249.9120	6	263.1209
7	210.5495	7	223.7584	7	236.9673	7	250.1762	7	263.3851
8	210.8137	8	224.0226	8	237.2315	8	250.4404	8	263.6492
9	211.0779	9	224.2868	9	237.4957	9	250.7045	9	263.9134

CAPACITY—GALLONS TO LITRES

[Reduction factor: 1 gallon = 3.7853323 litres]

Gallons	Litres	Gallons	Litres	Gallons	Litres	Gallons	Litres	Gallons	Litres
0		50	189.2666	100	378.533	150	567.800	200	757.066
1	3.7853	1	193.0519	1	382.319	1	571.585	1	760.852
2	7.5707	2	196.8373	2	386.104	2	575.371	2	764.637
3	11.3560	3	200.6226	3	389.889	3	579.156	3	768.422
4	15.1413	4	204.4079	4	393.675	4	582.941	4	772.208
5	18.9267	5	208.1933	5	397.460	5	586.727	5	775.993
6	22.7120	6	211.9786	6	401.245	6	590.512	6	779.778
7	26.4973	7	215.7639	7	405.031	7	594.297	7	783.564
8	30.2827	8	219.5493	8	408.816	8	598.083	8	787.349
9	34.0680	9	223.3346	9	412.601	9	601.868	9	791.134
10	37.8533	60	227.1199	110	416.387	160	605.653	210	794.920
1	41.6387	1	230.9053	1	420.172	1	609.438	1	798.705
2	45.4240	2	234.6906	2	423.957	2	613.224	2	802.490
3	49.2093	3	238.4759	3	427.743	3	617.009	3	806.276
4	52.9947	4	242.2613	4	431.528	4	620.794	4	810.061
5	56.7800	5	246.0466	5	435.313	5	624.580	5	813.846
6	60.5653	6	249.8319	6	439.099	6	628.365	6	817.632
7	64.3506	7	253.6173	7	442.884	7	632.150	7	821.417
8	68.1360	8	257.4026	8	446.669	8	635.936	8	825.202
9	71.9213	9	261.1879	9	450.455	9	639.721	9	828.988
20	75.7066	70	264.9733	120	454.240	170	643.506	220	832.773
1	79.4920	1	268.7586	1	458.025	1	647.292	1	836.558
2	83.2773	2	272.5439	2	461.811	2	651.077	2	840.344
3	87.0626	3	276.3293	3	465.596	3	654.862	3	844.129
4	90.8480	4	280.1146	4	469.381	4	658.648	4	847.914
5	94.6333	5	283.8999	5	473.167	5	662.433	5	851.700
6	98.4186	6	287.6853	6	476.952	6	666.218	6	855.485
7	102.2040	7	291.4706	7	480.737	7	670.004	7	859.270
8	105.9893	8	295.2559	8	484.523	8	673.789	8	863.056
9	109.7746	9	299.0413	9	488.308	9	677.574	9	866.841
30	113.5600	80	302.8266	130	492.093	180	681.360	230	870.626
1	117.3453	1	306.6119	1	495.879	1	685.145	1	874.412
2	121.1306	2	310.3972	2	499.664	2	688.930	2	878.197
3	124.9160	3	314.1826	3	503.449	3	692.716	3	881.982
4	128.7013	4	317.9679	4	507.235	4	696.501	4	885.768
5	132.4866	5	321.7532	5	511.020	5	700.286	5	889.553
6	136.2720	6	325.5386	6	514.805	6	704.072	6	893.338
7	140.0573	7	329.3239	7	518.591	7	707.857	7	897.124
8	143.8426	8	333.1092	8	522.376	8	711.642	8	900.909
9	147.6280	9	336.8946	9	526.161	9	715.428	9	904.694
40	151.4133	90	340.6799	140	529.947	190	719.213	240	908.480
1	155.1986	1	344.4652	1	533.732	1	722.998	1	912.265
2	158.9840	2	348.2506	2	537.517	2	726.784	2	916.050
3	162.7693	3	352.0359	3	541.303	3	730.569	3	919.836
4	166.5546	4	355.8212	4	545.088	4	734.354	4	923.621
5	170.3400	5	359.6066	5	548.873	5	738.140	5	927.406
6	174.1253	6	363.3919	6	552.659	6	741.925	6	931.192
7	177.9106	7	367.1772	7	556.444	7	745.710	7	934.977
8	181.6960	8	370.9626	8	560.229	8	749.496	8	938.762
9	185.4813	9	374.7479	9	564.015	9	753.281	9	942.548

CAPACITY—GALLONS TO LITRES

[Reduction factor: 1 gallon = 3.7853323 litres]

Gallons	Litres	Gallons	Litres	Gallons	Litres	Gallons	Litres	Gallons	Litres
250	946.333	300	1,135.600	350	1,324.866	400	1,514.133	450	1,703.400
1	950.118	1	1,139.385	1	1,328.652	1	1,517.918	1	1,707.185
2	953.904	2	1,143.170	2	1,332.437	2	1,521.704	2	1,710.970
3	957.689	3	1,146.956	3	1,336.222	3	1,525.489	3	1,714.756
4	961.474	4	1,150.741	4	1,340.008	4	1,529.274	4	1,718.541
5	965.260	5	1,154.526	5	1,343.793	5	1,533.060	5	1,722.326
6	969.045	6	1,158.312	6	1,347.578	6	1,536.845	6	1,726.112
7	972.830	7	1,162.097	7	1,351.364	7	1,540.630	7	1,729.897
8	976.616	8	1,165.882	8	1,355.149	8	1,544.416	8	1,733.682
9	980.401	9	1,169.668	9	1,358.934	9	1,548.201	9	1,737.468
260	984.186	310	1,173.453	360	1,362.720	410	1,551.986	460	1,741.253
1	987.972	1	1,177.238	1	1,366.525	1	1,555.772	1	1,745.038
2	991.757	2	1,181.024	2	1,370.290	2	1,559.557	2	1,748.824
3	995.542	3	1,184.809	3	1,374.076	3	1,563.342	3	1,752.609
4	999.328	4	1,188.594	4	1,377.851	4	1,567.128	4	1,756.394
5	1,003.113	5	1,192.380	5	1,381.646	5	1,570.913	5	1,760.180
6	1,006.898	6	1,196.165	6	1,385.432	6	1,574.698	6	1,763.965
7	1,010.684	7	1,199.950	7	1,389.217	7	1,578.484	7	1,767.750
8	1,014.469	8	1,203.736	8	1,393.002	8	1,582.269	8	1,771.536
9	1,018.254	9	1,207.521	9	1,396.788	9	1,586.054	9	1,775.321
270	1,022.040	320	1,211.306	370	1,400.573	420	1,589.840	470	1,779.106
1	1,025.825	1	1,215.092	1	1,404.358	1	1,593.625	1	1,782.892
2	1,029.610	2	1,218.877	2	1,408.144	2	1,597.410	2	1,786.677
3	1,033.396	3	1,222.662	3	1,411.929	3	1,601.196	3	1,790.462
4	1,037.181	4	1,226.448	4	1,415.714	4	1,604.981	4	1,794.248
5	1,040.966	5	1,230.233	5	1,419.500	5	1,608.766	5	1,798.033
6	1,044.752	6	1,234.018	6	1,423.285	6	1,612.552	6	1,801.818
7	1,048.537	7	1,237.804	7	1,427.070	7	1,616.337	7	1,805.604
8	1,052.322	8	1,241.589	8	1,430.856	8	1,620.122	8	1,809.389
9	1,056.108	9	1,245.374	9	1,434.641	9	1,623.908	9	1,813.174
280	1,059.893	330	1,249.160	380	1,438.426	430	1,627.693	480	1,816.960
1	1,063.678	1	1,252.945	1	1,442.212	1	1,631.478	1	1,820.745
2	1,067.464	2	1,256.730	2	1,445.997	2	1,635.264	2	1,824.530
3	1,071.249	3	1,260.516	3	1,449.782	3	1,639.049	3	1,828.316
4	1,075.034	4	1,264.301	4	1,453.568	4	1,642.834	4	1,832.101
5	1,078.820	5	1,268.086	5	1,457.353	5	1,646.620	5	1,835.886
6	1,082.605	6	1,271.872	6	1,461.138	6	1,650.405	6	1,839.671
7	1,086.390	7	1,275.657	7	1,464.924	7	1,654.190	7	1,843.457
8	1,090.176	8	1,279.442	8	1,468.709	8	1,657.976	8	1,847.242
9	1,093.961	9	1,283.228	9	1,472.494	9	1,661.761	9	1,851.027
290	1,097.746	340	1,287.013	390	1,476.280	440	1,665.546	490	1,854.813
1	1,101.532	1	1,290.798	1	1,480.065	1	1,669.332	1	1,858.598
2	1,105.317	2	1,294.584	2	1,483.850	2	1,673.117	2	1,862.383
3	1,109.102	3	1,298.369	3	1,487.636	3	1,676.902	3	1,866.169
4	1,112.888	4	1,302.154	4	1,491.421	4	1,680.688	4	1,869.954
5	1,116.673	5	1,305.940	5	1,495.206	5	1,684.473	5	1,873.739
6	1,120.458	6	1,309.725	6	1,498.992	6	1,688.258	6	1,877.525
7	1,124.244	7	1,313.510	7	1,502.777	7	1,692.044	7	1,881.310
8	1,128.029	8	1,317.296	8	1,506.562	8	1,695.829	8	1,885.095
9	1,131.814	9	1,321.081	9	1,510.348	9	1,699.614	9	1,888.881

CAPACITY—GALLONS TO LITRES

[Reduction factor: 1 gallon = 3.7853323 litres]

Gallons	Litres	Gallons	Litres	Gallons	Litres	Gallons	Litres	Gallons	Litres
500	1,892.666	550	2,081.933	600	2,271.199	650	2,460.466	700	2,649.733
1	1,896.451	1	2,085.718	1	2,274.985	1	2,464.251	1	2,653.518
2	1,900.237	2	2,089.503	2	2,278.770	2	2,468.037	2	2,657.303
3	1,904.022	3	2,093.289	3	2,282.555	3	2,471.822	3	2,661.089
4	1,907.807	4	2,097.074	4	2,286.341	4	2,475.607	4	2,664.874
5	1,911.593	5	2,100.859	5	2,290.126	5	2,479.393	5	2,668.659
6	1,915.378	6	2,104.645	6	2,293.911	6	2,483.178	6	2,672.445
7	1,919.163	7	2,108.430	7	2,297.697	7	2,486.963	7	2,676.230
8	1,922.949	8	2,112.215	8	2,301.482	8	2,490.749	8	2,680.015
9	1,926.734	9	2,116.001	9	2,305.267	9	2,494.534	9	2,683.801
510	1,930.519	560	2,119.786	610	2,309.053	660	2,498.319	710	2,687.586
1	1,934.305	1	2,123.571	1	2,312.838	1	2,502.105	1	2,691.371
2	1,938.090	2	2,127.357	2	2,316.623	2	2,505.890	2	2,695.157
3	1,941.875	3	2,131.142	3	2,320.409	3	2,509.675	3	2,698.942
4	1,945.661	4	2,134.927	4	2,324.194	4	2,513.461	4	2,702.727
5	1,949.446	5	2,138.713	5	2,327.979	5	2,517.246	5	2,706.513
6	1,953.231	6	2,142.498	6	2,231.765	6	2,521.031	6	2,710.298
7	1,957.017	7	2,146.283	7	2,335.550	7	2,524.817	7	2,714.083
8	1,960.802	8	2,150.069	8	2,339.335	8	2,528.602	8	2,717.869
9	1,964.587	9	2,153.854	9	2,343.121	9	2,532.387	9	2,721.654
520	1,968.373	570	2,157.639	620	2,346.906	670	2,536.173	720	2,725.439
1	1,972.158	1	2,161.425	1	2,350.691	1	2,539.958	1	2,729.225
2	1,975.943	2	2,165.210	2	2,354.477	2	2,543.743	2	2,733.010
3	1,979.729	3	2,168.995	3	2,358.262	3	2,547.529	3	2,736.795
4	1,983.514	4	2,172.781	4	2,362.047	4	2,551.314	4	2,740.581
5	1,987.299	5	2,176.566	5	2,365.833	5	2,555.099	5	2,744.366
6	1,991.085	6	2,180.351	6	2,369.618	6	2,558.885	6	2,748.151
7	1,994.870	7	2,184.137	7	2,373.403	7	2,562.670	7	2,751.937
8	1,998.655	8	2,187.922	8	2,377.189	8	2,566.455	8	2,755.722
9	2,002.441	9	2,191.707	9	2,380.974	9	2,570.241	9	2,759.507
530	2,006.226	580	2,195.493	630	2,384.759	680	2,574.026	730	2,763.293
1	2,010.011	1	2,199.278	1	2,388.545	1	2,577.811	1	2,767.078
2	2,013.797	2	2,203.063	2	2,392.330	2	2,581.597	2	2,770.863
3	2,017.582	3	2,206.849	3	2,396.115	3	2,585.382	3	2,774.649
4	2,021.367	4	2,210.634	4	2,399.901	4	2,589.167	4	2,778.434
5	2,025.153	5	2,214.419	5	2,403.686	5	2,592.953	5	2,782.219
6	2,028.938	6	2,218.205	6	2,407.471	6	2,596.738	6	2,786.005
7	2,032.723	7	2,221.990	7	2,411.257	7	2,600.523	7	2,789.790
8	2,036.509	8	2,225.775	8	2,415.042	8	2,604.309	8	2,793.575
9	2,040.294	9	2,229.561	9	2,418.827	9	2,608.094	9	2,797.361
540	2,044.079	590	2,233.346	640	2,422.613	690	2,611.879	740	2,801.146
1	2,047.865	1	2,237.131	1	2,426.398	1	2,615.665	1	2,804.931
2	2,051.650	2	2,240.917	2	2,430.183	2	2,619.450	2	2,808.717
3	2,055.435	3	2,244.702	3	2,433.969	3	2,623.235	3	2,812.502
4	2,059.221	4	2,248.487	4	2,437.754	4	2,627.021	4	2,816.287
5	2,063.006	5	2,252.273	5	2,441.539	5	2,630.806	5	2,820.073
6	2,066.791	6	2,256.058	6	2,445.325	6	2,634.591	6	2,823.858
7	2,070.577	7	2,259.843	7	2,449.110	7	2,638.377	7	2,827.643
8	2,074.362	8	2,263.629	8	2,452.895	8	2,642.162	8	2,831.429
9	2,078.147	9	2,267.414	9	2,456.681	9	2,645.947	9	2,835.214

CAPACITY—GALLONS TO LITRES

[Reduction factor: 1 gallon = 3.7853323 litres]

Gallons	Litres	Gallons	Litres	Gallons	Litres	Gallons	Litres	Gallons	Litres
750	2,838.999	800	3,028.266	850	3,217.532	900	3,406.799	950	3,596.066
1	2,842.785	1	3,032.051	1	3,221.318	1	3,410.584	1	3,599.851
2	2,846.570	2	3,035.837	2	3,225.103	2	3,414.370	2	3,603.636
3	2,850.355	3	3,039.622	3	3,228.888	3	3,418.155	3	3,607.422
4	2,854.141	4	3,043.407	4	3,232.674	4	3,421.940	4	3,611.207
5	2,857.926	5	3,047.193	5	3,236.459	5	3,425.726	5	3,614.992
6	2,861.711	6	3,050.978	6	3,240.244	6	3,429.511	6	3,618.778
7	2,865.497	7	3,054.763	7	3,244.030	7	3,433.296	7	3,622.563
8	2,869.282	8	3,058.548	8	3,247.815	8	3,437.082	8	3,626.348
9	2,873.067	9	3,062.334	9	3,251.600	9	3,440.867	9	3,630.134
760	2,876.853	810	3,066.119	860	3,255.386	910	3,444.652	960	3,633.919
1	2,880.638	1	3,069.904	1	3,259.171	1	3,448.438	1	3,637.704
2	2,884.423	2	3,073.690	2	3,262.956	2	3,452.223	2	3,641.490
3	2,888.209	3	3,077.475	3	3,266.742	3	3,456.008	3	3,645.275
4	2,891.994	4	3,081.260	4	3,270.527	4	3,459.794	4	3,649.060
5	2,895.779	5	3,085.046	5	3,274.312	5	3,463.579	5	3,652.846
6	2,899.565	6	3,088.831	6	3,278.098	6	3,467.364	6	3,656.631
7	2,903.350	7	3,092.616	7	3,281.883	7	3,471.150	7	3,660.416
8	2,907.135	8	3,096.402	8	3,285.668	8	3,474.935	8	3,664.202
9	2,910.921	9	3,100.187	9	3,289.454	9	3,478.720	9	3,667.987
770	2,914.706	820	3,103.972	870	3,293.239	920	3,482.506	970	3,671.772
1	2,918.491	1	3,107.758	1	3,297.024	1	3,486.291	1	3,675.558
2	2,922.277	2	3,111.543	2	3,300.810	2	3,490.076	2	3,679.343
3	2,926.062	3	3,115.328	3	3,304.595	3	3,493.862	3	3,683.128
4	2,929.847	4	3,119.114	4	3,308.380	4	3,497.647	4	3,686.914
5	2,933.633	5	3,122.899	5	3,312.166	5	3,501.432	5	3,690.699
6	2,937.418	6	3,126.684	6	3,315.951	6	3,505.218	6	3,694.484
7	2,941.203	7	3,130.470	7	3,319.736	7	3,509.003	7	3,698.270
8	2,944.989	8	3,134.255	8	3,323.522	8	3,512.788	8	3,702.055
9	2,948.774	9	3,138.040	9	3,327.307	9	3,516.574	9	3,705.840
780	2,952.559	830	3,141.826	880	3,331.092	930	3,520.359	980	3,709.626
1	2,956.345	1	3,145.611	1	3,334.878	1	3,524.144	1	3,713.411
2	2,960.130	2	3,149.396	2	3,338.663	2	3,527.930	2	3,717.196
3	2,963.915	3	3,153.182	3	3,342.448	3	3,531.715	3	3,720.982
4	2,967.701	4	3,156.967	4	3,346.234	4	3,535.500	4	3,724.767
5	2,971.486	5	3,160.752	5	3,350.019	5	3,539.286	5	3,728.552
6	2,975.271	6	3,164.538	6	3,353.804	6	3,543.071	6	3,732.338
7	2,979.057	7	3,168.323	7	3,357.590	7	3,546.856	7	3,736.123
8	2,982.842	8	3,172.108	8	3,361.375	8	3,550.642	8	3,739.908
9	2,986.627	9	3,175.894	9	3,365.160	9	3,554.427	9	3,743.694
790	2,990.413	840	3,179.679	890	3,368.946	940	3,558.212	990	3,747.479
1	2,994.198	1	3,183.464	1	3,372.731	1	3,561.998	1	3,751.264
2	2,997.983	2	3,187.250	2	3,376.516	2	3,565.783	2	3,755.050
3	3,001.769	3	3,191.035	3	3,380.302	3	3,569.568	3	3,758.835
4	3,005.554	4	3,194.820	4	3,384.087	4	3,573.354	4	3,762.620
5	3,009.339	5	3,198.606	5	3,387.872	5	3,577.139	5	3,766.406
6	3,013.125	6	3,202.391	6	3,391.658	6	3,580.924	6	3,770.191
7	3,016.910	7	3,206.176	7	3,395.443	7	3,584.710	7	3,773.976
8	3,020.695	8	3,209.962	8	3,399.228	8	3,588.495	8	3,777.762
9	3,024.481	9	3,213.747	9	3,403.014	9	3,592.280	9	3,781.547

CAPACITY—HECTOLITRES TO BUSHELS

[Reduction factor: 1 hectolitre = 2.8378189 bushels]

Hecto-litres	Bush-els	Hecto-litres	Bush-els	Hecto-litres	Bush-els	Hecto-litres	Bush-els	Hecto-litres	Bush-els
0		50	141.8909	100	283.782	150	425.673	200	567.564
1	2.8378	1	144.7288	1	286.620	1	428.511	1	570.402
2	5.6756	2	147.5666	2	289.458	2	431.348	2	573.239
3	8.5135	3	150.4044	3	292.295	3	434.186	3	576.077
4	11.3513	4	153.2422	4	295.133	4	437.024	4	578.915
5	14.1891	5	156.0800	5	297.971	5	439.862	5	581.753
6	17.0269	6	158.9179	6	300.809	6	442.700	6	584.591
7	19.8647	7	161.7557	7	303.647	7	445.538	7	587.429
8	22.7026	8	164.5935	8	306.484	8	448.375	8	590.266
9	25.5404	9	167.4313	9	309.322	9	451.213	9	593.104
10	28.3782	60	170.2691	110	312.160	160	454.051	210	595.942
1	31.2160	1	173.1070	1	314.998	1	456.889	1	598.780
2	34.0538	2	175.9448	2	317.836	2	459.727	2	601.618
3	36.8916	3	178.7826	3	320.674	3	462.564	3	604.455
4	39.7295	4	181.6204	4	323.511	4	465.402	4	607.293
5	42.5673	5	184.4582	5	326.349	5	468.240	5	610.131
6	45.4051	6	187.2960	6	329.187	6	471.078	6	612.969
7	48.2429	7	190.1339	7	332.025	7	473.916	7	615.807
8	51.0807	8	192.9717	8	334.863	8	476.754	8	618.645
9	53.9186	9	195.8095	9	337.700	9	479.591	9	621.482
20	56.7564	70	198.6473	120	340.538	170	482.429	220	624.320
1	59.5942	1	201.4851	1	343.376	1	485.267	1	627.158
2	62.4320	2	204.3230	2	346.214	2	488.105	2	629.996
3	65.2698	3	207.1608	3	349.052	3	490.943	3	632.834
4	68.1077	4	209.9986	4	351.890	4	493.780	4	635.671
5	70.9455	5	212.8364	5	354.727	5	496.618	5	638.509
6	73.7833	6	215.6742	6	357.565	6	499.456	6	641.347
7	76.6211	7	218.5121	7	360.403	7	502.294	7	644.185
8	79.4589	8	221.3499	8	363.241	8	505.132	8	647.023
9	82.2967	9	224.1877	9	366.079	9	507.970	9	649.861
30	85.1346	80	227.0255	130	368.916	180	510.807	230	652.698
1	87.9724	1	229.8633	1	371.754	1	513.645	1	655.536
2	90.8102	2	232.7012	2	374.592	2	516.483	2	658.374
3	93.6480	3	235.5390	3	377.430	3	519.321	3	661.212
4	96.4858	4	238.3768	4	380.268	4	522.159	4	664.050
5	99.3237	5	241.2146	5	383.106	5	524.996	5	666.887
6	102.1615	6	244.0524	6	385.943	6	527.834	6	669.725
7	104.9993	7	246.8902	7	388.781	7	530.672	7	672.563
8	107.8371	8	249.7281	8	391.619	8	533.510	8	675.401
9	110.6749	9	252.5659	9	394.457	9	536.348	9	678.239
40	113.5128	90	255.4037	140	397.295	190	539.186	240	681.077
1	116.3506	1	258.2415	1	400.132	1	542.023	1	683.914
2	119.1884	2	261.0793	2	402.970	2	544.861	2	686.752
3	122.0262	3	263.9172	3	405.808	3	547.699	3	689.590
4	124.8640	4	266.7550	4	408.646	4	550.537	4	692.428
5	127.7019	5	269.5928	5	411.484	5	553.375	5	695.266
6	130.5397	6	272.4306	6	414.322	6	556.213	6	698.103
7	133.3775	7	275.2684	7	417.159	7	559.050	7	700.941
8	136.2153	8	278.1063	8	419.997	8	561.888	8	703.779
9	139.0531	9	280.9441	9	422.835	9	564.726	9	706.617

CAPACITY—HECTOLITRES TO BUSHELS

[Reduction factor: 1 hectolitre = 2.8378189 bushels]

Hecto-litres	Bush-els	Hecto-litres	Bush-els	Hecto-litres	Bush-els	Hecto-litres	Bush-els	Hecto-litres	Bush-els
250	709.455	300	851.346	350	993.237	400	1,135.128	450	1,277.019
1	712.293	1	854.183	1	996.074	1	1,137.965	1	1,279.856
2	715.130	2	857.021	2	998.912	2	1,140.803	2	1,282.694
3	717.968	3	859.859	3	1,001.750	3	1,143.641	3	1,285.532
4	720.806	4	862.697	4	1,004.588	4	1,146.479	4	1,288.370
5	723.644	5	865.535	5	1,007.426	5	1,149.317	5	1,291.208
6	726.482	6	868.373	6	1,010.264	6	1,152.154	6	1,294.045
7	729.319	7	871.210	7	1,013.101	7	1,154.992	7	1,296.883
8	732.157	8	874.048	8	1,015.939	8	1,157.830	8	1,299.721
9	734.995	9	876.886	9	1,018.777	9	1,160.668	9	1,302.559
260	737.833	310	879.724	360	1,021.615	410	1,163.506	460	1,305.397
1	740.671	1	882.562	1	1,024.453	1	1,166.344	1	1,308.235
2	743.509	2	885.400	1	1,027.290	2	1,169.181	2	1,311.072
3	746.346	3	888.237	3	1,030.128	3	1,172.019	3	1,313.910
4	749.184	4	891.075	4	1,032.966	4	1,174.857	4	1,316.748
5	752.022	5	893.913	5	1,035.804	5	1,177.695	5	1,319.586
6	754.860	6	896.751	6	1,038.642	6	1,180.533	6	1,322.424
7	757.698	7	899.589	7	1,041.480	7	1,183.370	7	1,325.261
8	760.535	8	902.426	8	1,044.317	8	1,186.208	8	1,328.099
9	763.373	9	905.264	9	1,047.155	9	1,189.046	9	1,330.937
270	766.211	320	908.102	370	1,049.993	420	1,191.884	470	1,333.775
1	769.049	1	910.940	1	1,052.831	1	1,194.722	1	1,336.613
2	771.887	2	913.778	2	1,055.669	2	1,197.560	2	1,339.451
3	774.725	3	916.616	3	1,058.506	3	1,200.397	3	1,342.288
4	777.562	4	919.453	4	1,061.344	4	1,203.235	4	1,345.126
5	780.400	5	922.291	5	1,064.182	5	1,206.073	5	1,347.964
6	783.238	6	925.129	6	1,067.020	6	1,208.911	6	1,350.802
7	786.076	7	927.967	7	1,069.858	7	1,211.749	7	1,353.640
8	788.914	8	930.805	8	1,072.696	8	1,214.586	8	1,356.477
9	791.751	9	933.642	9	1,075.533	9	1,217.424	9	1,359.315
280	794.589	330	936.480	380	1,078.371	430	1,220.262	480	1,362.153
1	797.427	1	939.318	1	1,081.209	1	1,223.100	1	1,364.991
2	800.265	2	942.156	2	1,084.047	2	1,225.938	2	1,367.829
3	803.103	3	944.994	3	1,086.885	3	1,228.776	3	1,370.667
4	805.941	4	947.832	4	1,089.722	4	1,231.613	4	1,373.504
5	808.778	5	950.669	5	1,092.560	5	1,234.451	5	1,376.342
6	811.616	6	953.507	6	1,095.398	6	1,237.289	6	1,379.180
7	814.454	7	956.345	7	1,098.236	7	1,240.127	7	1,382.018
8	817.292	8	959.183	8	1,101.074	8	1,242.965	8	1,384.856
9	820.130	9	962.021	9	1,103.912	9	1,245.803	9	1,387.693
290	822.967	340	964.858	390	1,106.749	440	1,248.640	490	1,390.531
1	825.805	1	967.696	1	1,109.587	1	1,251.478	1	1,393.369
2	828.643	2	970.534	2	1,112.425	2	1,254.316	2	1,396.207
3	831.481	3	973.372	3	1,115.263	3	1,257.154	3	1,399.045
4	834.319	4	976.210	4	1,118.101	4	1,259.992	4	1,401.883
5	837.157	5	979.048	5	1,120.938	5	1,262.829	5	1,404.720
6	839.994	6	981.885	6	1,123.776	6	1,265.667	6	1,407.558
7	842.832	7	984.723	7	1,126.614	7	1,268.505	7	1,410.396
8	845.670	8	987.561	8	1,129.452	8	1,271.343	8	1,413.234
9	848.508	9	990.399	9	1,132.290	9	1,274.181	9	1,416.072

CAPACITY—HECTOLITRES TO BUSHELS

[Reduction factor: 1 hectolitre = 2.8378189 bushels]

Hecto-litres	Bushels	Hecto-litres	Bushels	Hecto-litres	Bushels	Hecto-litres	Bushels	Hecto-litres	Bushels
500	1,418.909	550	1,560.800	600	1,702.691	650	1,844.582	700	1,986.473
1	1,421.747	1	1,563.638	1	1,705.529	1	1,847.420	1	1,989.311
2	1,424.585	2	1,566.476	2	1,708.367	2	1,850.258	2	1,992.149
3	1,427.423	3	1,569.314	3	1,711.205	3	1,853.096	3	1,994.987
4	1,430.261	4	1,572.152	4	1,714.043	4	1,855.934	4	1,997.825
5	1,433.099	5	1,574.989	5	1,716.880	5	1,858.771	5	2,000.662
6	1,435.936	6	1,577.827	6	1,719.718	6	1,861.609	6	2,003.500
7	1,438.774	7	1,580.665	7	1,722.556	7	1,864.447	7	2,006.338
8	1,441.612	8	1,583.503	8	1,725.394	8	1,867.285	8	2,009.176
9	1,444.450	9	1,586.341	9	1,728.232	9	1,870.123	9	2,012.014
510	1,447.288	560	1,589.179	610	1,731.070	660	1,872.960	710	2,014.851
1	1,450.125	1	1,592.016	1	1,733.907	1	1,875.798	1	2,017.689
2	1,452.963	2	1,594.854	2	1,736.745	2	1,878.636	2	2,020.527
3	1,455.801	3	1,597.692	3	1,739.583	3	1,881.474	3	2,023.365
4	1,458.639	4	1,600.530	4	1,742.421	4	1,884.312	4	2,026.203
5	1,461.477	5	1,603.368	5	1,745.259	5	1,887.150	5	2,029.041
6	1,464.315	6	1,606.206	6	1,748.096	6	1,889.987	6	2,031.878
7	1,467.152	7	1,609.043	7	1,750.934	7	1,892.825	7	2,034.716
8	1,469.990	8	1,611.881	8	1,753.772	8	1,895.663	8	2,037.554
9	1,472.828	9	1,614.719	9	1,756.610	9	1,898.501	9	2,040.392
520	1,475.666	570	1,617.557	620	1,759.448	670	1,901.339	720	2,043.230
1	1,478.504	1	1,620.395	1	1,762.286	1	1,904.176	1	2,046.067
2	1,481.341	2	1,623.232	2	1,765.123	2	1,907.014	2	2,048.905
3	1,484.179	3	1,626.070	3	1,767.961	3	1,909.852	3	2,051.743
4	1,487.017	4	1,628.908	4	1,770.799	4	1,912.690	4	2,054.581
5	1,489.855	5	1,631.746	5	1,773.637	5	1,915.528	5	2,057.419
6	1,492.693	6	1,634.584	6	1,776.475	6	1,918.366	6	2,060.257
7	1,495.531	7	1,637.422	7	1,779.312	7	1,921.203	7	2,063.094
8	1,498.368	8	1,640.259	8	1,782.150	8	1,924.041	8	2,065.932
9	1,501.206	9	1,643.097	9	1,784.988	9	1,926.879	9	2,068.770
530	1,504.044	580	1,645.935	630	1,787.826	680	1,929.717	730	2,071.608
1	1,506.882	1	1,648.773	1	1,790.664	1	1,932.555	1	2,074.446
2	1,509.720	2	1,651.611	2	1,793.502	2	1,935.393	2	2,077.283
3	1,512.557	3	1,654.448	3	1,796.339	3	1,938.230	3	2,080.121
4	1,515.395	4	1,657.286	4	1,799.177	4	1,941.068	4	2,082.959
5	1,518.233	5	1,660.124	5	1,802.015	5	1,943.906	5	2,085.797
6	1,521.071	6	1,662.962	6	1,804.853	6	1,946.744	6	2,088.635
7	1,523.909	7	1,665.800	7	1,807.691	7	1,949.582	7	2,091.473
8	1,526.747	8	1,668.638	8	1,810.528	8	1,952.419	8	2,094.310
9	1,529.584	9	1,671.475	9	1,813.366	9	1,955.257	9	2,097.148
540	1,532.422	590	1,674.313	640	1,816.204	690	1,958.095	740	2,099.986
1	1,535.260	1	1,677.151	1	1,819.042	1	1,960.933	1	2,102.824
2	1,538.098	2	1,679.989	2	1,821.880	2	1,963.771	2	2,105.662
3	1,540.936	3	1,682.827	3	1,824.718	3	1,966.609	3	2,108.499
4	1,543.773	4	1,685.664	4	1,827.555	4	1,969.446	4	2,111.337
5	1,546.611	5	1,688.502	5	1,830.393	5	1,972.284	5	2,114.175
6	1,549.449	6	1,691.340	6	1,833.231	6	1,975.122	6	2,117.013
7	1,552.287	7	1,694.178	7	1,836.069	7	1,977.960	7	2,119.851
8	1,555.125	8	1,697.016	8	1,838.907	8	1,980.798	8	2,122.689
9	1,557.963	9	1,699.854	9	1,841.744	9	1,983.635	9	2,125.526

CAPACITY—HECTOLITRES TO BUSHELS

[Reduction factor: 1 hectolitre = 2.8378189 bushels]

Hecto-litres	Bush-els	Hecto-litres	Bush-els	Hecto-litres	Bush-els	Hecto-litres	Bush-els	Hecto-litres	Bush-els
750	2,128.364	800	2,270.255	850	2,412.146	900	2,554.037	950	2,695.928
1	2,131.202	1	2,273.093	1	2,414.984	1	2,556.875	1	2,698.766
2	2,134.040	2	2,275.931	2	2,417.822	2	2,559.713	2	2,701.604
3	2,136.878	3	2,278.769	3	2,420.660	3	2,562.550	3	2,704.441
4	2,139.715	4	2,281.606	4	2,423.497	4	2,565.388	4	2,707.279
5	2,142.553	5	2,284.444	5	2,426.335	5	2,568.226	5	2,710.117
6	2,145.391	6	2,287.282	6	2,429.173	6	2,571.064	6	2,712.955
7	2,148.229	7	2,290.120	7	2,432.011	7	2,573.902	7	2,715.793
8	2,151.067	8	2,292.958	8	2,434.849	8	2,576.740	8	2,718.631
9	2,153.905	9	2,295.796	9	2,437.686	9	2,579.577	9	2,721.468
760	2,156.742	810	2,298.633	860	2,440.524	910	2,582.415	960	2,724.306
1	2,159.580	1	2,301.471	1	2,443.362	1	2,585.253	1	2,727.144
2	2,162.418	2	2,304.309	2	2,446.200	2	2,588.091	2	2,729.982
3	2,165.256	3	2,307.147	3	2,449.038	3	2,590.929	3	2,732.820
4	2,168.094	4	2,309.985	4	2,451.876	4	2,593.766	4	2,735.657
5	2,170.931	5	2,312.822	5	2,454.713	5	2,596.604	5	2,738.495
6	2,173.769	6	2,315.660	6	2,457.551	6	2,599.442	6	2,741.333
7	2,176.607	7	2,318.498	7	2,460.389	7	2,602.280	7	2,744.171
8	2,179.445	8	2,321.336	8	2,463.227	8	2,605.118	8	2,747.009
9	2,182.283	9	2,324.174	9	2,466.065	9	2,607.956	9	2,749.847
770	2,185.121	820	2,327.012	870	2,468.902	920	2,610.793	970	2,752.684
1	2,187.958	1	2,329.849	1	2,471.740	1	2,613.631	1	2,755.522
2	2,190.796	2	2,332.687	2	2,474.578	2	2,616.469	2	2,758.360
3	2,193.634	3	2,335.525	3	2,477.416	3	2,619.307	3	2,761.198
4	2,196.472	4	2,338.363	4	2,480.254	4	2,622.145	4	2,764.036
5	2,199.310	5	2,341.201	5	2,483.092	5	2,624.982	5	2,766.873
6	2,202.147	6	2,344.038	6	2,485.929	6	2,627.820	6	2,769.711
7	2,204.985	7	2,346.876	7	2,488.767	7	2,630.658	7	2,772.549
8	2,207.823	8	2,349.714	8	2,491.605	8	2,633.496	8	2,775.387
9	2,210.661	9	2,352.552	9	2,494.443	9	2,636.334	9	2,778.225
780	2,213.499	830	2,355.390	880	2,497.281	930	2,639.172	980	2,781.063
1	2,216.337	1	2,358.228	1	2,500.118	1	2,642.009	1	2,783.900
2	2,219.174	2	2,361.065	2	2,502.956	2	2,644.847	2	2,786.738
3	2,222.012	3	2,363.903	3	2,505.794	3	2,647.685	3	2,789.576
4	2,224.850	4	2,366.741	4	2,508.632	4	2,650.523	4	2,792.414
5	2,227.688	5	2,369.579	5	2,511.470	5	2,653.361	5	2,795.252
6	2,230.526	6	2,372.417	6	2,514.308	6	2,656.199	6	2,798.089
7	2,233.363	7	2,375.254	7	2,517.145	7	2,659.036	7	2,800.927
8	2,236.201	8	2,378.092	8	2,519.983	8	2,661.874	8	2,803.765
9	2,239.039	9	2,380.930	9	2,522.821	9	2,664.712	9	2,806.603
790	2,241.877	840	2,383.768	890	2,525.659	940	2,667.550	990	2,809.441
1	2,244.715	1	2,386.606	1	2,528.497	1	2,670.388	1	2,812.279
2	2,247.553	2	2,389.444	2	2,531.334	2	2,673.225	2	2,815.116
3	2,250.390	3	2,392.281	3	2,534.172	3	2,676.063	3	2,817.954
4	2,253.228	4	2,395.119	4	2,537.010	4	2,678.901	4	2,820.792
5	2,256.066	5	2,397.957	5	2,539.848	5	2,681.739	5	2,823.630
6	2,258.904	6	2,400.795	6	2,542.686	6	2,684.577	6	2,826.468
7	2,261.742	7	2,403.633	7	2,545.524	7	2,687.415	7	2,829.305
8	2,264.579	8	2,406.470	8	2,548.361	8	2,690.252	8	2,832.143
9	2,267.417	9	2,409.308	9	2,551.199	9	2,693.090	9	2,834.981

CAPACITY—BUSHELS TO HECTOLITRES

[Reduction factor: 1 bushel = 0.35238330 hectolitre]

Bush-els	Hecto-litres	Bush-els	Hecto-litres	Bush-els	Hecto-litres	Bush-els	Hecto-litres	Bush-els	Hecto-litres
0		50	17.61917	100	35.2383	150	52.8575	200	70.4767
1	0.35238	1	17.97155	1	35.5907	1	53.2099	1	70.8290
2	0.70477	2	18.32393	2	35.9431	2	53.5623	2	71.1814
3	1.05715	3	18.67631	3	36.2955	3	53.9146	3	71.5338
4	1.40953	4	19.02870	4	36.6479	4	54.2670	4	71.8862
5	1.76192	5	19.38108	5	37.0002	5	54.6194	5	72.2386
6	2.11430	6	19.73346	6	37.3526	6	54.9718	6	72.5910
7	2.46668	7	20.08585	7	37.7050	7	55.3242	7	72.9433
8	2.81907	8	20.43823	8	38.0574	8	55.6766	8	73.2957
9	3.17145	9	20.79061	9	38.4098	9	56.0289	9	73.6481
10	3.52383	60	21.14300	110	38.7622	160	56.3813	210	74.0005
1	3.87622	1	21.49538	1	39.1145	1	56.7337	1	74.3529
2	4.22860	2	21.84776	2	39.4669	2	57.0861	2	74.7053
3	4.58098	3	22.20015	3	39.8193	3	57.4385	3	75.0576
4	4.93337	4	22.55253	4	40.1717	4	57.7909	4	75.4100
5	5.28575	5	22.90491	5	40.5241	5	58.1432	5	75.7624
6	5.63813	6	23.25730	6	40.8765	6	58.4956	6	76.1148
7	5.99052	7	23.60968	7	41.2288	7	58.8480	7	76.4672
8	6.34290	8	23.96206	8	41.5812	8	59.2004	8	76.8196
9	6.69528	9	24.31445	9	41.9336	9	59.5528	9	77.1719
20	7.04767	70	24.66683	120	42.2860	170	59.9052	220	77.5243
1	7.40005	1	25.01921	1	42.6384	1	60.2575	1	77.8767
2	7.75243	2	25.37160	2	42.9908	2	60.6099	2	78.2291
3	8.10482	3	25.72398	3	43.3431	3	60.9623	3	78.5815
4	8.45720	4	26.07636	4	43.6955	4	61.3147	4	78.9339
5	8.80958	5	26.42875	5	44.0479	5	61.6671	5	79.2862
6	9.16197	6	26.78113	6	44.4003	6	62.0195	6	79.6386
7	9.51435	7	27.13351	7	44.7527	7	62.3718	7	79.9910
8	9.86673	8	27.48590	8	45.1051	8	62.7242	8	80.3434
9	10.21912	9	27.83828	9	45.4574	9	63.0766	9	80.6958
30	10.57150	80	28.19066	130	45.8098	180	63.4290	230	81.0482
1	10.92388	1	28.54305	1	46.1622	1	63.7814	1	81.4005
2	11.27627	2	28.89543	2	46.5146	2	64.1338	2	81.7529
3	11.62865	3	29.24781	3	46.8670	3	64.4861	3	82.1053
4	11.98103	4	29.60020	4	47.2194	4	64.8385	4	82.4577
5	12.33342	5	29.95258	5	47.5717	5	65.1909	5	82.8101
6	12.68580	6	30.30496	6	47.9241	6	65.5433	6	83.1625
7	13.03818	7	30.65735	7	48.2765	7	65.8957	7	83.5148
8	13.39057	8	31.00973	8	48.6289	8	66.2481	8	83.8672
9	13.74295	9	31.36211	9	48.9813	9	66.6004	9	84.2196
40	14.09533	90	31.71450	140	49.3337	190	66.9528	240	84.5720
1	14.44772	1	32.06688	1	49.6860	1	67.3052	1	84.9244
2	14.80010	2	32.41926	2	50.0384	2	67.6576	2	85.2768
3	15.15248	3	32.77165	3	50.3908	3	68.0100	3	85.6291
4	15.50487	4	33.12403	4	50.7432	4	68.3624	4	85.9815
5	15.85725	5	33.47641	5	51.0956	5	68.7147	5	86.3339
6	16.20963	6	33.82880	6	51.4480	6	69.0671	6	86.6863
7	16.56202	7	34.18118	7	51.8003	7	69.4195	7	87.0387
8	16.91440	8	34.53356	8	52.1527	8	69.7719	8	87.3911
9	17.26678	9	34.88595	9	52.5051	9	70.1243	9	87.7434

CAPACITY—BUSHELS TO HECTOLITRES

[Reduction factor: 1 bushel = 0.35238330 hectolitre]

Bush-els	Hecto-litres	Bush-els	Hecto-litres	Bush-els	Hecto-litres	Bush-els	Hecto-litres	Bush-els	Hecto-litres
250	88.0958	300	105.7150	350	123.3342	400	140.9533	450	158.5725
1	88.4482	1	106.0674	1	123.6865	1	141.3057	1	158.9249
2	88.8006	2	106.4198	2	124.0389	2	141.6581	2	159.2773
3	89.1530	3	106.7721	3	124.3913	3	142.0105	3	159.6296
4	89.5054	4	107.1245	4	124.7437	4	142.3629	4	159.9820
5	89.8577	5	107.4769	5	125.0961	5	142.7152	5	160.3344
6	90.2101	6	107.8293	6	125.4485	6	143.0676	6	160.6868
7	90.5625	7	108.1817	7	125.8008	7	143.4200	7	161.0392
8	90.9149	8	108.5341	8	126.1532	8	143.7724	8	161.3916
9	91.2673	9	108.8864	9	126.5056	9	144.1248	9	161.7439
260	91.6197	310	109.2388	360	126.8580	410	144.4772	460	162.0963
1	91.9720	1	109.5912	1	127.2104	1	144.8295	1	162.4487
2	92.3244	2	109.9436	2	127.5628	2	145.1819	2	162.8011
3	92.6768	3	110.2960	3	127.9151	3	145.5343	3	163.1535
4	93.0292	4	110.6484	4	128.2675	4	145.8867	4	163.5059
5	93.3816	5	111.0007	5	128.6199	5	146.2391	5	163.8582
6	93.7340	6	111.3531	6	128.9723	6	146.5915	6	164.2106
7	94.0863	7	111.7055	7	129.3247	7	146.9438	7	164.5630
8	94.4387	8	112.0579	8	129.6771	8	147.2962	8	164.9154
9	94.7911	9	112.4103	9	130.0294	9	147.6486	9	165.2678
270	95.1435	320	112.7627	370	130.3818	420	148.0010	470	165.6202
1	95.4959	1	113.1150	1	130.7342	1	148.3534	1	165.9725
2	95.8483	2	113.4674	2	131.0866	2	148.7058	2	166.3249
3	96.2006	3	113.8198	3	131.4390	3	149.0581	3	166.6773
4	96.5530	4	114.1722	4	131.7914	4	149.4105	4	167.0297
5	96.9054	5	114.5746	5	132.1437	5	149.7629	5	167.3821
6	97.2578	6	114.8770	6	132.4961	6	150.1153	6	167.7345
7	97.6102	7	115.2293	7	132.8485	7	150.4677	7	168.0868
8	97.9626	8	115.5817	8	133.2009	8	150.8201	8	168.4392
9	98.3149	9	115.9341	9	133.5533	9	151.1724	9	168.7916
280	98.6673	330	116.2865	380	133.9057	430	151.5248	480	169.1440
1	99.0197	1	116.6389	1	134.2580	1	151.8772	1	169.4964
2	99.3721	2	116.9913	2	134.6104	2	152.2296	2	169.8488
3	99.7245	3	117.3436	3	134.9628	3	152.5820	3	170.2011
4	100.0769	4	117.6960	4	135.3152	4	152.9344	4	170.5535
5	100.4292	5	118.0484	5	135.6676	5	153.2867	5	170.9059
6	100.7816	6	118.4008	6	136.0200	6	153.6391	6	171.2583
7	101.1340	7	118.7532	7	136.3723	7	153.9915	7	171.6107
8	101.4864	8	119.1056	8	136.7247	8	154.3439	8	171.9631
9	101.8388	9	119.4579	9	137.0771	9	154.6963	9	172.3154
290	102.1912	340	119.8103	390	137.4295	440	155.0487	490	172.6678
1	102.5435	1	120.1627	1	137.7819	1	155.4010	1	173.0202
2	102.8959	2	120.5151	2	138.1343	2	155.7534	2	173.3726
3	103.2483	3	120.8675	3	138.4866	3	156.1058	3	173.7250
4	103.6007	4	121.2199	4	138.8390	4	156.4582	4	174.0774
5	103.9531	5	121.5722	5	139.1914	5	156.8106	5	174.4297
6	104.3055	6	121.9246	6	139.5438	6	157.1630	6	174.7821
7	104.6578	7	122.2770	7	139.8962	7	157.5153	7	175.1345
8	105.0102	8	122.6294	8	140.2486	8	157.8677	8	175.4869
9	105.3626	9	122.9818	9	140.6009	9	158.2201	9	175.8393

CAPACITY—BUSHELS TO HECTOLITRES

[Reduction factor: 1 bushel = 0.35238330 hectolitre]

Bush-els	Hecto-litres	Bush-els	Hecto-litres	Bush-els	Hecto-litres	Bush-els	Hecto-litres	Bush-els	Hecto-litres
500	176. 1917	550	193. 8108	600	211. 4300	650	229. 0491	700	246. 6683
1	176. 5440	1	194. 1632	1	211. 7824	1	229. 4015	1	247. 0207
2	176. 8964	2	194. 5156	2	212. 1347	2	229. 7539	2	247. 3731
3	177. 2488	3	194. 8680	3	212. 4871	3	230. 1063	3	247. 7255
4	177. 6012	4	195. 2203	4	212. 8395	4	230. 4587	4	248. 0778
5	177. 9536	5	195. 5727	5	213. 1919	5	230. 8111	5	248. 4302
6	178. 3060	6	195. 9251	6	213. 5443	6	231. 1634	6	248. 7826
7	178. 6583	7	196. 2775	7	213. 8967	7	231. 5158	7	249. 1350
8	179. 0107	8	196. 6299	8	214. 2490	8	231. 8682	8	249. 4874
9	179. 3631	9	196. 9823	9	214. 6014	9	232. 2206	9	249. 8398
510	179. 7155	560	197. 3346	610	214. 9538	660	232. 5730	710	250. 1921
1	180. 0679	1	197. 6870	1	215. 3062	1	232. 9254	1	250. 5445
2	180. 4203	2	198. 0394	2	215. 6586	2	233. 2777	2	250. 8969
3	180. 7726	3	198. 3918	3	216. 0110	3	233. 6301	3	251. 2493
4	181. 1250	4	198. 7442	4	216. 3633	4	233. 9825	4	251. 6017
5	181. 4774	5	199. 0966	5	216. 7157	5	234. 3349	5	251. 9541
6	181. 8298	6	199. 4489	6	217. 0681	6	234. 6873	6	252. 3064
7	182. 1822	7	199. 8013	7	217. 4205	7	235. 0397	7	252. 6588
8	182. 5346	8	200. 1537	8	217. 7729	8	235. 3920	8	253. 0112
9	182. 8869	9	200. 5061	9	218. 1253	9	235. 7444	9	253. 3636
520	183. 2393	570	200. 8585	620	218. 4776	670	236. 0968	720	253. 7160
1	183. 5917	1	201. 2109	1	218. 8300	1	236. 4492	1	254. 0684
2	183. 9441	2	201. 5632	2	219. 1824	2	236. 8016	2	254. 4207
3	184. 2965	3	201. 9156	3	219. 5348	3	237. 1540	3	254. 7731
4	184. 6489	4	202. 2680	4	219. 8872	4	237. 5063	4	255. 1255
5	185. 0012	5	202. 6204	5	220. 2396	5	237. 8587	5	255. 4779
6	185. 3536	6	202. 9728	6	220. 5919	6	238. 2111	6	255. 8303
7	185. 7060	7	203. 3252	7	220. 9443	7	238. 5635	7	256. 1827
8	186. 0584	8	203. 6775	8	221. 2967	8	238. 9159	8	256. 5350
9	186. 4108	9	204. 0299	9	221. 6491	9	239. 2683	9	256. 8874
530	186. 7631	580	204. 3823	630	222. 0015	680	239. 6206	730	257. 2398
1	187. 1155	1	204. 7347	1	222. 3539	1	239. 9730	1	257. 5922
2	187. 4679	2	205. 0871	2	222. 7062	2	240. 3254	2	257. 9446
3	187. 8203	3	205. 4395	3	223. 0586	3	240. 6778	3	258. 2970
4	188. 1727	4	205. 7918	4	223. 4110	4	241. 0302	4	258. 6493
5	188. 5251	5	206. 1442	5	223. 7634	5	241. 3826	5	259 0017
6	188. 8774	6	206. 4966	6	224. 1158	6	241. 7349	6	259. 3541
7	189. 2298	7	206. 8490	7	224. 4682	7	242. 0873	7	259. 7065
8	189. 5822	8	207. 2014	8	224. 8205	8	242. 4397	8	260. 0589
9	189. 9346	9	207. 5538	9	225. 1729	9	242. 7921	9	260. 4113
540	190. 2870	590	207. 9061	640	225. 5253	690	243. 1445	740	260. 7636
1	190. 6394	1	208. 2585	1	225. 8777	1	243. 4969	1	261. 1160
2	190. 9917	2	208. 6109	2	226. 2301	2	243. 8492	2	261. 4684
3	191. 3441	3	208. 9633	3	226. 5825	3	244. 2016	3	261. 8208
4	191. 6965	4	209. 3157	4	226. 9348	4	244. 5540	4	262. 1732
5	192. 0489	5	209. 6681	5	227. 2872	5	244. 9064	5	262. 5256
6	192. 4013	6	210. 0204	6	227. 6396	6	245. 2588	6	262. 8779
7	192. 7537	7	210. 3728	7	227. 9920	7	245. 6112	7	263. 2303
8	193. 1060	8	210. 7252	8	228. 3444	8	245. 9635	8	263. 5827
9	193. 4584	9	211. 0776	9	228. 6968	9	246. 3159	9	263. 9351

CAPACITY—BUSHELS TO HECTOLITRES

[Reduction factor: 1 bushel = 0.35238330 hectolitre]

Bushels	Hectolitres	Bushels	Hectolitres	Bushels	Hectolitres	Bushels	Hectolitres	Bushels	Hectolitres
750	264.2875	800	281.9066	850	299.5258	900	317.1450	950	334.7641
1	264.6399	1	282.2590	1	299.8782	1	317.4974	1	335.1165
2	264.9922	2	282.6114	2	300.2306	2	317.8497	2	335.4689
3	265.3446	3	282.9638	3	300.5830	3	318.2021	3	335.8213
4	265.6970	4	283.3162	4	300.9353	4	318.5545	4	336.1737
5	266.0494	5	283.6686	5	301.2877	5	318.9069	5	336.5261
6	266.4018	6	284.0209	6	301.6401	6	319.2593	6	336.8784
7	266.7542	7	284.3733	7	301.9925	7	319.6117	7	337.2308
8	267.1065	8	284.7257	8	302.3449	8	319.9640	8	337.5832
9	267.4589	9	285.0781	9	302.6973	9	320.3164	9	337.9356
760	267.8113	810	285.4305	860	303.0496	910	320.6688	960	338.2880
1	268.1637	1	285.7829	1	303.4020	1	321.0212	1	338.6404
2	268.5161	2	286.1352	2	303.7544	2	321.3736	2	338.9927
3	268.8685	3	286.4876	3	304.1068	3	231.7260	3	339.3451
4	269.2208	4	286.8400	4	304.4592	4	322.0783	4	339.6975
5	269.5732	5	287.1924	5	304.8116	5	322.4307	5	340.0499
6	269.9256	6	287.5448	6	305.1639	6	322.7831	6	340.4023
7	270.2780	7	287.8972	7	305.5163	7	323.1355	7	340.7547
8	270.6304	8	288.2495	8	305.8687	8	323.4879	8	341.1070
9	270.9828	9	288.6019	9	306.2211	9	323.8403	9	341.4594
770	271.3351	820	288.9543	870	306.5735	920	324.1926	970	341.8118
1	271.6875	1	289.3067	1	306.9259	1	324.5450	1	342.1642
2	272.0399	2	289.6591	2	307.2782	2	324.8974	2	342.5166
3	272.3923	3	290.0115	3	307.6306	3	325.2498	3	342.8690
4	272.7447	4	290.3638	4	307.9830	4	325.6022	4	343.2213
5	273.0971	5	290.7162	5	308.3354	5	325.9546	5	343.5737
6	273.4494	6	291.0686	6	308.6878	6	326.3069	6	343.9261
7	273.8018	7	291.4210	7	309.0402	7	326.6593	7	344.2785
8	274.1542	8	291.7734	8	309.3925	8	327.0117	8	344.6309
9	274.5066	9	292.1258	9	309.7449	9	327.3641	9	344.9833
780	274.8590	830	292.4781	880	310.0973	930	327.7165	980	345.3356
1	275.2114	1	292.8305	1	310.4497	1	328.0689	1	345.6880
2	275.5637	2	293.1829	2	310.8021	2	328.4212	2	346.0404
3	275.9161	3	293.5353	3	311.1545	3	328.7736	3	346.3928
4	276.2685	4	293.8877	4	311.5068	4	329.1260	4	346.7452
5	276.6209	5	294.2401	5	311.8592	5	329.4784	5	347.0976
6	276.9733	6	294.5924	6	312.2116	6	329.8308	6	347.4499
7	277.3257	7	294.9448	7	312.5640	7	330.1832	7	347.8023
8	277.6780	8	295.2972	8	312.9164	8	330.5355	8	348.1547
9	278.0304	9	295.6496	9	313.2688	9	330.8879	9	348.5071
790	278.3828	840	296.0020	890	313.6211	940	331.2403	990	348.8595
1	278.7352	1	296.3544	1	313.9735	1	331.5927	1	349.2119
2	279.0876	2	296.7067	2	314.3259	2	331.9451	2	349.5642
3	279.4400	3	297.0591	3	314.6783	3	332.2975	3	349.9166
4	279.7923	4	297.4115	4	315.0307	4	332.6498	4	350.2690
5	280.1447	5	297.7639	5	315.3831	5	333.0022	5	350.6214
6	280.4971	6	298.1163	6	315.7354	6	333.3546	6	350.9738
7	280.8495	7	298.4687	7	316.0878	7	333.7070	7	351.3262
8	281.2019	8	298.8210	8	316.4402	8	334.0594	8	351.6785
9	281.5543	9	299.1734	9	316.7926	9	334.4118	9	352.0309

MASS—KILOGRAMS TO AVOIRDUPOIS POUNDS

[Reduction factor: 1 kilogram = 2.204622341 avoirdupois pounds]

Kilos	Pounds	Kilos	Pounds	Kilos	Pounds	Kilos	Pounds	Kilos	Pounds
0		50	110.2311	100	220.4622	150	330.6934	200	440.9245
1	2.2046	1	112.4357	1	222.6669	1	332.8980	1	443.1291
2	4.4092	2	114.6404	2	224.8715	2	335.1026	2	445.3337
3	6.6139	3	116.8450	3	227.0761	3	337.3072	3	447.5383
4	8.8185	4	119.0496	4	229.2807	4	339.5118	4	449.7430
5	11.0231	5	121.2542	5	231.4853	5	341.7165	5	451.9476
6	13.2277	6	123.4589	6	233.6900	6	343.9211	6	454.1522
7	15.4324	7	125.6635	7	235.8946	7	346.1257	7	456.3568
8	17.6370	8	127.8681	8	238.0992	8	348.3303	8	458.5614
9	19.8416	9	130.0727	9	240.3038	9	350.5350	9	460.7661
10	22.0462	60	132.2773	110	242.5085	160	352.7396	210	462.9707
1	24.2508	1	134.4820	1	244.7131	1	354.9442	1	465.1753
2	26.4555	2	136.6866	2	246.9177	2	357.1488	2	467.3799
3	28.6601	3	138.8912	3	249.1223	3	359.3534	3	469.5846
4	30.8647	4	141.0958	4	251.3269	4	361.5581	4	471.7892
5	33.0693	5	143.3005	5	253.5316	5	363.7627	5	473.9938
6	35.2740	6	145.5051	6	255.7362	6	365.9673	6	476.1984
7	37.4786	7	147.7097	7	257.9408	7	368.1719	7	478.4030
8	39.6832	8	149.9143	8	260.1454	8	370.3766	8	480.6077
9	41.8878	9	.152.1189	9	262.3501	9	372.5812	9	482.8123
20	44.0924	70	154.3236	120	264.5547	170	374.7858	220	485.0169
1	46.2971	1	156.5282	1	266.7593	1	376.9904	1	487.2215
2	48.5017	2	158.7328	2	268.9639	2	379.1950	2	489.4262
3	50.7063	3	160.9374	3	271.1685	3	381.3997	3	491.6308
4	52.9109	4	163.1421	4	273.3732	4	383.6043	4	493.8354
5	55.1156	5	165.3467	5	275.5778	5	385.8089	5	496.0400
6	57.3202	6	167.5513	6	277.7824	6	388.0135	6	498.2446
7	59.5248	7	169.7559	7	279.9870	7	390.2182	7	500.4493
8	61.7294	8	171.9605	8	282.1917	8	392.4228	8	502.6539
9	63.9340	9	174.1652	9	284.3963	9	394.6274	9	504.8585
30	66.1387	80	176.3698	130	286.6009	180	396.8320	230	507.0631
1	68.3433	1	178.5744	1	288.8055	1	399.0366	1	509.2678
2	70.5479	2	180.7790	2	291.0101	2	401.2413	2	511.4724
3	72.7525	3	182.9837	3	293.2148	3	403.4459	3	513.6770
4	74.9572	4	185.1883	4	295.4194	4	405.6505	4	515.8816
5	77.1618	5	187.3929	5	297.6240	5	407.8551	5	518.0863
6	79.3664	6	189.5975	6	299.8286	6	410.0598	6	520.2909
7	81.5710	7	191.8021	7	302.0333	7	412.2644	7	522.4955
8	83.7756	8	194.0068	8	304.2379	8	414.4690	8	524.7001
9	85.9803	9	196.2114	9	306.4425	9	416.6736	9	526.9047
40	88.1849	90	198.4160	140	308.6471	190	418.8782	240	529.1094
1	90.3895	1	200.6206	1	310.8518	1	421.0829	1	531.3140
2	92.5941	2	202.8253	2	313.0564	2	423.2875	2	533.5186
3	94.7988	3	205.0299	3	315.2610	3	425.4921	3	535.7232
4	97.0034	4	207.2345	4	317.4656	4	427.6967	4	537.9279
5	99.2080	5	209.4391	5	319.6702	5	429.9014	5	540.1325
6	101.4126	6	211.6437	6	321.8749	6	432.1060	6	542.3371
7	103.6173	7	213.8484	7	324.0795	7	434.3106	7	544.5417
8	105.8219	8	216.0530	8	326.2841	8	436.5152	8	546.7463
9	108.0265	9	218.2576	9	328.4887	9	438.7198	9	548.9510

MASS—KILOGRAMS TO AVOIRDUPOIS POUNDS

[Reduction factor: 1 kilogram = 2.204622341 avoirdupois pounds]

Kilos	Pounds	Kilos	Pounds	Kilos	Pounds	Kilos	Pounds	Kilos	Pounds
250	551.1556	300	661.3867	350	771.6178	400	881.8489	450	992.0801
1	553.3602	1	663.5913	1	773.8224	1	884.0536	1	994.2847
2	555.5648	2	665.7959	2	776.0271	2	886.2582	2	996.4893
3	557.7695	3	668.0006	3	778.2317	3	888.4628	3	998.6939
4	559.9741	4	670.2052	4	780.4363	4	890.6674	4	1,000.8985
5	562.1787	5	672.4098	5	782.6409	5	892.8720	5	1,003.1032
6	564.3833	6	674.6144	6	784.8456	6	895.0767	6	1,005.3078
7	566.5879	7	676.8191	7	787.0502	7	897.2813	7	1,007.5124
8	568.7926	8	679.0237	8	789.2548	8	899.4859	8	1,009.7170
9	570.9972	9	681.2283	9	791.4594	9	901.6905	9	1,011.9217
260	573.2018	310	683.4329	360	793.6640	410	903.8952	460	1,014.1263
1	575.4064	1	685.6375	1	795.8687	1	906.0998	1	1,016.3309
2	577.6111	2	687.8422	2	798.0733	2	908.3044	2	1,018.5355
3	579.8157	3	690.0468	3	800.2779	3	910.5090	3	1,020.7401
4	582.0203	4	692.2514	4	802.4825	4	912.7136	4	1,022.9448
5	584.2249	5	694.4560	5	804.6872	5	914.9183	5	1,025.1494
6	586.4295	6	696.6607	6	806.8918	6	917.1229	6	1,027.3540
7	588.6342	7	698.8653	7	809.0964	7	919.3275	7	1,029.5586
8	590.8388	8	701.0699	8	811.3010	8	921.5321	8	1,031.7633
9	593.0434	9	703.2745	9	813.5056	9	923.7368	9	1,033.9679
270	595.2480	320	705.4791	370	815.7103	420	925.9414	470	1,036.1725
1	597.4527	1	707.6838	1	817.9149	1	928.1460	1	1,038.3771
2	599.6573	2	709.8884	2	820.1195	2	930.3506	2	1,040.5817
3	601.8619	3	712.0930	3	822.3241	3	932.5553	3	1,042.7864
4	604.0665	4	714.2976	4	824.5288	4	934.7599	4	1,044.9910
5	606.2711	5	716.5023	5	826.7334	5	936.9645	5	1,047.1956
6	608.4758	6	718.7069	6	828.9380	6	939.1691	6	1,049.4002
7	610.6804	7	720.9115	7	831.1426	7	941.3737	7	1,051.6049
8	612.8850	8	723.1161	8	833.3472	8	943.5784	8	1,053.8095
9	615.0896	9	725.3208	9	835.5519	9	945.7830	9	1,056.0141
280	617.2943	330	727.5254	380	837.7565	430	947.9876	480	1,058.2187
1	619.4989	1	729.7300	1	839.9611	1	950.1922	1	1,060.4233
2	621.7035	2	731.9346	2	842.1657	2	952.3969	2	1,062.6280
3	623.9081	3	734.1392	3	844.3704	3	954.6015	3	1,064.8326
4	626.1127	4	736.3439	4	846.5750	4	956.8061	4	1,067.0372
5	628.3174	5	738.5485	5	848.7796	5	959.0107	5	1,069.2418
6	630.5220	6	740.7531	6	850.9842	6	961.2153	6	1,071.4465
7	632.7266	7	742.9577	7	853.1888	7	963.4200	7	1,073.6511
8	634.9312	8	745.1624	8	855.3935	8	965.6246	8	1,075.8557
9	637.1359	9	747.3670	9	857.5981	9	967.8292	9	1,078.0603
290	639.3405	340	749.5716	390	859.8027	440	970.0338	490	1,080.2649
1	641.5451	1	751.7762	1	862.0073	1	972.2385	1	1,082.4696
2	643.7497	2	753.9808	2	864.2120	2	974.4431	2	1,084.6742
3	645.9543	3	756.1855	3	866.4166	3	976.6477	3	1,086.8788
4	648.1590	4	758.3901	4	868.6212	4	978.8523	4	1,089.0834
5	650.3636	5	760.5947	5	870.8258	5	981.0569	5	1,091.2881
6	652.5682	6	762.7993	6	873.0304	6	983.2616	6	1,093.4927
7	654.7728	7	765.0040	7	875.2351	7	985.4662	7	1,095.6973
8	656.9775	8	767.2086	8	877.4397	8	987.6708	8	1,097.9019
9	659.1821	9	769.4132	9	879.6443	9	989.8754	9	1,100.1065

MASS—KILOGRAMS TO AVOIRDUPOIS POUNDS

[Reduction factor: 1 kilogram = 2.204622341 avoirdupois pounds]

Kilos	Pounds	Kilos	Pounds	Kilos	Pounds	Kilos	Pounds	Kilos	Pounds
500	1,102.3112	550	1,212.5423	600	1,322.7734	650	1,433.0045	700	1,543.2356
1	1,104.5158	1	1,214.7469	1	1,324.9780	1	1,435.2091	1	1,545.4403
2	1,106.7204	2	1,216.9515	2	1,327.1826	2	1,437.4138	2	1,547.6449
3	1,108.9250	3	1,219.1562	3	1,329.3873	3	1,439.6184	3	1,549.8495
4	1,111.1297	4	1,221.3608	4	1,331.5919	4	1,441.8230	4	1,552.0541
5	1,113.3343	5	1,223.5654	5	1,333.7965	5	1,444.0276	5	1,554.2588
6	1,115.5389	6	1,225.7700	6	1,336.0011	6	1,446.2323	6	1,556.4634
7	1,117.7435	7	1,227.9746	7	1,338.2058	7	1,448.4369	7	1,558.6680
8	1,119.9481	8	1,230.1793	8	1,340.4104	8	1,450.6415	8	1,560.8726
9	1,122.1528	9	1,232.3839	9	1,342.6150	9	1,452.8461	9	1,563.0772
510	1,124.3574	560	1,234.5885	610	1,344.8196	660	1,455.0507	710	1,565.2819
1	1,126.5620	1	1,236.7931	1	1,347.0243	1	1,457.2554	1	1,567.4865
2	1,128.7666	2	1,238.9978	2	1,349.2289	2	1,459.4600	2	1,569.6911
3	1,130.9713	3	1,241.2024	3	1,351.4335	3	1,461.6646	3	1,571.8957
4	1,133.1759	4	1,243.4070	4	1,353.6381	4	1,463.8692	4	1,574.1004
5	1,135.3805	5	1,245.6116	5	1,355.8427	5	1,466.0739	5	1,576.3050
6	1,137.5851	6	1,247.8162	6	1,358.0474	6	1,468.2785	6	1,578.5096
7	1,139.7898	7	1,250.0209	7	1,360.2520	7	1,470.4831	7	1,580.7142
8	1,141.9944	8	1,252.2255	8	1,362.4566	8	1,472.6877	8	1,582.9188
9	1,144.1990	9	1,254.4301	9	1,364.6612	9	1,474.8923	9	1,585.1235
520	1,146.4036	570	1,256.6347	620	1,366.8659	670	1,477.0970	720	1,587.3281
1	1,148.6082	1	1,258.8394	1	1,369.0705	1	1,479.3016	1	1,589.5327
2	1,150.8129	2	1,261.0440	2	1,371.2751	2	1,481.5062	2	1,591.7373
3	1,153.0175	3	1,263.2486	3	1,373.4797	3	1,483.7108	3	1,593.9420
4	1,155.2221	4	1,265.4532	4	1,375.6843	4	1,485.9155	4	1,596.1466
5	1,157.4267	5	1,267.6578	5	1,377.8890	5	1,488.1201	5	1,598.3512
6	1,159.6314	6	1,269.8625	6	1,380.0936	6	1,490.3247	6	1,600.5558
7	1,161.8360	7	1,272.0671	7	1,382.2982	7	1,492.5293	7	1,602.7604
8	1,164.0406	d	1,274.2717	8	1,384.5028	8	1,494.7339	8	1,604.9651
9	1,166.2452	9	1,276.4763	9	1,386.7075	9	1,496.9386	9	1,607.1697
530	1,168.4498	580	1,278.6810	630	1,388.9121	680	1,499.1432	730	1,609.3743
1	1,170.6545	1	1,280.8856	1	1,391.1167	1	1,501.3478	1	1,611.5789
2	1,172.8591	2	1,283.0902	2	1,393.3213	2	1,503.5524	2	1,613.7836
3	1,175.0637	3	1,285.2948	3	1,395.5259	3	1,505.7571	3	1,615.9882
4	1,177.2683	4	1,287.4994	4	1,397.7306	4	1,507.9617	4	1,618.1928
5	1,179.4730	5	1,289.7041	5	1,399.9352	5	1,510.1663	5	1,620.3974
6	1,181.6776	6	1,291.9087	6	1,402.1398	6	1,512.3709	6	1,622.6020
7	1,183.8822	?	1,294.1133	7	1,404.3444	7	1,514.5755	7	1,624.8067
8	1,186.0868	8	1,296.3179	8	1,406.5491	8	1,516.7802	8	1,627.0113
9	1,188.2914	9	1,298.5226	9	1,408.7537	9	1,518.9848	9	1,629.2159
540	1,190.4961	590	1,300.7272	640	1,410.9583	690	1,521.1894	740	1,631.4205
1	1,192.7007	1	1,302.9318	1	1,413.1629	1	1,523.3940	1	1,633.6252
2	1,194.9053	2	1,305.1364	2	1,415.3675	2	1,525.5987	2	1,635.8298
3	1,197.1099	3	1,307.3410	3	1,417.5722	3	1,527.8033	3	1,638.0344
4	1,199.3146	4	1,309.5457	4	1,419.7768	4	1,530.0079	4	1,640.2390
5	1,201.5192	5	1,311.7503	5	1,421.9814	5	1,532.2125	5	1,642.4436
6	1,203.7238	6	1,313.9549	6	1,424.1860	6	1,534.4171	6	1,644.6483
7	1,205.9284	7	1,316.1595	7	1,426.3907	7	1,536.6218	7	1,646.8529
8	1,208.1330	8	1,318.3642	8	1,428.5953	8	1,538.8264	8	1,649.0575
9	1,210.3377	9	1,320.5688	9	1,430.7999	9	1,541.0310	9	1,651.2621

MASS—KILOGRAMS TO AVOIRDUPOIS POUNDS

[Reduction factor: 1 kilogram = 2.204622341 avoirdupois pounds]

Kilos	Pounds	Kilos	Pounds	Kilos	Pounds	Kilos	Pounds	Kilos	Pounds
750	1,653.4668	800	1,763.6979	850	1,873.9290	900	1,984.1601	950	2,094.3912
1	1,655.6714	1	1,765.9025	1	1,876.1336	1	1,986.3647	1	2,096.5958
2	1,657.8760	2	1,768.1071	2	1,878.3382	2	1,988.5694	2	2,098.8005
3	1,660.0806	3	1,770.3117	3	1,880.5429	3	1,990.7740	3	2,101.0051
4	1,662.2852	4	1,772.5164	4	1,882.7475	4	1,992.9786	4	2,103.2097
5	1,664.4899	5	1,774.7210	5	1,884.9521	5	1,995.1832	5	2,105.4143
6	1,666.6945	6	1,776.9256	6	1,887.1567	6	1,997.3878	6	2,107.6190
7	1,668.8991	7	1,779.1302	7	1,889.3613	7	1,999.5925	7	2,109.8236
8	1,671.1037	8	1,781.3349	8	1,891.5660	8	2,001.7971	8	2,112.0282
9	1,673.3084	9	1,783.5395	9	1,893.7706	9	2,004.0017	9	2,114.2328
760	1,675.5130	810	1,785.7441	860	1,895.9752	910	2,006.2063	960	2,116.4374
1	1,677.7176	1	1,787.9487	1	1,898.1798	1	2,008.4110	1	2,118.6421
2	1,679.9222	2	1,790.1533	2	1,900.3845	2	2,010.6156	2	2,120.8467
3	1,682.1268	3	1,792.3580	3	1,902.5891	3	2,012.8202	3	2,123.0513
4	1,684.3315	4	1,794.5626	4	1,904.7937	4	2,015.0248	4	2,125.2559
5	1,686.5361	5	1,796.7672	5	1,906.9983	5	2,017.2294	5	2,127.4606
6	1,688.7407	6	1,798.9718	6	1,909.2029	6	2,019.4341	6	2,129.6652
7	1,690.9453	7	1,801.1765	7	1,911.4076	7	2,021.6387	7	2,131.8698
8	1,693.1500	8	1,803.3811	8	1,913.6122	8	2,023.8433	8	2,134.0744
9	1,695.3546	9	1,805.5857	9	1,915.8168	9	2,026.0479	9	2,136.2790
770	1,697.5592	820	1,807.7903	870	1,918.0214	920	2,028.2526	970	2,138.4837
1	1,699.7638	1	1,809.9949	1	1,920.2261	1	2,030.4572	1	2,140.6883
2	1,701.9684	2	1,812.1996	2	1,922.4307	2	2,032.6618	2	2,142.8929
3	1,704.1731	3	1,814.4042	3	1,924.6353	3	2,034.8664	3	2,145.0975
4	1,706.3777	4	1,816.6088	4	1,926.8399	4	2,037.0710	4	2,147.3022
5	1,708.5823	5	1,818.8134	5	1,929.0445	5	2,039.2757	5	2,149.5068
6	1,710.7869	6	1,821.0181	6	1,931.2492	6	2,041.4803	6	2,151.7114
7	1,712.9916	7	1,823.2227	7	1,933.4538	7	2,043.6849	7	2,153.9160
8	1,715.1962	8	1,825.4273	8	1,935.6584	8	2,045.8895	8	2,156.1206
9	1,717.4008	9	1,827.6319	9	1,937.8630	9	2,048.0942	9	2,158.3253
780	1,719.6054	830	1,829.8365	880	1,940.0677	930	2,050.2988	980	2,160.5299
1	1,721.8100	1	1,832.0412	1	1,942.2723	1	2,052.5034	1	2,162.7345
2	1,724.0147	2	1,834.2458	2	1,944.4769	2	2,054.7080	2	2,164.9391
3	1,726.2193	3	1,836.4504	3	1,946.6815	3	2,056.9126	3	2,167.1438
4	1,728.4239	4	1,838.6550	4	1,948.8861	4	2,059.1173	4	2,169.3484
5	1,730.6285	5	1,840.8597	5	1,951.0908	5	2,061.3219	5	2,171.5530
6	1,732.8332	6	1,843.0643	6	1,953.2954	6	2,063.5265	6	2,173.7576
7	1,735.0378	7	1,845.2689	7	1,955.5000	7	2,065.7311	7	2,175.9623
8	1,737.2424	8	1,847.4735	8	1,957.7046	8	2,067.9358	8	2,178.1669
9	1,739.4470	9	1,849.6781	9	1,959.9093	9	2,070.1404	9	2,180.3715
790	1,741.6516	840	1,851.8828	890	1,962.1139	940	2,072.3450	990	2,182.5761
1	1,743.8563	1	1,854.0874	1	1,964.3185	1	2,074.5496	1	2,184.7807
2	1,746.0609	2	1,856.2920	2	1,966.5231	2	2,076.7542	2	2,186.9854
3	1,748.2655	3	1,858.4966	3	1,968.7278	3	2,078.9589	3	2,189.1900
4	1,750.4701	4	1,860.7013	4	1,970.9324	4	2,081.1635	4	2,191.3946
5	1,752.6748	5	1,862.9059	5	1,973.1370	5	2,083.3681	5	2,193.5992
6	1,754.8794	6	1,865.1105	6	1,975.3416	6	2,085.5727	6	2,195.8039
7	1,757.0840	7	1,867.3151	7	1,977.5462	7	2,087.7774	7	2,198.0085
8	1,759.2886	8	1,869.5197	8	1,979.7509	8	2,089.9820	8	2,200.2131
9	1,761.4933	9	1,871.7244	9	1,981.9555	9	2,092.1866	9	2,202.4177

MASS—AVOIRDUPOIS POUNDS TO KILOGRAMS

[Reduction factor: 1 avoirdupois pound = 0.4535924277 kilogram]

Pounds	Kilos	Pounds	Kilos	Pounds	Kilos	Pounds	Kilos	Pounds	Kilos
0		50	22.67962	100	45.35924	150	68.03886	200	90.71849
1	0.45359	1	23.13321	1	45.81284	1	68.49246	1	91.17208
2	.90718	2	23.58681	2	46.26643	2	68.94605	2	91.62567
3	1.36078	3	24.04040	3	46.72002	3	69.39964	3	92.07926
4	1.81437	4	24.49399	4	47.17361	4	69.85323	4	92.53286
5	2.26796	5	24.94758	5	47.62720	5	70.30683	5	92.98645
6	2.72155	6	25.40118	6	48.08080	6	70.76042	6	93.44004
7	3.17515	7	25.85477	7	48.53439	7	71.21401	7	93.89363
8	3.62874	8	26.30836	8	48.98798	8	71.66760	8	94.34722
9	4.08233	9	26.76195	9	49.44157	9	72.12120	9	94.80082
10	4.53592	60	27.21555	110	49.89517	160	72.57479	210	95.25441
1	4.98952	1	27.66914	1	50.34876	1	73.02838	1	95.70800
2	5.44311	2	28.12273	2	50.80235	2	73.48197	2	96.16159
3	5.89670	3	28.57632	3	51.25594	3	73.93557	3	96.61519
4	6.35029	4	29.02992	4	51.70954	4	74.38916	4	97.06878
5	6.80389	5	29.48351	5	52.16313	5	74.84275	5	97.52237
6	7.25748	6	29.93710	6	52.61672	6	75.29634	6	97.97596
7	7.71107	7	30.39069	7	53.07031	7	75.74994	7	98.42956
8	8.16466	8	30.84429	8	53.52391	8	76.20353	8	98.88315
9	8.61826	9	31.29788	9	53.97750	9	76.65712	9	99.33674
20	9.07185	70	31.75147	120	54.43109	170	77.11071	220	99.79033
1	9.52544	1	32.20506	1	54.88468	1	77.56431	1	100.24393
2	9.97903	2	32.65865	2	55.33828	2	78.01790	2	100.69752
3	10.43263	3	33.11225	3	55.79187	3	78.47149	3	101.15111
4	10.88622	4	33.56584	4	56.24546	4	78.92509	4	101.60470
5	11.33981	5	34.01943	5	56.69905	5	79.37867	5	102.05830
6	11.79340	6	34.47302	6	57.15265	6	79.83227	6	102.51189
7	12.24700	7	34.92662	7	57.60624	7	80.28586	7	102.96548
8	12.70059	8	35.38021	8	58.05983	8	80.73945	8	103.41907
9	13.15418	9	35.83380	9	58.51342	9	81.19304	9	103.87267
30	13.60777	80	36.28739	130	58.96702	180	81.64664	230	104.32626
1	14.06137	1	36.74099	1	59.42061	1	82.10023	1	104.77985
2	14.51496	2	37.19458	2	59.87420	2	82.55382	2	105.23344
3	14.96855	3	37.64817	3	60.32779	3	83.00741	3	105.68704
4	15.42214	4	38.10176	4	60.78139	4	83.46101	4	106.14063
5	15.87573	5	38.55536	5	61.23498	5	83.91460	5	106.59422
6	16.32933	6	39.00895	6	61.68857	6	84.36819	6	107.04781
7	16.78292	7	39.46254	7	62.14216	7	84.82178	7	107.50141
8	17.23651	8	39.91613	8	62.59576	8	85.27538	8	107.95500
9	17.69010	9	40.36973	9	63.04935	9	85.72897	9	108.40859
40	18.14370	90	40.82332	140	63.50294	190	86.18256	240	108.86218
1	18.59729	1	41.27691	1	63.95653	1	86.63615	1	109.31578
2	19.05088	2	41.73050	2	64.41012	2	87.08975	2	109.76937
3	19.50447	3	42.18410	3	64.86372	3	87.54334	3	110.22296
4	19.95807	4	42.63769	4	65.31731	4	87.99693	4	110.67655
5	20.41166	5	43.09128	5	65.77090	5	88.45052	5	111.13014
6	20.86525	6	43.54487	6	66.22449	6	88.90412	6	111.58374
7	21.31884	7	43.99847	7	66.67809	7	89.35771	7	112.03733
8	21.77244	8	44.45206	8	67.13168	8	89.81130	8	112.49092
9	22.22603	9	44.90565	9	67.58527	9	90.26489	9	112.94451

MASS—AVOIRDUPOIS POUNDS TO KILOGRAMS

[Reduction factor: 1 avoirdupois pound = 0.4535924277 kilogram]

Pounds	Kilos	Pounds	Kilos	Pounds	Kilos	Pounds	Kilos	Pounds	Kilos
250	113. 39811	300	136. 07773	350	158. 75735	400	181. 43697	450	204. 11659
1	113. 85170	1	136. 53132	1	159. 21094	1	181. 89056	1	204. 57018
2	114. 30529	2	136. 98491	2	159. 66453	2	182. 34416	2	205. 02378
3	114. 75888	3	137. 43851	3	160. 11813	3	182. 79775	3	205. 47737
4	115. 21248	4	137. 89210	4	160. 57172	4	183. 25134	4	205. 93096
5	115. 66607	5	138. 34569	5	161. 02531	5	183. 70493	5	206. 38455
6	116. 11966	6	138. 79928	6	161. 47890	6	184. 15853	6	206. 83815
7	116. 57325	7	139. 25288	7	161. 93250	7	184. 61212	7	207. 29174
8	117. 02685	8	139. 70647	8	162. 38609	8	185. 06571	8	207. 74533
9	117. 48044	9	140. 16006	9	162. 83968	9	185. 51930	9	208. 19892
260	117. 93403	310	140. 61365	360	163. 29327	410	185. 97290	460	208. 65252
1	118. 38762	1	141. 06725	1	163. 74687	1	186. 42649	1	209. 10611
2	118. 84122	2	141. 52084	2	164. 20046	2	186. 88008	2	209. 55970
3	119. 29481	3	141. 97443	3	164. 65405	3	187. 33367	3	210. 01329
4	119. 74840	4	142. 42802	4	165. 10764	4	187. 78727	4	210. 46689
5	120. 20199	5	142. 88161	5	165. 56124	5	188. 24086	5	210. 92048
6	120. 65559	6	143. 33521	6	166. 01483	6	188. 69445	6	211. 37407
7	121. 10918	7	143. 78880	7	166. 46842	7	189. 14804	7	211. 82766
8	121. 56277	8	144. 24239	8	166. 92201	8	189. 60163	8	212. 28126
9	122. 01636	9	144. 69598	9	167. 37561	9	190. 05523	9	212. 73485
270	122. 46996	320	145. 14958	370	167. 82920	420	190. 50882	470	213. 18844
1	122. 92355	1	145. 60317	1	168. 28279	1	190. 96241	1	213. 64203
2	123. 37714	2	146. 05676	2	168. 73638	2	191. 41600	2	214. 09563
3	123. 83073	3	146. 51035	3	169. 18998	3	191. 86960	3	214. 54922
4	124. 28433	4	146. 96395	4	169. 64357	4	192. 32319	4	215. 00281
5	124. 73792	5	147. 41754	5	170. 09716	5	192. 77678	5	215. 45640
6	125. 19151	6	147. 87113	6	170. 55075	6	193. 23037	6	215. 91000
7	125. 64510	7	148. 32472	7	171. 00435	7	193. 68397	7	216. 36359
8	126. 09869	8	148. 77832	8	171. 45794	8	194. 13756	8	216. 81718
9	126. 55229	9	149. 23191	9	171. 91153	9	194. 59115	9	217. 27077
280	127. 00588	330	149. 68550	380	172. 36512	430	195. 04474	480	217. 72437
1	127. 45947	1	150. 13909	1	172. 81871	1	195. 49834	1	218. 17796
2	127. 91306	2	150. 59269	2	173. 27231	2	195. 95193	2	218. 63155
3	128. 36666	3	151. 04628	3	173. 72590	3	196. 40552	3	219. 08514
4	128. 82025	4	151. 49987	4	174. 17949	4	196. 85911	4	219. 53874
5	129. 27384	5	151. 95346	5	174. 63308	5	197. 31271	5	219. 99233
6	129. 72743	6	152. 40706	6	175. 08668	6	197. 76630	6	220. 44592
7	130. 18103	7	152. 86065	7	175. 54027	7	198. 21989	7	220. 89951
8	130. 63462	8	153. 31424	8	175. 99386	8	198. 67348	8	221. 35310
9	131. 08821	9	153. 76783	9	176. 44745	9	199. 12708	9	221. 80670
290	131. 54180	340	154. 22143	390	176. 90105	440	199. 58067	490	222. 26029
1	131. 99540	1	154. 67502	1	177. 35464	1	200. 03426	1	222. 71388
2	132. 44899	2	155. 12861	2	177. 80823	2	200. 48785	2	223. 16747
3	132. 90258	3	155. 58220	3	178. 26182	3	200. 94145	3	223. 62107
4	133. 35617	4	156. 03580	4	178. 71542	4	201. 39504	4	224. 07466
5	133. 80977	5	156. 48939	5	179. 16901	5	201. 84863	5	224. 52825
6	134. 26336	6	156. 94298	6	179. 62260	6	202. 30222	6	224. 98184
7	134. 71695	7	157. 39657	7	180. 07619	7	202. 75582	7	225. 43544
8	135. 17054	8	157. 85016	8	180. 52979	8	203. 20941	8	225. 88903
9	135. 62414	9	158. 30376	9	180. 98338	9	203. 66300	9	226. 34262

MASS—AVOIRDUPOIS POUNDS TO KILOGRAMS

[Reduction factor: 1 avoirdupois pound = 0.4535924277 kilogram]

Pounds	Kilos	Pounds	Kilos	Pounds	Kilos	Pounds	Kilos	Pounds	Kilos
500	226.79621	550	249.47584	600	272.15546	650	294.83508	700	317.51470
1	227.24981	1	249.92943	1	272.60905	1	295.28867	1	317.96829
2	227.70340	2	250.38302	2	273.06264	2	295.74226	2	318.42188
3	228.15699	3	250.83661	3	273.51623	3	296.19586	3	318.87548
4	228.61058	4	251.29020	4	273.96983	4	296.64945	4	319.32907
5	229.06418	5	251.74380	5	274.42342	5	297.10304	5	319.78266
6	229.51777	6	252.19739	6	274.87701	6	297.55663	6	320.23625
7	229.97136	7	252.65098	7	275.33060	7	298.01022	7	320.68985
8	230.42495	8	253.10457	8	275.78420	8	298.46382	8	321.14344
9	230.87855	9	253.55817	9	276.23779	9	298.91741	9	321.59703
510	231.33214	560	254.01176	610	276.69138	660	299.37100	710	322.05062
1	231.78573	1	254.46535	1	277.14497	1	299.82459	1	322.50422
2	232.23932	2	254.91894	2	277.59857	2	300.27819	2	322.95781
3	232.69292	3	255.37254	3	278.05216	3	300.73178	3	323.41140
4	233.14651	4	255.82613	4	278.50575	4	301.18537	4	323.86499
5	233.60010	5	256.27972	5	278.95934	5	301.63896	5	324.31859
6	234.05369	6	256.73331	6	279.41294	6	302.09256	6	324.77218
7	234.50729	7	257.18691	7	279.86653	7	302.54615	7	325.22577
8	234.96088	8	257.64050	8	280.32012	8	302.99974	8	325.67936
9	235.41447	9	258.09409	9	280.77371	9	303.45333	9	326.13296
520	235.86806	570	258.54768	620	281.22731	670	303.90693	720	326.58655
1	236.32165	1	259.00128	1	281.68090	1	304.36052	1	327.04014
2	236.77525	2	259.45487	2	282.13449	2	304.81411	2	327.49373
3	237.22884	3	259.90846	3	282.58808	3	305.26770	3	327.94733
4	237.68243	4	260.36205	4	283.04167	4	305.72130	4	328.40092
5	238.13602	5	260.81565	5	283.49527	5	306.17489	5	328.85451
6	238.58962	6	261.26924	6	283.94886	6	306.62848	6	329.30810
7	239.04321	7	261.72283	7	284.40245	7	307.08207	7	329.76169
8	239.49680	8	262.17642	8	284.85604	8	307.53567	8	330.21529
9	239.95039	9	262.63002	9	285.30964	9	307.98926	9	330.66888
530	240.40399	580	263.08361	630	285.76323	680	308.44285	730	331.12247
1	240.85758	1	263.53720	1	286.21682	1	308.89644	1	331.57606
2	241.31117	2	263.99079	2	286.67041	2	309.35004	2	332.02966
3	241.76476	3	264.44439	3	287.12401	3	309.80363	3	332.48325
4	242.21836	4	264.89798	4	287.57760	4	310.25722	4	332.93684
5	242.67195	5	265.35157	5	288.03119	5	310.71081	5	333.39043
6	243.12554	6	265.80516	6	288.48478	6	311.16441	6	333.84403
7	243.57913	7	266.25876	7	288.93838	7	311.61800	7	334.29762
8	244.03273	8	266.71235	8	289.39197	8	312.07159	8	334.75121
9	244.48632	9	267.16594	9	289.84556	9	312.52518	9	335.20480
540	244.93991	590	267.61953	640	290.29915	690	312.97878	740	335.65840
1	245.39350	1	268.07312	1	290.75275	1	313.43237	1	336.11199
2	245.84710	2	268.52672	2	291.20634	2	313.88596	2	336.56558
3	246.30069	3	268.98031	3	291.65993	3	314.33955	3	337.01917
4	246.75428	4	269.43390	4	292.11352	4	314.79314	4	337.47277
5	247.20787	5	269.88749	5	292.56712	5	315.24674	5	337.92636
6	247.66147	6	270.34109	6	293.02071	6	315.70033	6	338.37995
7	248.11506	7	270.79468	7	293.47430	7	316.15392	7	338.83354
8	248.56865	8	271.24827	8	293.92789	8	316.60751	8	339.28714
9	249.02224	9	271.70186	9	294.38149	9	317.06111	9	339.74073

MASS—AVOIRDUPOIS POUNDS TO KILOGRAMS

[Reduction factor: 1 avoirdupois pound = 0.4535924277 kilogram]

Pounds	Kilos	Pounds	Kilos	Pounds	Kilos	Pounds	Kilos	Pounds	Kilos
750	340.19432	800	362.87394	850	385.55356	900	408.23318	950	430.91281
1	340.64791	1	363.32753	1	386.00716	1	408.68678	1	431.36640
2	341.10151	2	363.78113	2	386.46075	2	409.14037	2	431.81999
3	341.55510	3	364.23472	3	386.91434	3	409.59396	3	432.27358
4	342.00869	4	364.68831	4	387.36793	4	410.04755	4	432.72718
5	342.46228	5	365.14190	5	387.82153	5	410.50115	5	433.18077
6	342.91588	6	365.59550	6	388.27512	6	410.95474	6	433.63436
7	343.36947	7	366.04909	7	388.72871	7	411.40833	7	434.08795
8	343.82306	8	366.50268	8	389.18230	8	411.86192	8	434.54155
9	344.27665	9	366.95627	9	389.63590	9	412.31552	9	434.99514
760	344.73025	810	367.40987	860	390.08949	910	412.76911	960	435.44873
1	345.18384	1	367.86346	1	390.54308	1	413.22270	1	435.90232
2	345.63743	2	368.31705	2	390.99667	2	413.67629	2	436.35592
3	346.09102	3	368.77064	3	391.45027	3	414.12989	3	436.80951
4	346.54461	4	369.22424	4	391.90386	4	414.58348	4	437.26310
5	346.99821	5	369.67783	5	392.35745	5	415.03707	5	437.71669
6	347.45180	6	370.13142	6	392.81104	6	415.49066	6	438.17029
7	347.90539	7	370.58501	7	393.26463	7	415.94426	7	438.62388
8	348.35898	8	371.03861	8	393.71823	8	416.39785	8	439.07747
9	348.81258	9	371.49220	9	394.17182	9	416.85144	9	439.53106
770	349.26617	820	371.94579	870	394.62541	920	417.30503	970	439.98465
1	349.71976	1	372.39938	1	395.07900	1	417.75863	1	440.43825
2	350.17335	2	372.85298	2	395.53260	2	418.21222	2	440.89184
3	350.62695	3	373.30657	3	395.98619	3	418.66581	3	441.34543
4	351.08054	4	373.76016	4	396.43978	4	419.11940	4	441.79902
5	351.53413	5	374.21375	5	396.89337	5	419.57300	5	442.25262
6	351.98772	6	374.66735	6	397.34697	6	420.02659	6	442.70621
7	352.44132	7	375.12094	7	397.80056	7	420.48018	7	443.15980
8	352.89491	8	375.57453	8	398.25415	8	420.93377	8	443.61339
9	353.34850	9	376.02812	9	398.70774	9	421.38737	9	444.06699
780	353.80209	830	376.48171	880	399.16134	930	421.84096	980	444.52058
1	354.25569	1	376.93531	1	399.61493	1	422.29455	1	444.97417
2	354.70928	2	377.38890	2	400.06852	2	422.74814	2	445.42776
3	355.16287	3	377.84249	3	400.52211	3	423.20174	3	445.88136
4	355.61646	4	378.29608	4	400.97571	4	423.65533	4	446.33495
5	356.07006	5	378.74968	5	401.42930	5	424.10892	5	446.78854
6	356.52365	6	379.20327	6	401.88289	6	424.56251	6	447.24213
7	356.97724	7	379.65686	7	402.33648	7	425.01610	7	447.69573
8	357.43083	8	380.11045	8	402.79008	8	425.46970	8	448.14932
9	357.88443	9	380.56405	9	403.24367	9	425.92329	9	448.60291
790	358.33802	840	381.01764	890	403.69726	940	426.37688	990	449.05650
1	358.79161	1	381.47123	1	404.15085	1	426.83047	1	449.51010
2	359.24520	2	381.92482	2	404.60445	2	427.28407	2	449.96369
3	359.69880	3	382.37842	3	405.05804	3	427.73766	3	450.41729
4	360.15239	4	382.83201	4	405.51163	4	428.19125	4	450.87087
5	360.60598	5	383.28560	5	405.96522	5	428.64484	5	451.32447
6	361.05957	6	383.73919	6	406.41882	6	429.09844	6	451.77806
7	361.51316	7	384.19279	7	406.87241	7	429.55203	7	452.23165
8	361.96676	8	384.64638	8	407.32600	8	430.00562	8	452.68534
9	362.42035	9	385.09997	9	407.77959	9	430.45921	9	453.13894

METRIC AND ENGLISH EQUIVALENTS OF DISTANCE IN TRACK AND FIELD EVENTS

Metric distances for track and field events to be run in athletic meets held under the jurisdiction of the Amateur Athletic Union were officially adopted by that body on November 22, 1932. The following tables have been included in this book to make it possible for those not familiar with the Metric system to know the various distances expressed in metres.

In Table 1 are given the equivalents of Metric and English distances for principal indoor and outdoor track events.

In Table 2 are given the Metric equivalents for distances in feet, inches and binary fractions of an inch.

The metric equivalent of any distance may be conveniently found, to the nearest ⅛ inch, by breaking the distance down into convenient parts, obtaining the equivalent of each part and then adding them together to get the total equivalent.

For example the metric equivalent of 251 feet, 9½ inches is found as follows:

200 feet	=	60.960 metres
50 feet	=	15.240 metres
1 foot	=	.0305 metre
9 inches	=	.229 metre
½ inch	=	.013 metre

251 feet, 9½ inches = 76.4725 metres

DISTANCE EQUIVALENTS

Basis $\begin{cases} \text{1 metre} = 39.37 \text{ inches} = 3.280\ 8 \text{ feet} = 1.093\ 6 \text{ yards} \\ \text{1 kilometre} = 1\ 000 \text{ metres} = 0.621\ 370 \text{ mile} \end{cases}$

TABLE 1.—*Track events*

Yards : Metres	Metres : Yards
40 = 36. 58	50 = 54. 68
50 = 45. 72	60 = 65. 62
60 = 54. 86	65 = 71. 08
70 = 64. 01	80 = 87. 49
75 = 68. 58	100 = 109. 36
100 = 91. 44	110 = 120. 30
110 = 100. 58	200 = 218. 72
120 = 109. 73	300 = 328. 08
220 = 201. 17	400 = 437. 44
300 = 274. 32	500 = 546. 81
440 = 402. 34 = ¼ mi	600 = 656. 16
600 = 548. 64	800 = 874. 89
880 = 804. 67 = ½ mi	1 000 = 1 093. 61
1 000 = 914. 40	1 500 = 1 640. 42
1 320 = 1 207. 01 = ¾ mi	1 600 = 1 749. 78

Miles : Metres	Metres : Miles		Yards and inches		Miles (approx.)
1 = 1 609. 3	2 000 =	1		427	8	1. 24
2 = 3 218. 7	2 400 =	1		864	24	1. 49
3 = 4 828. 0	3 000 =	1	1 520	30	1. 86
4 = 6 437. 4	3 200 =	1	1 739	20	1. 99
5 = 8 046. 7					
	5 000 =	3		188	2	3. 11
6 = 9 656. 1	6 000 =	3	1 281	24	3. 73
7 = 11 265. 4	10 000 =	6		376	4	6. 21
8 = 12 874. 8	15 000 =	9		564	6	9. 32
9 = 14 484. 1					
	20 000 =	12		752	8	12. 43
10 = 16 093. 5	25 000 =	15		940	10	15. 53
15 = 24 140. 2	30 000 =	18	1 128	12	18. 64
20 = 32 186. 9	50 000 =	31		120	20	31. 07
25 = 40 233. 7					

TABLE 2.—*Field events*

Feet : Metres		Inches : Metres	
1	= 0.305	1 =	0.025
2	= .610	2 =	.051
3	= .914	3 =	.076
4	= 1.219	4 =	.102
5	= 1.524		
		5 =	.127
6	= 1.829	6 =	.152
7	= 2.134	7 =	.178
8	= 2.438	8 =	.203
9	= 2.743		
		9 =	.229
10	= 3.048	10 =	.254
20	= 6.096	11 =	.279
30	= 9.144	12 =	.305
40	= 12.192		
50	= 15.240	Fractions	
		of an	
60	= 18.288	inch : Metre	
70	= 21.336		
80	= 24.384	$\frac{1}{8}$ =	0.003
90	= 27.432	$\frac{1}{4}$ =	.006
		$\frac{3}{8}$ =	.010
100	= 30.480	$\frac{1}{2}$ =	.013
200	= 60.960		
300	= 91.440	$\frac{5}{8}$ =	.016
400	= 121.920	$\frac{3}{4}$ =	.019
500	= 152.400	$\frac{7}{8}$ =	.022
		1 =	.025
600	= 182.880		
700	= 213.360		
800	= 243.840		
900	= 274.321		

The precision of measurement of distance and of time, as ordinarily carried out in track and field events, received consideration in determining the number of decimal places to be carried out in these tables.

Distances in field events are customarily measured in feet and inches to the nearest eighth of an inch. This is about 3 millimetres or 0.0003 metres. In order to convert these measured distances from feet and inches to metres with maximum accuracy, the metric equivalents are given to the nearest 0.001 metre.

The same consideration has been given to the accuracy of measurement of both distance and time as carried out with track events. It should be noted that when time is taken with a stop watch it is usually given to the fifth or tenth of a second. When taken with electrical timing devices it may be given to the hundredth of a second.

In dashes, where 1 second represents a distance of approximately 10 yards or 10 metres, $\frac{1}{10}$ second represents about 1 yard or 1 metre, and $\frac{1}{100}$ second represents a distance of $\frac{1}{10}$ yard or $\frac{1}{10}$ metre. There is no need at present, therefore, to give metric equivalents of distances more precision than the nearest $\frac{1}{10}$ metre, even when the most precise timing methods are used. For distances of less than a mile, however, they have been given to the nearest $\frac{1}{100}$ metre in order to allow for possible future improvement in timing devices.

The Metric Technical Language

The change over to the SI presents a unique opportunity to use a correct unambiguous terminology in connection with concepts such as *mass, weight, measure, dimension*, etc. from the start.

It is recommended that the following terms be consistently used in the future. The first column gives the terms used at present. The second column gives the terms that should be used to make a clear distinction between the concepts *mass* and *weight*. Use of these terms will ensure that the units kilogram (kg) and newton (N) are applied correctly.

Existing term	New English term
A	
apothecaries' weight	apothecaries' masspiece
assize weight	assize masspiece
avoirdupois weight	avoirdupois masspiece
B	
balance weight	balance piece
basis weight	basis mass
beam scale	beam balance
	beam massmeter
box-end beam scale	box-end beam massmeter
bulk handling	bulk handling
bulk installation	bulk installation
bulk intake	bulk intake
bulk price	bulk price
bulk storage	bulk storage
bulk store	bulk store
bulk transport	bulk transport
bulk weight	bulk mass
bushel weight	mass per hectolitre
C	
carat weight	carat masspiece
counterpoise	counterpoise
counter scale	counter massmeter
	counter scale
counting scale	counting scale
crane scale	crane massmeter
	crane scale
crane weigher	crane massmeter
	crane scale
cream test scale	cream test massmeter
	cream test scale
	cream test balance

D

dead-weight scale	dead-mass balance
denomination of measure	denomination of measure
dimension	dimension
drained weight	drained mass

F

fine weighing	fine mass-measuring

G

grain in bulk	grain in bulk
grain weight	grain masspiece
gross weight	gross mass

H

heavy-weight material	heavy-weight material *or* high-mass material
hopper scale	hopper massmeter
	hopper scale

L

lightweight material	lightweight material *or* low-mass material

M

material weight	material mass
measure	measure
measure of weight (e.g. measure of weight may be applied in selling liquids)	mass unit
	unit of mass (e.g. certain liquids may be sold in mass units)
measuring unit	measuring unit, unit of measurement
medium-weight material	medium-weight material *or* medium-mass material
micrometer scale	micrometer massmeter
	micrometer scale

N

net weight	net mass

P

person weigher	person massmeter
	person scale
platform scale	platform massmeter
	platform scale
post office beam scale	post office massmeter
	post office scale
	post office balance

S

scale	massmeter
	scale
short weight	short mass (expressed in kg)
sliding poise	sliding poise
spring balance 1. (calibrated in kg)	spring massmeter
	spring balance
spring balance 2. (calibrated in N)	spring weightmeter
	spring balance
standard weight 1.	standard mass
standard weight 2.	standard masspiece
steelyard	steelyard
suspended weigher	suspended massmeter
	suspended scale
swan-neck beam scale	swan-neck massmeter
	swan-neck balance
system of measures	system of measurement
system of weights and measures	system of measuring units

T

tare weight	tare
troy weight	troy masspiece

U

underweight

unit of measurement

unit of weight 1.
unit of weight 2.

undermass (e.g. the bag is
   10   kg undermass)
unit of measurement,
   measuring unit
unit of mass (the kilogram)
unit of weight (the newton)

W

wall beam

weigh 1. (the process of determining mass)
weigh 2. (v.i., e.g. the object
   weighs 2 lb)
weighbridge
weighing

weighing balance

weighing capacity
weighing instrument
weighing process
weighing system
weigh out

weight 1. (quantity of matter
   expressed in lb, e.g. the butter has a weight of 1 lb)
weight 2. (object of known
   mass used to determine the
   mass of other objects by
   using a balance, e.g. place
   the 1 lb weight on the
   scale)
weight 3. (gravitational pull of
   the earth on an object expressed in newtons, e.g. the
   weight of a kilogram of butter is less than 2 newtons on
   the moon)

wall massmeter
wall scale
measure the mass
determine the mass
the mass is
has a mass of
mass-measuring bridge
1. mass-measuring
2. mass measurement

massmeter
balance
mass-measuring capacity
massmeter
mass-measuring process
mass-measuring system
measure out (e.g. measure out
   5 kg)
mass (e.g. the butter has a
   mass of 500 g)

masspiece (e.g. place a 500 g
   masspiece on the balance)

weight

weight 4. (object on which the weight in newtons is stamped as well as the locality where it has the weight in question, e.g. hang the 1 lb weight from the testing machine)

weightpiece (e.g. hang the 10 N weightpiece from the testing machine)

weight 5. (a general name for objects that have heaviness but are not connected with units, e.g. a paper weight, curtain weight)

weight

weight 6. (in everyday and idiomatic expressions having no connection with units, such as: pulls his weight; worth his weight in gold; an argument carries weight)

weight

weight 7. (v. to attach factors indicative of their relative frequency or importance to the various items of a frequency distribution, e.g. prices were weighted)

weight

weight change

mass change (expressed in kg)

weight class

weight class *or* mass class

weight determination 1. (in lb-mass)

mass determination (in kilograms)

weight determination 2. (in lb-force)

weight determination (in newtons)

weight lifter

weight lifter

weight limits

mass limits

weight pan

masspiece pan

weight problems

weight problems *or* mass problems

weight range

mass-measuring range

weight registering

mass-registering

weight return

mass return

weights and measures

measuring units

Conclusion

Because this glossary is to be used by metrication officers, translators, linguists, terminologists, educationists and other experts, it contains more terms than those normally encountered by the man in the street. This may create the impression that the whole subject is difficult. This is not the case. In everyday life it is quite sufficient to remember the following:

a) The United States is changing over to the *Metric System of Measuring Units.*

b) In this system the kilogram is the *base unit of mass.*

c) To determine mass we *measure it by means of a massmeter.*

d) The term *massmeter* includes all *instruments* capable of measuring mass, thus also *scales* and *balances,* terms that will continue to be used.

e) We place *masspieces* on a balance when measuring the mass of an object. The mass of a masspiece is constant everywhere on earth and in space and is indicated on the masspiece.

To clarify our terminology it is necessary that a specific meaning should consistently be attached to certain words and that we should not use the same word for different meanings in this context as has happened so often in the past. In this regard the following terms are of importance:

measure:	any physical object with a known denomination used to determine the value of a quantity by direct comparison. A ruler or measuring tape is a measure of length, a litre cup is a measure of volume and a masspiece is a mass measure.
measuring unit:	units such as the metre, kilogram, second, ampere. They should not be referred to as measures.
denomination of a measure:	the value or size of a measure. A masspiece of 2 kg has a denomination of 2 kg; a volume measure with a capacity of 500 m*l* has a denomination of 500 m*l.*
measurement:	the completed measuring process giving a result expressed in measuring units.

THE OFFICIAL VERSION OF THE INTERNATIONAL SYSTEM OF UNITS (SI) WITH A CHRONOLOGY OF THE RESOLUTIONS AND RECOMMENDATIONS OF THE GENERAL CONFERENCE OF WEIGHTS AND MEASURES (CGPM)

I. INTRODUCTION

I.1

In 1948 the 9th CGPM[1], by its Resolution 6, instructed the CIPM[1]: "to study the establishment of a complete set of rules for units of measurement"; "to find out for this purpose, by official inquiry, the opinion prevailing in scientific, technical, and educational circles in all countries" and "to make recommendations on the establishment of a *practical system of units of measurement* suitable for adoption by all signatories to the Metre Convention."

The same General Conference also laid down, by its Resolution 7, general principles for unit symbols (see II.1.2, page 6) and also gave a list of units with special names.

The 10th CGPM (1954), by its Resolution 6, and the 14th CGPM (1971) by its Resolution 3, adopted as base units of this "practical system of units", the units of the following seven quantities: length, mass, time, electric current, thermodynamic temperature, amount of substance, and luminous intensity (see II.1, page 3).

The 11th CGPM (1960), by its Resolution 12, adopted the name *International System of Units*, with the international abbreviation SI, for this practical system of units of measurement and laid down rules for the prefixes (see III.1, page 12), the derived and supplementary units (see II.2.2, page 10 and II.3, page 11) and other matters, thus establishing a comprehensive specification for units of measurement.

In the present document the expressions "SI units", "SI prefixes", "supplementary units" are used in accordance with Recommendation 1 (1969) of the CIPM.

---

[1]For the meaning of these abbreviations, see page x.

I.2 The three classes of SI units

SI units are divided into three classes:
> base units,
> derived units,
> supplementary units.

From the scientific point of view division of SI units into these three classes is to a certain extent arbitrary, because it is not essential to the physics of the subject.

Nevertheless the General Conference, considering the advantages of a single, practical, worldwide system for international relations, for teaching and for scientific work, decided to base the International System on a choice of seven well-defined units which by convention are regarded as dimensionally independent: the metre, the kilogram, the second, the ampere, the kelvin, the mole, and the candela (see II.1, page 3). These SI units are called *base units*.[2]

The second class of SI units contains *derived units*, i.e., units that can be formed by combining base units according to the algebraic relations linking the corresponding quantities. Several of these algebraic expressions in terms of base units can be replaced by special names and symbols which can themselves be used to form other derived units (see II.2, page 6).

Although it might be thought that SI units can only be base units or derived units, the 11th CGPM (1960) admitted a third class of SI units, called *supplementary units*, for which it declined to state whether they were base units or derived units (see II.3, page 11).

The SI units of these three classes form a coherent set in the sense normally attributed to the expression "coherent system of units".

The decimal multiples and sub-multiples of SI units formed by means of SI prefixes must be given their full name *multiples and sub-multiples of SI units* when it is desired to make a distinction between them and the coherent set of SI units.

---

[2] *Translators' note.* The spellings "metre" and "kilogram" are used in this USA/UK translation in the hope of securing worldwide uniformity in the English spelling of the names of the units of the International System.

II. SI UNITS

II.1 Base units

1. Definitions

a) Unit of length.—The 11th CGPM (1960) replaced the definition of the metre based on the international prototype of platinum-iridium, in force since 1889 and amplified in 1927, by the following definition:

> *The metre is the length equal* to 1 650 763.73 *wavelengths in vacuum of the radiation corresponding to the transition between the levels* $2p_{10}$ *and* $5d_5$ *of the krypton*-86 *atom.* (11th CGPM (1960), Resolution 6).

The old international prototype of the metre which was legalized by the 1st CGPM in 1889 is still kept at the International Bureau of Weights and Measures under the conditions specified in 1889.

b) Unit of mass.—The 1st CGPM (1889) legalized the international prototype of the kilogram and declared: *this prototype shall henceforth be considered to be the unit of mass.*

With the object of removing the ambiguity which still occurred in the common use of the word "weight", the 3rd CGPM (1901) declared: *the kilogram is the unit of mass* [and not of weight or of force]; *it is equal to the mass of the international prototype of the kilogram.*

This international prototype made of platinum-iridium is kept at the BIPM under conditions specified by the 1st CGPM in 1889.

c) Unit of time.—Originally the unit of time, the second, was defined as the fraction 1/86 400 of the mean solar day. The exact definition of "mean solar day" was left to astronomers, but their measurements have shown that on account of irregularities in the rotation of the Earth the mean solar day does not guarantee the desired accuracy. In order to define the unit of time more precisely the 11th CGPM (1960) adopted a definition given by the International Astronomical Union which was based on the tropical year. Experimental work had however already shown that an atomic standard of time-interval, based on a transition between two energy levels of an atom or a molecule, could be realized and reproduced much more accurately. Considering that a very precise definition of the unit of time of the International System, the second, is indispensable for the needs of advanced metrology, the 13th CGPM (1967) decided to replace the definition of the second by the following:

The second is the duration of 9 192 631 770 *periods of the radiation corresponding to the transition between the two hyperfine levels of the ground state of the cesium*-133 *atom.* (13th CGPM (1967), Resolution 1).

d) Unit of electric current.—Electric units, called "international", for current and resistance, had been introduced by the International Electrical Congress held in Chicago in 1893, and the definitions of the "international" ampere and the "international" ohm were confirmed by the International Conference of London in 1908.

Although it was already obvious on the occasion of the 8th CGPM (1933) that there was a unanimous desire to replace those "international" units by so-called "absolute" units, the official decision to abolish them was only taken by the 9th CGPM (1948), which adopted for the unit of electric current, the ampere, the following definition:

The ampere is that constant current which, if maintained in two straight parallel conductors of infinite length, of negligible circular cross section, and placed 1 metre apart in vacuum, would produce between these conductors a force equal to 2×10^{-7} newton per metre of length. (CIPM (1946), Resolution 2 approved by the 9th CGPM, 1948)

The expression "MKS unit of force" which occurs in the original text has been replaced here by "newton" adopted by the 9th CGPM (1948, Resolution 7).

e) Unit of thermodynamic temperature.—The definition of the unit of thermodynamic temperature was given in substance by the 10th CGPM (1954, Resolution 3) which selected the triple point of water as fundamental fixed point and assigned to it the temperature 273.16 °K by definition. The 13th CGPM (1967, Resolution 3) adopted the name *kelvin* (symbol K) instead of "degree Kelvin" (symbol °K) and in its Resolution 4 defined the unit of thermodynamic temperature as follows:

The kelvin, unit of thermodynamic temperature, is the fraction 1/273.16 of the thermodynamic temperature of the triple point of water. (13th CGPM (1967), Resolution 4).

The 13th CGPM (1967, Resolution 3) also decided that the unit kelvin and its symbol K should be used to express an interval or a difference of temperature.

Note.—In addition to the thermodynamic temperature (symbol T), expressed in kelvins, use is also made of Celsius temperature (symbol t) defined by the equation

$$t = T - T_0$$

where $T_0 = 273.15$ K by definition. The Celsius temperature is expressed in degrees Celsius (symbol °C). The unit "degree Celsius" is thus equal to the unit "kelvin" and an interval or a difference of Celsius temperature may also be expressed in degrees Celsius.

f) Unit of amount of substance.—Since the discovery of the fundamental laws of chemistry, units of amount of substance called, for instance, "gram-atom" and "gram-molecule", have been used to specify amounts of chemical elements or compounds. These units had a direct connection with "atomic weights" and "molecular weights", which were in fact relative masses. "Atomic weights" were originally referred to the atomic weight of oxygen (by general agreement taken as 16). But whereas physicists separated isotopes in the mass spectrograph and attributed the value 16 to one of the isotopes of oxygen, chemists attributed that same value to the (slightly variable) mixture of isotopes 16, 17, and 18, which was for them the naturally occurring element oxygen. Finally an agreement between the International Union of Pure and Applied Physics (IUPAP) and the International Union of Pure and Applied Chemistry (IUPAC) brought this duality to an end in 1959/60. Physicists and chemists have ever since agreed to assign the value 12 to the isotope 12 of carbon, The unified scale thus obtained gives values of "relative atomic mass".

It remained to define the unit of amount of substance by fixing the corresponding mass of carbon 12; by international agreement, this mass has been fixed at 0.012 kg, and the unit of the quantity, "amount of substance",[3] has been given the name *mole* (symbol mol).

Following proposals of IUPAP, IUPAC, and ISO, the CIPM gave in 1967, and confirmed in 1969, the following definition of the mole, adopted by the 14th CGPM (1971, Resolution 3):

The mole is the amount of substance of a system which contains as many elementary entities as there are atoms in 0.012 kilogram of carbon 12.

Note. *When the mole is used, the elementary entities must be specified and may be atoms, molecules, ions, electrons, other particles, or specified groups of such particles.*

Note that this definition specifies at the same time the nature of the quantity whose unit is the mole.[3]

g) Unit of luminous intensity.—The units of luminous intensity based on flame or incandescent filament standards in use in various countries were replaced in 1948 by the "new candle". This decision had been prepared by the International Commission on Illumination (CIE) and by the CIPM before 1937, and was promulgated by the CIPM at its meeting in 1946 in virtue of powers conferred on it in 1933 by the 8th CGPM. The 9th CGPM (1948) ratified the decision of the CIPM and gave a new international name, *candela* (symbol cd), to the unit of luminous intensity. The text of the definition of the candela, as amended in 1967, is as follows.

The candela is the luminous intensity, in the perpendicular direction, of a surface of 1/600 000 square metre of a blackbody at the tem-

---

[3] The name of this quantity, adopted by IUPAP, IUPAC, and ISO is in French "quantité de matière" and in English "amount of substance"; (the German and Russian translations are "Stoffmenge" and "количество вещества"). The French name recalls "quantitas materiae" by which in the past the quantity now called mass used to be known; we must forget this old meaning, for mass and amount of substance are entirely different quantities.

perature of freezing platinum under a pressure of 101 325 *newtons per square metre.* (13th CGPM (1967). Resolution 5).

2. Symbols

The base units of the International System are collected in table 1 with their names and their symbols (10th CGPM (1954), Resolution 6; 11th CGPM (1960), Resolution 12; 13th CGPM (1967), Resolution 3; 14th CGPM (1971), Resolution 3.

TABLE 1

SI base units

Quantity	Name	Symbol
length	metre	m
mass	kilogram	kg
time	second	s
electric current	ampere	A
thermodynamic temperature*	kelvin	K
amount of substance	mole	mol
luminous intensity	candela	cd

*Celsius temperature is in general expressed in degrees Celsius (symbol °C) (see Note, p. 4).

The general principle governing the writing of unit symbols had already been adopted by the 9th CGPM (1958), Resolution 7, according to which:

Roman (upright) *type, in general lower case, is used for symbols of units; if however the symbols are derived from proper names, capital roman type is used* [for the first letter]. *These symbols are not followed by a full stop* (period).

Unit symbols do not change in the plural.

II.2 Derived units

1. Expressions

Derived units are expressed algebraically in terms of base units by means of the mathematical symbols of multiplication and division. Several derived units have been given special names and symbols which may themselves be used to express other derived units in a simpler way than in terms of the base units.

Derived units may therfore be classified under three headings. Some of them are given in tables 2, 3, and 4.

TABLE 2
*Examples of SI derived units
expressed in terms of base units*

Quantity	SI unit	
	Name	Symbol
area	square metre	m^2
volume	cubic metre	m^3
speed, velocity	metre per second	m/s
acceleration	metre per second squared	m/s^2
wave number	1 per metre	m^{-1}
density, mass density	kilogram per cubic metre	kg/m^3
current density	ampere per square metre	A/m^2
magnetic field strength	ampere per metre	A/m
concentration (of amount of substance)	mole per cubic metre	mol/m^3
activity (radioactive)	1 per second	s^{-1}
specific volume	cubic metre per kilogram	m^3/kg
luminance	candela per square metre	cd/m^2

TABLE 3

SI derived units with special names

Quantity	SI unit			
	Name	Sym-bol	Expression in terms of other units	Expression in terms of SI base units
frequency	hertz	Hz		s^{-1}
force	newton	N		$m \cdot kg \cdot s^{-2}$
pressure, stress	pascal	Pa	N/m^2	$m^{-1} \cdot kg \cdot s^{-2}$
energy, work, quantity of heat	joule	J	$N \cdot m$	$m^2 \cdot kg \cdot s^{-2}$
power, radiant flux	watt	W	J/s	$m^2 \cdot kg \cdot s^{-3}$
quantity of electricity, electric charge	coulomb	C	$A \cdot s$	$s \cdot A$
electric potential, potential difference, electromotive force	volt	V	W/A	$m^2 \cdot kg \cdot s^{-3} \cdot A^{-1}$
capacitance	farad	F	C/V	$m^{-2} \cdot kg^{-1} \cdot s^4 \cdot A^2$
electric resistance	ohm	Ω	V/A	$m^2 \cdot kg \cdot s^{-3} \cdot A^{-2}$
conductance	siemens	S	A/V	$m^{-2} \cdot kg^{-1} \cdot s^3 \cdot A^2$
magnetic flux	weber	Wb	$V \cdot s$	$m^2 \cdot kg \cdot s^{-2} \cdot A^{-1}$
magnetic flux density	tesla	T	Wb/m^2	$kg \cdot s^{-2} \cdot A^{-1}$
inductance	henry	H	Wb/A	$m^2 \cdot kg \cdot s^{-2} \cdot A^{-2}$
luminous flux	lumen	lm		$cd \cdot sr$ (ᵃ)
illuminance	lux	lx		$m^{-2} \cdot cd \cdot sr$ (ᵃ)

(ᵃ) In this expression the steradian (sr) is treated as a base unit.

TABLE 4
Examples of SI derived units
expressed by means of special names

Quantity	SI unit		
	Name	Symbol	Expression in terms of SI base units
dynamic viscosity	pascal second	Pa•s	m^{-1}•kg•s^{-1}
moment of force	metre newton	N•m	m^2•kg•s^{-2}
surface tension	newton per metre	N/m	kg•s^{-2}
heat flux density, irradiance	watt per square metre	W/m^2	kg•s^{-3}
heat capacity, entropy	joule per kelvin	J/K	m^2•kg•s^{-2}•K^{-1}
specific heat capacity, specific entropy	joule per kilogram kelvin	J/(kg•K)	m^2•s^{-2}•K^{-1}
specific energy	joule per kilogram	J/kg	m^2•s^{-2}
thermal conductivity	watt per metre kelvin	W/(m•K)	m•kg•s^{-3}•K^{-1}
energy density	joule per cubic metre	J/m^3	m^{-1}•kg•s^{-2}
electric field strength	volt per metre	V/m	m•kg•s^{-3}•A^{-1}
electric charge density	coulomb per cubic metre	C/m^3	m^{-3}•s•A
electric flux density	coulomb per square metre	C/m^2	m^{-2}•s•A
permittivity	farad per metre	F/m	m^{-3}•kg^{-1}•s^4•A^2
permeability	henry per metre	H/m	m•kg•s^{-2}•A^{-2}
molar energy	joule per mole	J/mol	m^2•kg•s^{-2}•mol^{-1}
molar entropy, molar heat capacity	joule per mole kelvin	J/(mol•K)	m^2•kg•s^{-2}•K^{-1}•mol^{-1}

Note a—The values of certain so-called dimensionless quantities, as for example refractive index, relative permeability or relative permittivity, are expressed by pure numbers. In this case the corresponding SI unit is the ratio of the same two SI units and may be expressed by the number 1.

Note b—Although a derived unit can be expressed in several equivalent ways by using names of base units and special names of derived units, CIPM sees no objection to the preferential use of certain combinations or of certain special names in order to distinguish more easily between quantities of the same dimension; for example, the hertz is often used in preference to the reciprocal second for the frequency of a periodic phenomenon, and the newton-metre in preference to the joule for the moment of a force, although, rigorously, 1 Hz$=1$s^{-1}, and 1 N$\cdot$m$=1$ J.

2. *Recommendations*

The International Organization for Standardization (ISO) has issued additional recommendations with the aim of securing uniformity in the use of units, in particular those of the International System (see the series of Recommendations R 31 and Recommendation R 1000 of Technical Committee ISO/TC 12 "Quantities, units, symbols, conversion factors and conversion tables").

According to these recommendations:

a) The product of two or more units is preferably indicated by a dot. The dot may be dispensed with when there is no risk of confusion with another unit symbol

for example: N$\cdot$m or N m *but not:* mN

b) A solidus (oblique stroke, /), a horizontal line, or negative powers may be used to express a derived unit formed from two others by division

for example: m/s, $\dfrac{m}{s}$ or m$\cdot$s^{-1}

c) The solidus must not be repeated on the same line unless ambiguity is avoided by parentheses. In complicated cases negative powers or parentheses should be used

for example: m/s^2 or   m$\cdot$s^{-2} *but not:* m/s/s
m$\cdot$kg/(s$^3\cdot$A) or m$\cdot$kg$\cdot$s$^{-3}\cdot$A^{-1} m$\cdot$kg/s^3/A

II.3 Supplementary units

The General Conference has not yet classified certain units of the International System under either base units or derived units. These SI units are assigned to the third class called "supplementary units", and may be regarded either as base units or as derived units.

For the time being this class contains only two, purely geometrical, units: the SI unit of plane angle, the *radian*, and the SI unit of solid angle, the *steradian* (11th CGPM (1960), Resolution 12).

TABLE 5

SI supplementary units

Quantity	SI unit	
	Name	Symbol
plane angle	radian	rad
solid angle	steradian	sr

The radian is the plane angle between two radii of a circle which cut off on the circumference an arc equal in length to the radius.

The steradian is the solid angle which, having its vertex in the center of a sphere, cuts off an area of the surface of the sphere equal to that of a square with sides of length equal to the radius of the sphere.

(ISO Recommendation R 31, part 1, second edition, December 1965).

Supplementary units may be used to form derived units. Examples are given in table 6.

TABLE 6

Examples of SI derived units formed by using supplementary units

Quantity	SI unit	
	Name	Symbol
angular velocity	radian per second	rad/s
angular acceleration	radian per second squared	rad/s^2
radiant intensity	watt per steradian	W/sr
radiance	watt per square metre steradian	W$\cdot$m$^{-2}\cdot$sr^{-1}

III. DECIMAL MULTIPLES AND SUB-MULTIPLES OF SI UNITS

III.1 SI Prefixes

The 11th CGPM (1960, Resolution 12) adopted a first series of names and symbols of prefixes to form decimal multiples and sub-multiples of SI units. Prefixes for 10^{-15} and 10^{-18} were added by the 12th CGPM (1964, Resolution 8).

TABLE 7

SI prefixes

Factor	Prefix	Symbol	Factor	Prefix	Symbol
10^{12}	tera	T	10^{-1}	deci	d
10^9	giga	G	10^{-2}	centi	c
10^6	mega	M	10^{-3}	milli	m
10^3	kilo	k	10^{-6}	micro	μ
10^2	hecto	h	10^{-9}	nano	n
10^1	deka	da	10^{-12}	pico	p
			10^{-15}	femto	f
			10^{-18}	atto	a

III.2 Recommendations

ISO recommends the following rules for the use of SI prefixes:

a) Prefix symbols are printed in roman (upright) type without spacing between the prefix symbol and the unit symbol.

b) An exponent attached to a symbol containing a prefix indicates that the multiple or sub-multiple of the unit is raised to the power expressed by the exponent,

$$for\ example: \quad 1\ cm^3 = 10^{-6}\ m^3$$
$$1\ cm^{-1} = 10^2\ m^{-1}$$

c) Compound prefixes, formed by the juxtaposition of two or more SI prefixes, are not to be used.

$$for\ example: \quad 1\ nm \quad but\ not: 1\ m\mu m$$

III.3 The kilogram

Among the base units of the International System, the unit of mass is the only one whose name, for historical reasons, contains a prefix. Names of decimal multiples and sub-multiples of the unit of mass are formed by attaching prefixes to the word "gram" (CIPM (1967), Recommendation 2).

IV. UNITS OUTSIDE THE INTERNATIONAL SYSTEM

IV.1 Units used with the International System

The CIPM (1969) recognized that users of SI will wish to employ with it certain units not part of it, but which are important and are widely used. These units are given in table 8. The combination of units of this table with SI units to form compound units should, however, be authorized only in limited cases; in particular, the kilowatt-hour should eventually be abandoned.

TABLE 8

Units in use with the International System

Name	Symbol	Value in SI unit
minute	min	1 min $= 60$ s
hour[a]	h	1 h $= 60$ min $= 3\ 600$ s
day	d	1 d $= 24$ h $= 86\ 400$ s
degree	°	1° $= (\pi/180)$ rad
minute	′	1′ $= (1/60)° = (\pi/10\ 800)$ rad
second	″	1″ $= (1/60)′ = (\pi/648\ 000)$ rad
litre[a]	l	1 l $= 1$ dm³ $= 10^{-3}$ m³
tonne[a]	t	1 t $= 10^3$ kg

[a] The symbol of this unit is included in Resolution 7 of the 9th CGPM (1948). The litre is defined in Resolution 6 of the 12th CGPM (1964).

It is likewise necessary to recognize, outside the International System, some others units which are useful in specialized fields, because their values expressed in SI units must be obtained by experiment, and are therefore not known exactly (table 9).

TABLE 9

Units used with the International System whose values in SI units are obtained experimentally

Name	Symbol	Definition
electronvolt	eV	$(^a)$
unified atomic mass unit	u	$(^b)$
astronomical unit	$(^c)$	$(^c)$
parsec	pc	$(^d)$

$(^a)$ 1 electronvolt is the kinetic energy acquired by an electron in passing through a potential difference of 1 volt in vacuum; 1 eV = 1.602 19 × 10⁻¹⁹ J approximately.

$(^b)$ The unified atomic mass unit is equal to the fraction $\frac{1}{12}$ of the mass of an atom of the nuclide ¹²C; 1 u = 1.660 53 × 10⁻²⁷ kg approximately.

$(^c)$ This unit does not have an international symbol; abbreviations are used, for example, AU in English, UA in French, AE in German, a.e.Д in Russian, etc. The astronomical unit of distance is the length of the radius of the unperturbed circular orbit of a body of negligible mass moving round the Sun with a sidereal angular velocity of 0.017 202 098 950 radian per day of 86 400 ephemeris seconds. In the system of astronomical constants of the International Astronomical Union the value adopted for it is: 1 AU = 149 600 × 10⁶ m.

$(^d)$ 1 parsec is the distance at which 1 astronomical unit subtends an angle of 1 second of arc; we thus have approximately, 1 pc = 206 265 AU = 30 857 × 10¹² m.

IV.2 Units accepted temporarily

In view of existing practice the CIPM (1969) considered it was preferable to keep for the time being, for use with those of the International System, the units listed in table 10.

TABLE 10

*Units to be used with the
International System for a limited time*

Name	Symbol	Value in SI units
nautical mile[a]		1 nautical mile $= 1\ 852$ m
knot		1 nautical mile per hour $=$ $(1852/3600)$ m/s
ångström	$\overset{\circ}{\text{A}}$	$1\ \overset{\circ}{\text{A}} = 0.1$ nm $= 10^{-10}$ m
are[b]	a	1 a $= 1$ dam^2 $= 10^2$ m^2
hectare[b]	ha	1 ha $= 1$ hm^2 $= 10^4$ m^2
barn[c]	b	1 b $= 100$ fm^2 $= 10^{-28}$ m^2
bar[d]	bar	1 bar $= 0.1$ MPa $= 10^5$ Pa
standard atmosphere[e]	atm	1 atm $= 101\ 325$ Pa
gal[f]	Gal	1 Gal $= 1$ cm/s^2 $= 10^{-2}$ m/s^2
curie[g]	Ci	1 Ci $= 3.7 \times 10^{10}$ s^{-1}
röntgen[h]	R	1 R $= 2.58 \times 10^{-4}$ C/kg
rad[i]	rad	1 rad $= 10^{-2}$ J/kg

(a) The nautical mile is a special unit employed for marine and aerial navigation to express distances. The conventional value given above was adopted by the First International Extraordinary Hydrographic Conference, Monaco, 1929, under the name "International nautical mile".

(b) This unit and its symbol were adopted by the CIPM in 1879 (*Procès-Verbaux CIPM,* 1879, p. 41).

(c) The barn is a special unit employed in nuclear physics to express effective cross sections.

(d) This unit and its symbol are included in Resolution 7 of the 9th CGPM (1948).

(e) Resolution 4 of 10th CGPM (1954).

(f) The gal is a special unit employed in geodesy and geophysics to express the acceleration due to gravity.

(g) The curie is a special unit employed in nuclear physics to express activity of radionuclides (12th CGPM (1964), Resolution 7).

(h) The röntgen is a special unit employed to express exposure of X or γ radiations.

(i) The rad is a special unit employed to express absorbed dose of ionizing radiations. When there is risk of confusion with the symbol for radian, rd may be used as symbol for rad.

IV.3 CGS units

The CIPM considers that it is in general preferable not to use, with the units of the International System, CGS units which have special names.[4] Such units are listed in table 11.

TABLE 11

CGS units with special names

Name	Symbol	Value in SI units
erg[a]	erg	$1 \text{ erg} = 10^{-7}$ J
dyne[a]	dyn	$1 \text{ dyn} = 10^{-5}$ N
poise[a]	P	$1 \text{ P} = 1 \text{ dyn·s/cm}^2 = 0.1 \text{ Pa· s}$
stokes	St	$1 \text{ St} = 1 \text{ cm}^2/\text{s} = 10^{-4} \text{ m}^2/\text{s}$
gauss[b]	Gs, G	$1 \text{ Gs corresponds to } 10^{-4}$ T
oersted[b]	Oe	$1 \text{ Oe corresponds to } \dfrac{1000}{4\pi} \text{ A/m}$
maxwell[b]	Mx	$1 \text{ Mx corresponds to } 10^{-8}$ Wb
stilb[a]	sb	$1 \text{ sb} = 1 \text{ cd/cm}^2 = 10^4/\text{m}^2$
phot	ph	$1 \text{ ph} = 10^4$ lx

[a] This unit and its symbol were included in Resolution 7 of the 9th CGPM (1948).
[b] This unit is part of the so-called "electromagnetic" 3-dimensional CGS system and cannot strictly speaking be compared to the corresponding unit of the International System, which has four dimensions when only electric quantities are considered.

[4] The aim of the International System of Units and of the recommendations contained in this document is to secure a greater degree of uniformity, hence a better mutual understanding of the general use of units. Nevertheless in certain specialized fields of scientific research, in particular in theoretical physics, there may sometimes be very good reasons for using other systems or other units.
Whichever units are used, it is important that the *symbols* employed for them follow current international recommendations.

IV.4 Other units

As regards units outside the International System which do not come under sections IV.1, 2, and 3, the CIPM considers that it is in general preferable to avoid them, and to use instead units of the International System. Some of those units are listed in table 12.

TABLE 12

Other units generally deprecated

Name	Value in SI units
fermi	1 fermi = 1 fm = 10^{-15} m
metric carat[a]	1 metric carat = 200 mg = 2×10^{-4} kg
torr	1 torr = $\dfrac{101\ 325}{760}$ Pa
kilogram-force (kgf)	1 kgf = 9.806 65 N
calorie (cal)	1 cal = 4.186 8 J[b]
micron (μ) [c]	1 μ = 1 μm = 10^{-6} m
X unit[d]	
stere (st) [e]	1 st = 1 m³
gamma (γ)	1 γ = 1 nT = 10^{-9} T
γ [f]	1 γ = 1 μg = 10^{-9} kg
λ [g]	1 λ = 1 μl = 10^{-6} l

(a) This name was adopted by the 4th CGPM (1907, pp. 89-91) for commercial dealings in diamonds, pearls, and precious stones.
(b) This value is that of the so-called "IT" calorie (5th International Conference on Properties of Steam, London, 1956).
(c) The name of this unit and its symbol, adopted by the CIPM in 1879 (*Procès-Verbaux CIPM*, 1879, p. 41) and retained in Resolution 7 of the 9th CGPM (1948) were abolished by the 13th CGPM (1967, Resolution 7).
(d) This special unit was employed to express wavelengths of X rays; 1 X unit = 1.002 $\times$ 10^{-4} nm approximately.
(e) This special unit employed to measure firewood was adopted by the CIPM in 1879 with the symbol "s" (*Procès-Verbaux CIPM*, 1879, p. 41). The 9th CGPM (1948, Resolution 7) changed the symbol to "st".
(f) This symbol is mentioned in *Procès-Verbaux CIPM*, 1880, p. 56.
(g) This symbol is mentioned in *Procès-Verbaux CIPM*, 1880, p. 30.

APPENDIX I
Decisions of the CGPM and the CIPM

CR: *Comptes rendus des séances de la Conférence Générale des Poids et Mesures (CGPM)*

PV: *Procès-Verbaux des séances du Comité International des Poids et Mesures (CIPM)*

1st CGPM, 1889

Sanction of the international prototypes of the metre and the kilogram (CR, 34-38)

The General Conference

considering

the "Compte rendu of the President of the CIPM" and the "Report of the CIPM", which show that, by the collaboration of the French section of the international Metre Commission and of the CIPM, the fundamental measurements of the international and national prototypes of the metre and of the kilogram have been made with all the accuracy and reliability which the present state of science permits; that the international and national prototypes of the metre and the kilogram are made of an alloy of platinum with 10 per cent iridium, to within 0.000 1; the equality in length of the international Metre and the equality in mass of the international Kilogram with the length of the Metre and the mass of the Kilogram kept in the Archives of France;

that the differences between the national Metres and the international Metre lie within 0.01 millimetre and that these differences are based on a hydrogen thermometer scale which can always be reproduced thanks to the stability of hydrogen, provided identical conditions are secured;

that the differences between the national Kilograms and the international Kilogram lie within 1 milligram;

that the international Metre and Kilogram and the national Metres and Kilograms fulfil the requirements of the Metre Convention,

sanctions

A. As regards international prototypes:

1 The Prototype of the metre chosen by the CIPM.

This prototype, at the temperature of melting ice, shall henceforth represent the metric unit of length.

2 The Prototype of the kilogram adopted by the CIPM.

This prototype shall henceforth be considered as the unit of mass.

3 The hydrogen thermometer centigrade scale in terms of which the equations of the prototype Metres have been established.

B. As regards national prototypes:

. . . .

3rd CGPM, 1901

Declaration concerning the definition of the litre (CR, 38)

. . . .

The Conference declares:

1   The unit of volume, for high accuracy determinations, is the volume occupied by a mass of 1 kilogram of pure water, at its maximum density and at standard atmospheric pressure; this volume is called "litre".

2   . . . .

Declaration on the unit of mass and on the definition of weight; conventional value of g_n (CR, 70)

Taking into account the decision of the CIPM of the 15 October 1887, according to which the kilogram has been defined as a unit of mass [5];

Taking into account the decision contained in the sanction of the prototypes of the Metric System, unanimously accepted by the CGPM on the 26 September 1889;

Considering the necessity to put an end to the ambiguity which in current practice still subsists on the meaning of the word *weight*, used sometimes for *mass*, sometimes for *mechanical force;*

The Conference declares:

"1   The kilogram is the unit of mass; it is equal to the mass of the international prototype of the kilogram;

"2   The word *weight* denotes a quantity of the same nature as a *force;* the weight of a body is the product of its mass and the acceleration due to gravity; in particular, the standard weight of a body is the product of its mass and the standard acceleration due to gravity;

"3   The value adopted in the international Service of Weights and Measures for the standard acceleration due to gravity is 980.665 cm/s², value already stated in the laws of some countries." [6]

---

[5] "The mass of the international Kilogram is taken as unit for the international Service of Weights and Measures" (PV, 1887, 88).
   [6] *Note of BIPM.* This conventional reference "standard value" ($g_n = 9.806\ 65$ m/s²) to be used in the reduction to standard gravity of measurements made in some place on the Earth has been reconfirmed in 1913 by the 5th CGPM (CR, 44).

7th CGPM, 1927

Definition of the metre by the international Prototype (CR, 49)

The unit of length is the metre, defined by the distance, at 0°, between the axes of the two central lines marked on the bar of platinum-iridium kept at the BIPM, and declared Prototype of the metre by the 1st CGPM, this bar being subject to standard atmospheric pressure and supported on two cylinders of at least one centimetre diameter, symmetrically placed in the same horizontal plane at a distance of 571 mm from each other.

CIPM, 1946

Definitions of photometric units (PV, **20**, 119)

RESOLUTION [7]

. . . .

4. The photometric units may be defined as follows:

New candle (unit of luminous intensity).—The value of the new candle is such that the brightness of the full radiator at the temperature of solidification of platinum is 60 new candles per square centimetre.

New lumen (unit of luminous flux).—The new lumen is the luminous flux emitted in unit solid angle (steradian) by a uniform point source having a luminous intensity of 1 new candle.

5. . . . .

Definitions of electric units (PV, **20**, 131)

RESOLUTION 2 [8]

. . . .

4. A) Definitions of the mechanical units which enter the definitions of electric units:

Unit of force.—The unit of force [in the MKS (Metre, Kilogram, Second) system] is that force which gives to a mass of 1 kilogram an acceleration of 1 metre per second, per second (*).

*The name "newton" has been proposed for the MKS unit of force.

---

[7] The two definitions contained in this Resolution were ratified by the 9th CGPM (1948), which also approved the name *candela* given to the "new candle" (CR, 54). For the lumen the qualifier "new" was later abandoned.
[8] The definitions contained in this Resolution 2 were approved by the 9th CGPM (1948), (CR, 49), which moreover adopted the name *newton* (Resolution 7).

Joule (unit of energy or work).—The joule is the work done when the point of application of 1 MKS unit of force [newton] moves a distance of 1 metre in the direction of the force.

Watt (unit of power).—The watt is that power which in one second gives rise to energy of 1 joule.

B) Definitions of electric units. The CIPM accepts the following propositions which define the theoretical value of the electric units:

Ampere (unit of electric current).—The ampere is that constant current which, if maintained in two straight parallel conductors of infinite length, of negligible circular cross-section, and placed 1 metre apart in vacuum, would produce between these conductors a force equal to 2×10^{-7} MKS unit of force [newton] per metre of length.

Volt (unit of potential difference and of electromotive force).— The volt is the difference of electric potential between two points of a conducting wire carrying a constant current of 1 ampere, when the power dissipated between these points is equal to 1 watt.

Ohm (unit of electric resistance).—The ohm is the electric resistance between two points of a conductor when a constant potential difference of 1 volt, applied to these points, produces in the conductor a current of 1 ampere, the conductor not being the seat of any electromotive force.

Coulomb (unit of quantity of electricity).—The coulomb is the quantity of electricity carried in 1 second by a current of 1 ampere.

Farad (unit of electric capacitance).—The farad is the capacitance of a capacitor between the plates of which there appears a potential difference of 1 volt when it is charged by a quantity of electricity of 1 coulomb.

Henry (unit of electric inductance).—The henry is the inductance of a closed circuit in which an electromotive force of 1 volt is produced when the electric current in the circuit varies uniformly at the rate of 1 ampere per second.

Weber (unit of magnetic flux).—The weber is that magnetic flux which, linking a circuit of one turn, would produce in it an electromotive force of 1 volt if it were reduced to zero at a uniform rate in 1 second.

9th CGPM, 1948

Triple point of water; thermodynamic scale with a single fixed point; unit of quantity of heat (joule) (CR, 55 and 63)

RESOLUTION 3 [9]

1. With present-day technique, the triple point of water is capable of providing a thermometric reference point with an accuracy higher than can be obtained from the melting point of ice.

In consequence the Consultative Committee [for Thermometry and Calorimetry] considers that the zero of the centesimal thermodynamic scale must be defined as the temperature 0.010 0 degree below that of the triple point of pure water.

2. The CCTC accepts the principle of an absolute thermodynamic scale with a single fundamental fixed point at present provided by the triple point of pure water, the absolute temperature of which will be fixed at a later date.

The introduction of this new scale does not affect in any way the use of the International Scale, which remains the recommended practical scale.

3. The unit of quantity of heat is the joule.

Note.—It is requested that the results of calorimetric experiments be as far as possible expressed in joules.

If the experiments are made by comparison with the rise of temperature of water (and that, for some reason, it is not possible to avoid using the calorie), the information necessary for conversion to joules must be provided.

The CIPM, advised by the CCTC, should prepare a table giving, in joules per degree, the most accurate values that can be obtained from experiments on the specific heat of water.

Adoption of "degree Celsius"

From three names ("degree centigrade", "centesimal degree", "degree Celsius") proposed to denote the degree of temperature, the CIPM has chosen "degree Celsius" (PV, 21, 1948, 88).

This name is also adopted by the General Conference (CR, 64).

---

[9] The three propositions contained in this Resolution 3 have been adopted by the General Conference.

Proposal for establishing a practical system of units of measurement (CR, 64).

RESOLUTION 6

The General Conference,

considering

that the CIPM has been requested by the International Union of Physics to adopt for international use a practical international system of units; that the International Union of Physics recommends the MKS system and one electric unit of the absolute practical system, but does not recommend that the CGS system be abandoned by physicists;

that the CGPM has itself received from the French Government a similar request, accompanied by a draft to be used as basis of discussion for the establishment of a complete specification of units of measurement;

instructs the CIPM:

to seek by an energetic, active, official enquiry the opinion of scientific, technical, and educational circles of all countries (offering them in effect the French document as basis);

to gather and study the answers;

to make recommendations for a single practical system of units of measurement, suitable for adoption by all countries adhering to the Metre Convention.

Writing and printing of unit symbols and of numbers

RESOLUTION 7

Principles

Roman (upright) type, in general lower case, is used for symbols of units; if however the symbols are derived from proper names, capital roman type is used. These symbols are not followed by a full stop.

In numbers, the comma (French practice) or the dot (British practice) are used only to separate the integral part of numbers from the decimal part. Numbers may be divided in groups of three in order to facilitate reading; neither dots nor commas are ever inserted in the spaces between groups.

Unit	Symbol	Unit	Symbol
.metre	m	ampere	A
.square metre	m²	volt	V
.cubic metre	m³	watt	W
.micron	μ	ohm	Ω
.litre	l	coulomb	C
.gram	g	farad	F
.tonne	t	henry	H
second	s	hertz	Hz
erg	erg	poise	P
dyne	dyn	newton	N
degree Celsius	°C	.candela ("new candle")	cd
.degree absolute	°K	lux	lx
calorie	cal	lumen	lm
bar	bar	stilb	sb
hour	h		

Notes

1. The symbols whose unit names are preceded by dots are those which had already been adopted by a decision of the CIPM.

2. The symbol for the stere, the unit of volume for firewood, shall be "st" and not "s", which had been previously assigned to it by the CIPM.

3. To indicate a temperature interval or difference, rather than a temperature, the word "degree" in full, or the abbreviation "deg", must be used.

10th CGPM, 1954

Definition of the thermodynamic temperature scale (CR, 79)

RESOLUTION 3

The 10th CGPM decides to define the thermodynamic temperature scale by choosing the triple point of water as the fundamental fixed point, and assigning to it the temperature 273.16 degrees Kelvin, exactly.

Definition of standard atmosphere (CR, 79)

RESOLUTION 4

The 10th CGPM, having noted that the definition of the standard atmosphere given by the 9th CGPM when defining the International Temperature Scale, led some physicists to believe that this definition of the standard atmosphere was valid only for accurate work in thermometry,

declares that it adopts, for general use, the definition:
1 standard atmosphere = 1 013 250 dynes per square centimetre,
i.e., 101 325 newtons per square metre.

Practical system of units (CR, 80)

RESOLUTION 6

In accordance with the wish expressed by the 9th CGPM in its Resolution 6 concerning the establishment of a practical system of units of measurement for international use, the 10th CGPM *decides* to adopt as base units of the system, the following units:

length _____ metre
mass _____ kilogram
time _____ second
electric current _____ ampere
thermodynamic temperature _____ degree Kelvin
luminous intensity _____ candela

CIPM, 1956

Definition of the unit of time (PV, 25, 77)

RESOLUTION 1

In virtue of the powers invested in it by Resolution 5 of the 10th CGPM, the CIPM
considering
1   that the 9th General Assembly of the International Astronomical Union (Dublin, 1955) declared itself in favor of linking the second to the tropical year;
2   that, according to the decisions of the 8th General Assembly of the International Astronomical Union (Rome, 1952), the second of ephemeris time (ET) is the fraction $\dfrac{12\ 960\ 276\ 813}{408\ 986\ 496} \times 10^{-9}$ of the tropical year for 1900 January 0 at 12 h ET,
decides
"The second is the fraction 1/31 556 925.974 7 of the tropical year for 1900 January 0 at 12 hours ephemeris time".

International System of Units (PV, 25, 83)

RESOLUTION 3

The CIPM
considering
the task entrusted to it by Resolution 6 of the 9th CGPM concerning the establishment of a practical system of units of measurement suitable for adoption by all countries adhering to the Metre Convention,

the documents received from twenty-one countries in reply to the enquiry requested by the 9th CGPM,

Resolution 6 of the 10th CGPM, fixing the base units of the system to be established

recommends

1   that the name "International System of Units" be given to the system founded on the base units adopted by the 10th CGPM, viz:

[here follows the list of the six base units with their symbols, reproduced in Resolution 12 of the 11th CGPM (1960)]

2   that the units listed in the table below be used, without excluding others which might be added later:

[here follows the table of units reproduced in paragraph 4 of Resolution 12 of the 11th CGPM (1960)]

11th CGPM, 1960

Definition of the metre (CR, 85)

RESOLUTION 6

The 11th CGPM

considering

that the international Prototype does not define the metre with an accuracy adequate for the present needs of metrology,

that it is moreover desirable to adopt a natural and indestructible standard,

decides

1   The metre is the length equal to 1 650 763.73 wavelengths in vacuum of the radiation corresponding to the transition between the levels 2 p_{10} and 5 d_5 of the krypton-86 atom.

2   The definition of the metre in force since 1889, based on the international Prototype of platinum-iridium, is abrogated.

3   The international Prototype of the metre sanctioned by the 1st CGPM in 1889 shall be kept at the BIPM under the conditions specified in 1889.

RESOLUTION 7

The 11th CGPM

requests the CIPM

1   to prepare specifications for the realization of the new definition of the metre [10];

2   to select secondary wavelength standards for measurement of length by interferometry, and to prepare specifications for their use;

3   to continue the work in progress on improvement of length standards.

---

[10] See Appendix 2, p 35, for the relevant Recommendation adopted by the CIPM.

Definition of the unit of time (CR, 86)

RESOLUTION 9

The 11th CGPM
considering
the powers given to the CIPM by the 10th CGPM, to define the
fundamental unit of time,
the decision taken by the CIPM in 1956,
ratifies the following definition:
"The second is the fraction 1/31 556 925.974 7 of the tropical year
for 1900 January 0 at 12 hours ephemeris time".
International System of Units (CR, 87)

RESOLUTION 12

The 11th CGPM
considering
Resolution 6 of the 10th CGPM, by which it adopted six base units
on which to establish a practical system of measurement for international use:

length	metre	m
mass	kilogram	kg
time	second	s
electric current	ampere	A
thermodynamic temperature	degree Kelvin	°K
luminous intensity	candela	cd

Resolution 3 adopted by the CIPM in 1956,
The recommendations adopted by the CIPM in 1958 concerning
an abbreviation for the name of the system, and prefixes to form
multiples and sub-multiples of the units,

decides
1   the system founded on the six base units above is called "International System of Units";
2   the international abbreviation of the name of the system is: SI;

3 names of multiples and sub-multiples of the units are formed by means of the following prefixes:

Multiplying factor	Prefix	Symbol
$1\ 000\ 000\ 000\ 000 = 10^{12}$	tera	T
$1\ 000\ 000\ 000 = 10^{9}$	giga	G
$1\ 000\ 000 = 10^{6}$	mega	M
$1\ 000 = 10^{3}$	kilo	k
$100 = 10^{2}$	hecto	h
$10 = 10^{1}$	deka	da
$0.1 = 10^{-1}$	deci	d
$0.01 = 10^{-2}$	centi	c
$0.001 = 10^{-3}$	milli	m
$0.000\ 001 = 10^{-6}$	micro	μ
$0.000\ 000\ 001 = 10^{-9}$	nano	n
$0.000\ 000\ 000\ 001 = 10^{-12}$	pico	p

4 the units listed below are used in the system, without excluding others which might be added later

	SUPPLEMENTARY UNITS		
plane angle	radian	rad	
solid angles	steradian	sr	
	DERIVED UNITS		
area	square metre	m²	
volume	cubic metre	m³	
frequency	hertz	Hz	1/s
mass density (density)	kilogram per cubic metre	kg/m³	
speed, velocity	metre per second	m/s	
angular velocity	radian per second	rad/s	
acceleration	metre per second squared	m/s²	
angular acceleration	radian per second squared	rad/s²	
force	newton	N	kg•m/s²
pressure (mechanical stress)	newton per square metre	N/m²	
kinematic viscosity	square metre per second	m²/s	
dynamic viscosity	newton-second per square metre	N•s/m²	
work, energy, quantity of heat	joule	J	N•m
power	watt	W	J/s
quantity of electricity	coulomb	C	A•s
potential difference, electromotive force	volt	V	W/A
electric field strength	volt per metre	V/m	
electric resistance	ohm	Ω	V/A
capacitance	farad	F	A•s/V
magnetic flux	weber	Wb	V•s
inductance	henry	H	V•s/A
magnetic flux density	tesla	T	Wb/m²
magnetic field strength	ampere per metre	A/m	
magnetomotive force	ampere	A	
luminous flux	lumen	lm	cd•sr
luminance	candela per square metre	cd/m²	
illuminance	lux	lx	lm/m²

Cubic decimetre and litre (CR, 88)

RESOLUTION 13

The 11th CGPM,
considering

that the cubic decimetre and the litre are unequal and differ by about 28 parts in 10⁶,

that determinations of physical quantities which involve measurements of volume are being made more and more accurately, thus increasing the risk of confusion between the cubic decimetre and the litre,

requests the CIPM to study the problem and submit its conclusions to the 12th CGPM.

CIPM, 1961
Cubic decimetre and litre (PV, 29, 34)

RECOMMENDATION

The CIPM recommends that the results of accurate measurements of volume be expressed in units of the International System and not in litres.

12th CGPM, 1964
Atomic standard of frequency (CR, 93)

RESOLUTION 5

The 12th CGPM,
considering

that the 11th CGPM noted in its Resolution 10 the urgency, in the interests of accurate metrology, of adopting an atomic or molecular standard of time interval, that, in spite of the results already obtained with cesium atomic frequency standards, the time has not yet come for the CGPM to adopt a new definition of the second, base unit of the International System of Units, because of the new and considerable improvements likely to be obtained from work now in progress,

considering also that it is not desirable to wait any longer before time measurements in physics are based on atomic or molecular frequency standards,

empowers the CIPM to name the atomic or molecular frequency standards to be employed for the time being,

requests the Organizations and Laboratories knowledgeable in this field to pursue work connected with a new definition of the second.

DECLARATION OF THE CIPM (1964) (PV, 32, 26 and CR, 93)
The CIPM,
empowered by Resolution 5 of the 12th CGPM to name atomic or molecular frequency standards for temporary use for time measurements in physics,

declares that the standard to be employed is the transition between the hyperfine levels $F = 4$, $M = 0$ and $F = 3$, $M = 0$ of the ground state $^2S_{1/2}$ of the cesium-133 atom, unperturbed by external fields, and that the frequency of this transition is assigned the value 9 192 631 770 hertz.

Litre (CR, 93)

RESOLUTION 6

The 12th CGPM,
considering Resolution 13 adopted by the 11th CGPM in 1960 and the Recommendation adopted by the CIPM in 1961,
1 *abrogates* the definition of the litre given in 1901 by the 3rd CGPM
2 *declares* that the word "litre" may be employed as a special name for the cubic decimetre,
3 *recommends* that the name litre should not be employed to give the results of high accuracy volume measurements.

Curie (CR, 94)

RESOLUTION 7

The 12th CGPM,
considering that the curie has been used for a long time in many countries as a unit of activity for radionuclides,
recognizing that in the International System of Units (SI), the unit of this activity is the second to the power of minus one (s^{-1}),
accepts that the curie be still retained outside SI as unit of activity, with the value 3.7×10^{10} s^{-1}. The symbol for this unit is Ci.

Prefixes femto and atto (CR, 94)

RESOLUTION 8

The 12 CGPM,
decides to add to the list of prefixes for the formation of names of multiples and sub-multiples of units, adopted by the 11th CGPM, Resolution 12, paragraph 3, the following two new prefixes:

Multiplying factor	Prefix	Symbol
10^{-15}	femto	f
10^{-18}	atto	a

13th CGPM, 1967-1968

SI unit of time (second) (CR, 103)

RESOLUTION 1

The 13th CGPM,

considering

that the definition of the second adopted by the CIPM in 1956 (Resolution 1) and ratified by Resolution 9 of the 11th CGPM (1960), later upheld by Resolution 5 of the 12th CGPM (1964), is inadequate for the present needs of metrology,

that at its meeting of 1964 the CIPM, empowered by Resolution 5 of the 12th CGPM (1964) recommended, in order to fulfil these requirements, a cesium atomic frequency standard for temporary use,

that this frequency standard has now been sufficiently tested and found sufficiently accurate to provide a definition of the second fulfilling present requirements,

that the time has now come to replace the definition now in force of the unit of time of the International System of Units by an atomic definition based on that standard,

decides

1   The unit of time of the International System of Units is the second defined as follows:

"The second is the duration of 9 192 631 770 periods of the radiation corresponding to the transition between the two hyperfine levels of the ground state of the cesium-133 atom".

2   Resolution 1 adopted by the CIPM at its meeting of 1956 and Resolution 9 of the 11th CGPM are now abrogated.

Unit of thermodynamic temperature (kelvin) (CR, 104)

RESOLUTION 3

The 13th CGPM

considering

the names "degree Kelvin" and "degree", the symbols "°K" and "deg" and the rules for their use given in Resolution 7 of the 9th CGPM (1948), in Resolution 12 of the 11th CGPM (1960) and the decision taken by the CIPM in 1962 (PV, 30, 27)[11], that the unit of thermodynamic temperature and the unit of temperature interval are one and the same unit, which ought to be denoted by a single name and single symbol,

[11] "1 The unit degree Kelvin (symbol °K) may be employed for a difference of two thermodynamic temperatures as well as for thermodynamic temperature itself.
"2 If it is found necessary to suppress the name Kelvin, the international symbol "deg" is recommended for the unit of difference of temperature. (The symbol "deg" is read, for example: "degré" in French, "degree" in English, "gradous" (градус) in Russian, "Grad" in German, "graad" in Dutch").

decides

1   the unit of thermodynamic temperature is denoted by the name "kelvin" and its symbol is "K";

2   the same name and the same symbol are used to express a temperature interval;

3   a temperature interval may also be expressed in degrees Celsius;

4   the decisions mentioned in the opening paragraph concerning the name of the unit of thermodynamic temperature, its symbol and the designation of the unit to express an interval or a difference of temperatures are abrogated, but the usages which derive from these decisions remain permissible for the time being.

RESOLUTION 4

The 13th CGPM,

considering that it is useful to formulate more explicitly the definition of the unit of thermodynamic temperature contained in Resolution 3 of the 10th CGPM (1954),

decides to express this definition as follows:

"The kelvin, unit of thermodynamic temperature, is the fraction 1/273.16 of the thermodynamic temperature of the triple point of water".

Unit of luminous intensity (candela) (CR, 104)

RESOLUTION 5

The 13th CGPM

considering

the definition of the unit of luminous intensity ratified by the 9th CGPM (1948) and contained in the "Resolution concerning the change of photometric units" adopted by the CIPM in 1946 (PV, **20,** 119) in virtue of the powers conferred by the 8th CGPM (1933),

that this definition fixes satisfactorily the unit of luminous intensity, but that its wording may be open to criticism,

decides to express the definition of the candela as follows:

"The candela is the luminous intensity, in the perpendicular direction, of a surface of 1/600 000 square metre of a blackbody at the temperature of freezing platinum under a pressure of 101 325 newtons per square metre."

Derived units (CR, 105)

RESOLUTION 6

The 13th CGPM
considering that it is useful to add some derived units to the list of paragraph 4 of Resolution 12 of the 11th CGPM (1960),
decides to add:

wave number	1 per metre	m⁻¹
entropy	joule per kelvin	J/K
specific heat capacity	joule per kilogram kelvin	J/(kg•K)
thermal conductivity	watt per metre kelvin	W/(m•K)
radiant intensity	watt per steradian	W/sr
activity (of a radioactive source)	1 per second	s⁻¹

Abrogation of earlier decisions (micron, new candle) (CR, 105)

RESOLUTION 7

The 13th CGPM,
considering that subsequent decisions of the General Conference concerning the International System of Units are incompatible with parts of Resolution 7 of the 9th CGPM (1948),

decides accordingly to remove from Resolution 7 of the 9th Conference:
1   the unit name "micron", and the symbol "μ" which had been given to that unit, but which has now become a prefix;
2   the unit name "new candle".

CIPM, 1967

Decimal multiples and sub-multiples of the unit of mass (PV **35**, 29)

RECOMMENDATION 2

The CIPM,
considering that the rule for forming names of decimal multiples and sub-multiples of the units of paragraph 3 of Resolution 12 of the 11th CGPM (1960) might be interpreted in different ways when applied to the unit of mass,
declares that the rules of Resolution 12 of the 11th CGPM apply to the kilogram in the following manner: the names of decimal multiples and sub-multiples of the unit of mass are formed by attaching prefixes to the word "gram".

CIPM, 1969

International System of Units: Rules for application of Resolution 12 of the 11th CGPM (1960) (PV, 37, 30)

RECOMMENDATION 1 (1969)

The CIPM,

considering that Resolution 12 of the 11th CGPM (1960) concerning the International System of Units, has provoked discussions on certain of its aspects,

declares

1 the base units, the supplementary units, and the derived units, of the International System of Units, which form a coherent set, are denoted by the name "SI units";

2 the prefixes adopted by the CGPM for the formation of decimal multiples and sub-multiples of SI units are called "SI prefixes"; and *recommends*

3 the use of SI units, and of their decimal multiples and sub-multiples whose names are formed by means of SI prefixes.

Note.—The name "supplementary units", appearing in Resolution 12 of the 11th CGPM (and in the present Recommendation) is given to SI units for which the General Conference declines to state whether they are base units or derived units.

14th CGPM, 1971

Pascal; siemens (CR, 77)

The 14th CGPM adopted the special names "pascal" (symbol Pa), for the SI unit newton per square metre, and "siemens" (symbol S), for the SI unit of electric conductance (reciprocal ohm).

International Atomic Time; function of CIPM (CR, 77)

RESOLUTION 1

The 14th CGPM

considering

that the second, unit of time of the International System of Units, has since 1967 been defined in terms of a natural atomic frequency, and no longer in terms of the time scales provided by astronomical motions,

that the need for an International Atomic Time (TAI) scale is a consequence of the atomic definition of the second,

that several international organizations have ensured and are still successfully ensuring the establishment of time scales based on astronomical motions, particularly thanks to the permanent services of the Bureau International de l'Heure (BIH),

that BIH has started to establish an atomic time scale of recognized quality and proven usefulness, that the atomic frequency standards for realizing the second have been considered and must continue to be considered by CIPM helped by a Consultative Committee, and that the unit interval of the International Atomic Time scale must be the second realized according to its atomic definition,

that all the competent international scientific organizations and the national laboratories active in this field have expressed the wish that CIPM and CGPM should give a definition of International Atomic Time, and should contribute to the establishment of the International Atomic Time scale,

that the usefulness of International Atomic Time entails close coordination with the time scales based on astronomical motions,

requests CIPM

1 to give a definition of International Atomic Time;*

2 to take the necessary steps, in agreement with the international organizations concerned, to ensure that available scientific competence and existing facilities are used in the best possible way to realize the International Atomic Time scale and to satisfy the requirements of users of International Atomic Time.

Unit of amount of substance (mole) (CR, 78)

RESOLUTION 3

The 14th CGPM

considering the advice of the International Union of Pure and Applied Physics, of the International Union of Pure and Applied Chemistry, and of the International Organization for Standardization, concerning the need to define a unit of amount of substance,

decides

1 The mole is the amount of substance of a system which contains as many elementary entities as there are atoms in 0.012 kilogram of carbon 12; its symbol is "mol".

2 When the mole is used, the elementary entities must be specified and may be atoms, molecules, ions, electrons, other particles, or specified groups of such particles.

3 The mole is a base unit of the International System of Units.

---

*In anticipation of this request, CIPM had asked the Consultative Committee for the Definition of the Second (CCDS), to prepare a definition of International Atomic Time. This definition, approved by CIPM at its 59th session (October 1970), is as follows:
'International Atomic Time [TAI] is the time reference coordinate established by the Bureau International de l'Heure on the basis of the readings of atomic clocks operating in various establishments in accordance with the definition of the second, the time unit of the International System of Units.'

APPENDIX II

Practical realization of the definitions
of some important units

1. Length

The following recommendation was adopted by the CIPM in 1960 to specify the characteristics of the discharge lamp radiating the standard line of krypton 86:

> In accordance with paragraph 1 of Resolution 7 adopted by the 11th CGPM (October 1960) the CIPM recommends that the line of krypton 86 adopted as primary standard of length be realized by means of a hot cathode discharge lamp containing krypton 86 of purity not less than 99% in sufficient quantity to ensure the presence of solid krypton at a temperature of 64 °K. The lamp shall have a capillary of internal diameter 2 to 4 millimetres, and wall thickness approximately 1 millimetre.
>
> It is considered that, provided the conditions listed below are satisfied, the wavelength of the radiation emitted by the positive column is equal to the wavelength corresponding to the transition between the unperturbed levels to within 1 in 10^8:
>
> 1. the capillary is observed end-on in a direction such that the light rays used travel from the cathode end to the anode end;
> 2. the lower part of the lamp including the capillary is immersed in a bath maintained to within 1 degree of the temperature of the triple point of nitrogen;
> 3. the current density in the capillary is 0.3 ± 0.1 ampere per square centimetre.
>
> (*Procès-Verbaux CIPM*, 1960, **28**, 71; *Comptes rendus* 11th *CGPM*, 1960, 85)

The ancillary apparatus comprises the stabilized current supply for the lamp, a vacuum-tight cryostat, a thermometer for use in the region of 63 K, a vacuum pump, and either a monochromator, to isolate the line or special interference filters.

The wavelength of the standard line, reproducible to 1 in 10^8 according to the above specifications, might be made reproducible to 1 in 10^9 approximately with more stringent specifications.

Other lines of krypton 86 and several lines of mercury 198 and of cadmium 114 are recommended as secondary standards (*Procès-Verbaux* CIPM, 1963, **31**, Recommendation 1, 26 and *Comptes rendus* 12th *CGPM*, 1964, 18).

The wavelength of these lines varies with pressure, temperature, and composition of the air in which the light travels; the refractive index of the air must therefore in general be measured *in situ*.

To measure end or line standards these radiations are used in an interference comparator a complicated instrument with mechanical, optical interference, and thermometric components.

2. Mass

The primary standard of the unit of mass is the international prototype of the kilogram kept at the BIPM. The mass of 1 kg secondary standards of platinum-iridium or of stainless steel is compared with the mass of the prototype by means of balances whose precision can reach 1 in 10^8 or better.

By an easy operation a series of masses can be standardized to obtain multiples and sub-multiples of the kilogram.

3. Time

Some laboratories are able to make the equipment required to produce electric oscillations at the frequency of vibration of the atom of cesium-133 which defines the second. This equipment includes a quartz oscillator, frequency multipliers and synthesizers, a klystron, phase-sensitive detectors, an apparatus for producing an atomic beam of cesium in vacuum, cavity resonators, uniform and non-uniform magnetic fields, and an ion detector.

Complete assemblies to produce this frequency are also commercially available.

By division it is possible to obtain pulses at the desired frequencies, for instance 1 Hz, 1 kHz, etc.

The stability and the reproducibility can exceed 1 in 10^{11}.

Radio stations broadcast waves whose frequencies are known to about the same accuracy.

There are other standards besides the cesium beam, among them the hydrogen maser, rubidium clocks, quartz frequency standards and clocks, etc. Their frequency is controlled by comparison with a cesium standard, either directly, or by means of radio transmissions.

Conforming to a decision of the 14th CGPM (1971, Resolution 1), the CIPM has given the following definition of International Atomic Time (TAI):

> "International Atomic Time is the time reference coordinate established by the Bureau International de l'Heure on the basis of the readings of atomic clocks operating in various establishments in accordance with the definition of the second, the time unit of the International system of Units.

Most time signals broadcast by radio waves are given in a time scale called Coordinated Universal Time (UTC). UTC is defined in such a manner that it differs from TAI[12] by an exact whole number of seconds. The difference UTC–TAI was set equal to −10 s starting the first of January 1972, the date of application of the reformulation of UTC which previously involved a frequency offset; this difference can be modified by 1 second, preferably on the first of January, and in case of need on the first of July, to keep UTC in agreement with the time defined by the rotation of the Earth with an approximation better than 0.7 s.[13] Furthermore, the legal times of most countries are offset by a whole number of hours (time zones and 'summer' time).

---

[12] See Appendix I, page 35, the definition of TAI given by CIPM at the request of the 14th CGPM (1971. Resolution 1).
[13] The difference UTC–TAI became −11 s on the 1st July 1972, and −12 s on the 1st January 1973.

4. Electric quantities

So-called "absolute" electrical measurements, i.e. those that realize the unit according to its definition, can be undertaken only by laboratories enjoying exceptional facilities.

Electric current is obtained in amperes by measuring the force between two coils, of measurable shape and size, that carry the current.

The ohm, the farad, and the henry are accurately linked by impedance measurements at a known frequency, and may be determined in absolute value by calculation (1) of the self-inductance of a coil, or the mutual inductance of two coils, in terms of their linear dimensions, or (2) of the change in capacitance of a capacitor in terms of the change in length of its electrodes (method of Thompson-Lampard).

The volt is deduced from the ampere and the ohm.

The accuracy of these measurements lies between 1 and 3 in 10^6.

The results of absolute measurements are obtained by means of secondary standards which are, for instance:

1. coils of manganin wire for resistance standards;
2. galvanic cells with cadmium sulphate electrolyte for standards of electromotive force;
3. capacitors for standards of capacitance (of 10 pF for example).

Application of recent techniques also provides means of checking the stability of the secondary standards which maintain the electric units: measurement of the gyromagnetic ratio of the proton γ_p' for the ampere, measurement of the ratio h/e by the Josephson effect for the volt.

5. Temperature

Absolute measurements of temperature in accordance with the definition of the unit of thermodynamic temperature, the kelvin, are related to thermodynamics, for example by the gas thermometer.

At 273.16 K accuracy is of the order of 1 in 10^6, but it is not as good at higher and at lower temperatures.

The International Practical Temperature Scale adopted by the CIPM in 1968 agrees with the best thermodynamic results to date. The text on this scale (which replaces the 1948 scale, amended in 1960) is published in *Comité Consultatif de Thermométrie*, 8th session, 1967, Annexe 18, and *Comptes rendus*, 13th *CGPM*, 1967-1968, Annexe 2; the English translation is published in *Metrologia*, 5, 35, 1969.

The instruments employed to measure temperatures in the International Scale are the platinum resistance thermometer, the platinum-10% rhodium/platinum thermocouple and the monochromatic optical pyrometer. These instruments are calibrated at a number of reproducible temperatures, called "defining fixed points," the values of which are assigned by agreement.

6. Amount of substance

All quantitative results of chemical analysis or of dosages can be expressed in moles, in other words in units of amount of substance of the constituent particles. The principle of physical measurements based on the definition of this unit is explained below.

The simplest case is that of a sample of a pure substance that is considered to be formed of atoms; call X the chemical symbol of these atoms. A mole of atoms X contains by definition as many atoms as there are ^{12}C atoms in 0.012 kilogram of carbon 12. As neither the mass $m(^{12}C)$ of an atom of carbon 12 nor the mass $m(X)$ of an atom X can be measured accurately, we use the ratio of these masses, $m(X)/m(^{12}C)$, which can be accurately determined.[14] The mass corresponding to 1 mole of X is then $[m(X)/m(^{12}C)] \times 0.012$ kg, which is expressed by saying that the molar mass $M(X)$ of X (quotient of mass by amount of substance) is

$$M(X) = [m(X)/m(^{12}C)] \times 0.012 \text{ kg/mol.}$$

For example, the atom of fluorine ^{19}F and the atom of carbon ^{12}C have masses which are in the ratio 18.9984/12. The molar mass of the molecular gas F_2 is:

$$M(F_2) = \frac{2 \times 18.9984}{12} \times 0.012 \text{ kg/mol} = 0.037\ 996\ 8 \text{ kg/mol.}$$

The amount of substance corresponding to a given mass of gas F_2, 0.05 kg for example, is:

$$\frac{0.05 \text{ kg}}{0.037\ 996\ 8 \text{ kg·mol}^{-1}} = 1.315\ 90 \text{ mol.}$$

In the case of a pure substance that is supposed made up of molecules B, which are combinations of atoms X, Y, . . . according to the chemical formula $B = X_\alpha Y_\beta$ . . ., the mass of one molecule is $m(B) = \alpha m(X) + \beta m(Y) + . . .$

This mass is not known with accuracy, but the ratio $m(B)/m(^{12}C)$ can be determined accurately. The molar mass of a molecular substance B is then

$$M(B) = \frac{m(B)}{m(^{12}C)} \times 0.012 \text{ kg/mol} = \left\{ \alpha \frac{m(X)}{m(^{12}C)} + \beta \frac{m(Y)}{m(^{12}C)} + . . . \right\}$$
$$\times 0.012 \text{ kg/mol.}$$

---

[14] There are many methods of measuring this ratio, the most direct one being by the mass spectrograph.

The same procedure is used in the more general case when the composition of the substance B is specified as $X_\alpha Y_\beta$ . . . even if α, β, . . . are not integers. If we denote the mass ratios $m(X)/m(^{12}C)$, $m(Y)/m(^{12}C)$, . . . by $r(X), r(Y)$, . . ., the molar mass of the substance B is given by the formula:

$$M(B) = [\alpha r(X) + \beta r(Y) + . . .] \times 0.012 \text{ kg/mol}.$$

There are other methods based on the laws of physics and physical chemistry for measuring amounts of substance; three examples are given below.

With perfect gases, 1 mole of particles of any gas occupies the same volume at a temperature T and a pressure p (approximately $0.022\ 4\ m^3$ at $T = 273.16$ K and $p = 101\ 325$ Pa); hence a method of measuring the ratio of amounts of substance for any two gases (the corrections to apply if the gases are not perfect are well known).

For quantitative electrolytic reactions the ratio of amounts of substance can be obtained by measuring quantities of electricity. For example, 1 mole of Ag and 1 mole of (1/2) Cu are deposited on a cathode by the same quantity of electricity (approximately 96 487 C).

Application of the laws of Raoult is yet another method of determining ratios of amounts of substance in extremely dilute solutions.

7. Photometric quantities

Absolute photometric measurements by comparison with the luminance of a blackbody at the temperature of freezing platinum can only be undertaken by a few well-equipped laboratories. The accuracy of these measurements is somewhat better than 1%.

The results of these measurements are maintained by means of incandescent lamps fed with d.c. in a specified manner. These lamps constitute standards of luminous intensity and of luminous flux.

The method approved by CIPM in 1937 (Procès-Verbaux CIPM, 18, 237) for determining the value of photometric quantities for luminous sources having a color other than that of the primary standard, utilizes a procedure taking account of the "spectral luminous efficiencies" $V(\lambda)$ adopted by it in 1933. They were at that time known as "relative visibility (or luminosity) factors", and had been recommended by the CIE in 1924.[15]

Photometric quantities are thereby defined in purely physical terms as quantities proportional to the sum or integral of a spectral power distribution, weighted according to a specified function of wavelength.

---

[15] CIE Publications No. 18 (1970), page 43, and No. 15 (1971), page 93 ; *Procès-Verbaux CIPM*, 40, 1972, Annexe 1. The $V(\lambda)$ [$=\bar{y}(\lambda)$] values are given for wavelengths in 1 nm steps from 360 to 830 nm ; they are an improvement on the values in 10 nm steps adopted by CIPM in 1933, and previously by CIE in 1924.

STATUS OF INTERNATIONAL METRIC SYSTEM IN THE UNITED STATES

1. CONSTITUTIONAL AUTHORITY TO FIX STANDARDS

"The Congress shall have power to * * * fix the standard of weights and measures." (Constitution of the United States, Art. 1, sec. 8, par. 5.)

2. METRIC SYSTEM LEGALIZED

"It shall be lawful throughout the United States of America to employ the weights and measures of the metric system, * * *." (Revised Statutes of the United States, sec. 3569.)

3. METRIC STANDARDS ADOPTED AS FUNDAMENTAL

"* * * the office of weights and measures * * * will in the future regard the international prototype meter and kilogram as fundamental standards, and the customary units, the yard and the pound, will be derived therefrom in accordance with the act of July 28, 1866." (Order approved by the Secretary of the Treasury, April 5, 1893.)

4. METRIC BALANCES FURNISHED CERTAIN POST OFFICES

"The Postmaster General shall furnish to the post offices exchanging mails with foreign countries, and to such other offices as he may deem expedient, postal balances denominated in grams of the metric system, fifteen grams of which shall be the equivalent, for postal purposes, of one-half ounce avoirdupois, and so on in progression." (Revised Statutes of the United States, sec. 3880.)

5. METRIC WEIGHTS USED FOR CERTAIN COINS

"* * * the weight of the half-dollar shall be twelve grams and one-half of a gram; the quarter-dollar and the dime shall be, respectively, one-half and one-fifth of the weight of said half-dollar." (Revised Statutes of the United States, sec. 3513.)

6. CONGRESS PROVIDES METRIC STANDARDS FOR THE STATES OF THE UNION, LAND-GRANT AGRICULTURAL COLLEGES, AND THE SMITHSONIAN INSTITUTION

"Be it resolved by the Senate and House of Representatives of the United States of America in Congress assembled, That the Secretary of the Treasury be, and he is hereby, authorized and directed to furnish to each State, to be delivered to the governor thereof, one set of the standard weights and measures of the metric system for the use of the States, respectively." (Joint resolution of Congress approved July 27, 1866.)
"Resolved by the Senate and House of Representatives of the United States of America in Congress assembled, That the Secretary of the Treasury be, and he is hereby, directed to cause a complete set of all the weights and measures adopted as standards to be delivered to the governor of each State in the Union, for the use of agricultural colleges in the States, respectively, which have received a grant of lands from the United States, and also one set of the same for the use of the Smithsonian Institution: * * *." (Joint resolution of Congress, approved March 3, 1881.)

7. UNITED STATES JOINS IN ESTABLISHING INTERNATIONAL BUREAU OF WEIGHTS AND MEASURES

"The high contracting parties engage to establish and maintain, at their common expense, a scientific and permanent international bureau * of weights and measures, the location of which shall be at Paris." (Extract from convention of 1875, signed for the United States by the United States ambassador to France.)

---

* This bureau has the cutody of the international standards of the metric system, to which all metric prototypes of the world are referred for verification. It was established and is maintained jointly by various governments.

8. CONGRESS ADOPTS THE METRIC UNITS FOR ELECTRICAL MEASURES

It was enacted by the Congress that the international electrical units shall be the legal units of electrical measure in the United States. These units were based on the centimeter-gram-second electromagnetic system of electrical units. (See Revised Statutes of the United States, Supplement, vol. 2, chap. 131, 1894.)

9. METRIC SYSTEM REQUIRED IN THE MEDICAL WORK OF THE WAR AND NAVY DEPARTMENTS AND THE U. S. PUBLIC HEALTH SERVICE OF THE TREASURY DEPARTMENT

(a) "Pharmacy management. * * *
"(b) Records.
"1. In time of peace and, so far as practicable, in time of war all prescriptions will be written in the metric system. * * *." (Army Regulations, 1929, Regulation 40–590, par. 18, sub.-par. 18–b (1).)
(b) "The metric system of weights and measures shall hereafter be employed in the Medical Department of the Navy." (Order approved by the Secretary of the Navy, April 15, 1878.)*
(c) "Officers shall, for all official, medical, and pharmacal purposes, make use of the metric system of weights and measures." (Regulations of the U. S. Public Health Service, 1931, sec. 856.)

10. METRIC CARAT ADOPTED AS UNIT OF WEIGHT FOR DIAMONDS AND OTHER PRECIOUS STONES

"Beginning July 1, 1913, the Bureau of Standards will recognize the international metric carat of 200 milligrams as the unit of weight for diamonds and other precious stones and will use this unit for the purposes of certification of all carat weights submitted to the bureau for test." (National Bureau of Standards, Circular C43, issued November 1, 1913.)
"On and after July 1, 1913, the unit of weight for imported diamonds, pearls, and other precious stones will be the metric carat of 200 milligrams.
"Collectors at ports now equipped with scales for weighing precious stones will make requisition for a new set of weights based upon such carat." (Treasury Department order, June 17, 1913, to collectors and other officers of the customs.)

11. METRIC SYSTEM OPTIONAL IN PUERTO RICO

"SECTION 1.—That the metric system of weights and measures and the imperial system customarily used in the United States, insofar as the same is described by this act, are hereby recognized and established in Porto Rico for use in all industrial and commercial transactions, * * *."
(Act No. 135, approved, August 18, 1913.)

12. METRIC SYSTEM MADE THE LEGAL SYSTEM IN THE PHILIPPINE ISLANDS

"The weights and measures to be used throughout the Philippine Islands are those of the metric system, with the following units: * * *
"The metric system of weights and measures, with its recognized scales, shall be used in all contracts, deeds, and other instruments publicly and officially attested, and in all official documents; and, except as hereinbelow provided, only weights and measures of the metric system shall be officially sealed and licensed.
"In the purchase and sale of manufactured lumber the English system of measures may be employed; and in ordering commodities or articles from abroad such

---

* The metric system is now used exclusively only in the medical prescription work of the Bureau of Medicine and Surgery.

weights and measures may be employed as are commonly used in the country to which the order is sent or from which the goods are shipped." (Administrative Code, 1917, vol. 2, Art. IX, p. 8, secs. 32 and 33.)

13. RELATION BETWEEN INCHES AND MILLIMETERS ADOPTED BY AMERICAN STANDARDS ASSOCIATION

For industrial purposes a simple relation between the inch and the millimeter has been adopted by the American Standards Association (ASA B48.1–1933), and by similar organizations in 15 other countries. This relation is

$$1 \text{ inch} = 25.4 \text{ millimeters (exactly)}$$

from which, 1 yard = 0.9144 meter (exactly).

The adoption of this relation by industry, for use in making conversions between inches and millimeters, has no effect upon the legal definition of the yard or of the meter.

14. DISTANCES IN MULTIPLES OF METRIC UNITS ADOPTED FOR AMATEUR ATHLETIC UNION TRACK EVENTS

On November 22, 1932, the Amateur Athletic Union took official action adopting metric distances for track events to be run in athletic meets held under the jurisdiction of that body. These metric distances given in this publication are also given in Letter Circular LC376, which may be obtained from the National Bureau of Standards.

TEXT OF JOINT RESOLUTION

Proposed by Department of Commerce and Introduced in 92nd Congress as
Senate Joint Resolution 219 and House Joint Resolutions 1092, 1132, and 1169

To establish a national policy relating to conversion to the metric system in
the United States.

Whereas the use of the metric system of weights and measures in the United
States was authorized by the Act of July 28, 1866 (14 Stat. 339); and

Whereas the United States was one of the original signatories to the Convention
of the Meter (20 Stat. 709), which established the General Conference of
Weights and Measures, the International Committee of Weights and Measures,
and the International Bureau of Weights and Measures; and

Whereas the metric measurement standards recognized and developed by the
International Bureau of Weights and Measures have been adopted as the
fundamental measurement standards of the United States and the customary
units of weights and measures used in the United States have been since
1893 based upon such metric measurement standards; and

Whereas the Governments of Australia, Canada, Great Britain, India, Japan,
New Zealand, and the Union of South Africa have determined to convert,
are converting, or have converted to the use of the metric system in
their respective jurisdictions; and

Whereas the United States is the only industrially developed nation which has
not established a national policy committing itself to and facilitating
conversion to the metric system; and

Whereas, as a result of the study to determine the advantages and disadvantages
of increased use of the metric system in the United States authorized by
Public Law 90-472 (82 Stat. 693), the Secretary of Commerce has found
that increased use of the metric system in the United States is inevitable,
and has concluded that a planned national program to achieve a metric
changeover is desirable; that maximum efficiency will result and minimum
costs to effect the conversion will be incurred if the conversion is
carried out in general without Federal subsidies; that the changeover
period be ten years, at the end of which the Nation would be predominantly,
although not exclusively, metric; that a central coordinating body be
established and assigned to coordinate the changeover in cooperation with
all sectors of our society; and that immediate attention be given to
public and formal education and to effective United States participation
in international standardsmaking: Now, therefore, be it

Resolved by the Senate and House of Representatives of the United States of
America in Congress assembled, That the policy of the United States shall
be—

(1) to facilitate and encourage the substitution of metric measurement
units for customary measurement units to education, trade, commerce, and all
other sectors of the economy of the United States with a view to making metric
units the predominant, although not exclusive, language of measurement with
respect to transactions occurring after ten years from the date of the enact-
ment of this resolution.

(2) to facilitate and encourage the development as rapidly as practicable of new or revised engineering standards based on metric measurement units in those specific fields or areas in the United States where such standards will result in rationalization or simplification of relationships, improvements of design, or increases in economy.

(3) to facilitate and encourage the retention in new metric language standards of those United States engineering designs, practices, and conventions that are internationally accepted or embody superior technology.

(4) to cooperate with foreign governments and public and private international organizations which are or become concerned with the encouragement and coordination of increased use of metric measurement units or engineering standards based on such units, or both, with a view to gaining international recognition for metric standards proposed by the United States and to encouraging retention of equivalent customary units in international recommendations during the United States changeover period.

(5) to assist the public through information and educational programs to become familiar with the meaning and applicability to metric terms and measures in daily life. Programs hereunder should include:

(a) Public information programs conducted by the Board through the use of newspapers, magazines, radio, television, other media, and through talks before appropriate citizens groups and public organizations.

(b) Counseling and consultation by the Secretary of Health, Education, and Welfare and the Director, National Science Foundation, with educational associations and groups so as to assure that the metric system of measurement is made a part of the curricula of the Nation's educational institutions and that teachers and other appropriate personnel are properly trained to teach the metric system of measurement.

(c) Consultation by the Secretary of Commerce with the National Conference of Weights and Measures so as to assure that State and local weights and measures officials are appropriately informed of the intended metric changeover and are thus assisted in their efforts to bring about timely amendments to weights and measures laws.

(d) Such other public information programs by any Federal agency in support of this resolution which relate to the mission of the agency.

Sec. 2. Definitions—For the purposes of this resolution—

(a) The term "metric system of measurement" means the international system of units as established by the General Conference of Weights and Measures in 1960 and interpreted or modified for the United States by the Secretary of Commerce.

(b) The term "engineering standard" means a standard which prescribes a concise set of conditions and requirements to be satisfied by a material, product, process, procedure, convention, test method, and the physical, functional, performance, and/or conformance characteristics thereof.

(c) The term "changeover period" means the length of time for the United States to become predominantly, although not exclusively, metric.

(d) The term "international recommendation" means a recommendation formulated and promulgated by an international organization and recommended for adoption by individual nations as a national standard of measurement.

Sec. 3. There is hereby established a National Metric Conversion Board (hereinafter referred to as the "Board") to implement the policy set out in this resolution.

Sec. 4. The composition of the Board shall be as follows:
(a) Not to exceed twenty-one persons appointed by the President who shall serve at his pleasure and for such terms as he shall specify and who shall be broadly representative of the American society. The President shall designate one of the members appointed by him to serve as Chairman and another to serve as the Vice Chairman of the Board;
(b) Two Members of the House of Representatives who shall not be members of the same political party shall be appointed by the Speaker of the House of Representatives; and
(c) Two Members of the Senate who shall not be members of the same political party shall be appointed by the President of the Senate.
Sec. 5. The Executive Director of the Board shall be appointed by the President and shall be responsible to the Board for carrying out its responsibilities according to the provisions of this resolution.
Sec. 6. (a) Within twelve months after funds have been appropriated to carry out the provisions of this resolution the Board shall, in furtherance and in support of the policy expressed in section 1 of this resolution, develop and submit to the Secretary of Commerce for his approval and transmittal to the President a comprehensive plan to accomplish a changeover to the metric system of measurement in the United States. If such plan is approved by the President, he shall transmit it to the Congress. Such plan may include recommendations for legislation deemed necessary and appropriate. In developing this plan the Board shall:
(1) Consult with and take into account the interests and views of United States commerce and industry, including small business; science; engineering; labor; education; consumers; government agencies at the Federal, State, and local level; nationally recognized standards developing and coordinating organizations; and such other individuals or groups as are considered appropriate by the Board to carry out the purposes of this section.
(2) Consult, to the extent deemed appropriate, with foreign governments, public international organizations, and, through appropriate member organizations, private international standards organizations. Contact with foreign governments and intergovernmental organizations shall be accomplished in consultation with the Department of State.
(b) Any amendment to an approved plan shall be submitted by the Board to the Secretary and the President under the provisions set out in subsection (a) of this section.
(c) Unless otherwise provided by the Congress, the Board shall have no compulsory powers.
Sec. 7. Upon approval of the plan by the President, the Board shall begin the implementation of the plan, except for those recommendations, if any, which require legislation.
Sec. 8. In carrying out its duties, the Board is authorized to:
(a) enter into contracts in accordance with the Federal Property and Administrative Services Act of 1949, as amended, with Federal or State agencies, private firms, institutions, and individuals for the conduct of research or surveys, the preparation of reports, and other activities necessary to the discharge of its duties;
(b) conduct hearings at such times and places as it deems appropriate;

(c) establish such committees and advisory panels as it deems necessary to work with the various sectors of the American economy and governmental agencies in the development and implementation of detailed changeover plans for those sectors; and

(d) perform such other acts as may be necessary to carry out the duties prescribed by this resolution.

Sec. 9. (a) Members of the Board who are not in the regular full-time employ of the United States shall, while attending meetings or conferences of the Board or otherwise engaged in the business of the Board, be entitled to receive compensation at a rate of $100 per day, including traveltime, and while so serving on the business of the Board away from their homes or regular places of business, they may be allowed travel expenses, including per diem in lieu of subsistence, as authorized by section 5703 of title 5, United States Code, for persons employed intermittently in the Government service. Payments under this section shall not render members of the Board employees or officials of the United States for any purpose.

(b) The Executive Director of the Board shall serve full time and receive basic pay at a rate not to exceed the rate provided for GS-18 in subchapter III of chapter 53 of title 5, United States Code.

Sec. 10. (a) The Board is authorized to appoint and fix the compensation of such staff personnel as may be necessary to carry out the provisions of this Act.

(b) The Board is authorized to employ experts and consultants or organizations thereof as authorized by section 3109 of title 5, United States Code, compensate individuals so employed at rates not in excess of the rate prescribed for grade 18 of the General Schedule under section 5332 of such title, including traveltime, and allow them, while away from their homes or regular places of business, travel expenses (including per diem in lieu of subsistence) as authorized by section 5703 of said title 5 for persons in the Government service employed: _Provided, however,_ That contracts for such employment may be renewed annually.

Sec. 11. Financial and administrative services (including those related to budgeting, accounting, financial reporting, personnel, and procurement) and such other staff services as may be requested by the Board shall be provided the Board by the Secretary of Commerce, for which payment shall be made in advance, or by reimbursement, from funds of the Board in such amounts as may be agreed upon by the Chairman of the Board and the Secretary of Commerce.

In performing these functions for the Board, the Secretary is authorized to obtain such information and assistance from other Federal agencies as may be necessary.

Sec. 12. (a) The Board is hereby authorized to accept, hold, administer, and utilize gifts, donations, and bequests of property, both real and personal, and personal services, for the purpose of aiding or facilitating the work of the Board. Gifts and bequests of money and the proceeds from sales of other property received as gifts or bequests shall be deposited in the Treasury in a separate fund and shall be disbursed upon order of the Board.

(b) For the purpose of Federal income, estate, and gift taxes, property accepted under subsection (a) of this section shall be considered as a gift or bequest to or for the use of the United States.

INDEX

OTHER METRIC BOOKS

THE COMPLETE METRIC SYSTEM with THE INTERNATIONAL
SYSTEM OF UNITS (SI)
L.C. Card Number 72-97799
ISBN Number 0-913768-00-6

THE TEACHER'S GUIDE TO THE METRIC SYSTEM
L.C. Card Number 74-3811 ISBN Number 0-913768-01-4

THE METRIC SYSTEM FOR BEGINNERS
L.C. Card Number 74-3812
ISBN Number 0-913768-02-2

THE METRIC SYSTEM FOR SECONDARY SCHOOLS
L.C. Card Number 74-1-176
ISBN Number 0-913768-04-9

METRIC CHARTS and POSTERS

No. C9131 - METRICS FOR THE CLASSROOM (Set of 5 Charts)
No. P9132 - THE METRIC SYSTEM FOR EVERYDAY USE
             (1 Poster)
No. TP9133 - METRIC CONVERSIONS AT A GLANCE
             (Set of 2 Posters)
U.S. Customary to Metric
Metric to U.S. Customary

No. CP9134 - COMBINATION KIT (All the 8 Charts and Posters
             mentioned above)

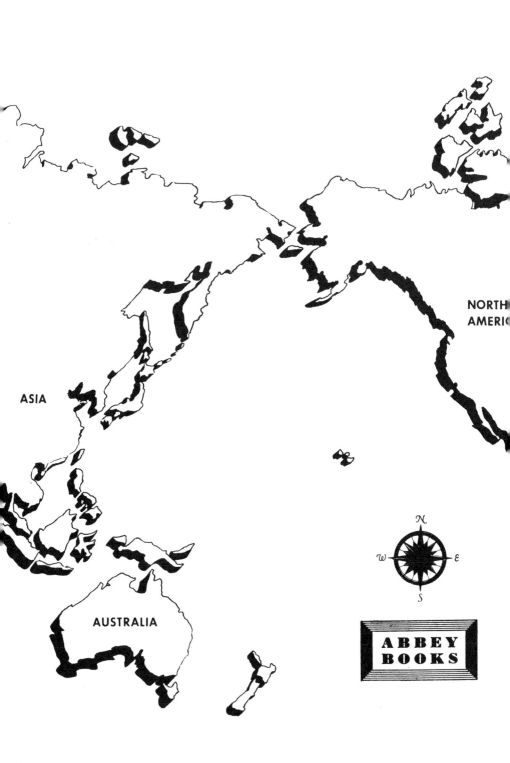

ASIA

NORTH
AMERIC

AUSTRALIA

ABBEY
BOOKS